D0899605

# Earth and People
## An Introduction to Geography
### Fourth Editon

William B. Kory

Geography Department
University of Pittsburgh at Johnstown

WILEY Custom
LEARNING SOLUTIONS

This custom textbook includes materials submitted by the Author for publication by John Wiley & Sons, Inc. The material has not been edited by Wiley and the Author is solely responsible for its content.

Copyright © 2011 by William B. Kory

All rights reserved.

No part of this publication may be reproduced, stored in a retrieval system or transmitted in any form or by any means, electronic, mechanical, photocopying, recording, scanning or otherwise, except as permitted under Sections 107 or 108 of the 1976 United States Copyright Act, without either the prior written permission of the Publisher, or authorization through payment of the appropriate per-copy fee to the Copyright Clearance Center, Inc., 222 Rosewood Drive, Danvers, MA 01923, website www.copyright.com. Requests to the Publisher for permission should be addressed to the Permissions Department, John Wiley & Sons, Inc., 111 River Street, Hoboken, NJ 07030-5774, (201)748-6011, fax (201)748-6008, website http://www.wiley.com/go/permissions.

To order books or for customer service, please call 1(800)-CALL-WILEY (225-5945).

Printed in the United States of America.

ISBN 978-0-470-94130-0

Printed and bound by Odyssey Press Inc.

10 9 8 7 6 5 4 3 2 1

## PREFACE

This book was prepared primarily for students who are taking their first geography class. It has evolved from the material used by the author in an introductory course over the past twenty-five years. The book is designed to give students some idea of the scope of geography and to stress the integrative nature of the field. Although geography is a social science discipline, it has links to natural sciences (biology, geology, oceanography, chemistry), to civil engineering, to computer science and especially to the environmental studies. The material in the book focuses on the regional and systematic approaches in the study of geography. It should serve as a guide to the topics which will be introduces and discusses in class to broaden the intellectual horizons of the students.

Geographers are interested, among other things, in understanding the spatial relationships among human and physical phenomenon, and the book stresses this approach to the discipline. It examines some of the problems of concern to geographers, investigates the methods used by geographers, looks at the human-environmental interaction, and focuses on specific regions of the world. The regional analyses should convey the exclusivity of each area and an understanding and appreciation of different cultures and peoples, allowing the students to better understand our complex world. Cartography, field research and other geographic tools will be examined, showing how geographers use these tools.

The various units in this book deal with specific sub-fields of geography, outlining major objectives, general concepts and various approaches to studying and comprehending the discipline. The topics have been selected to cover the human, cultural, physical and regional aspects of geography. The material is, therefore, designed to acquaint students with basic geographic ideas and give a broad view of the field. For those students who may wish to take additional courses in geography, or decode to major in the discipline, the "Earth and People" class will serve as a good foundation.

There are maps at the end of the book covering various regions of the world. The book was meant to be used with National Geographic's College Atlas of the World edited by Harm De Blij and Roger Downs.

William B. Kory
Summer, 2010

I would like to thank my colleagues in
the Geography Department at UPJ

*OLA JOHANSSON*
and
*GREGORY FAIERS*

for their.suggestions to this
edition of the book.

The Chapter on CHINA and much of the
editorial work was done by
Professor Johansson

# Contents

# I. *INTRODUCTION TO THE FIELD OF GEOGRAPHY*

Geographers interpret and explain the occurrence; distribution, and inter-relationships of physical and cultural patterns on the face of the earth. Geography's unique perspective is its <u>spatial</u> point of view.

> Geography is a study of places or space, in the same sense that history is a study of time. Thus, geography is more a point of view, or a method of inquiry, than it is a body of facts. The first question a geographer asks is "WHERE are things located?" Even more important, however, is concern with "WHY are they located where they are?" Therefore, the modern geographer is concerned primarily with interpreting and explaining the ties of physical and cultural landscape patterns of the earth's surface. As a synthesizing discipline, geography is an especially attractive major for Liberal Arts students.[1]

Although most geographers would agree on several common themes which identify geography as a distinct Social Science discipline, each would also have a personal interpretation on how geographers study various phenomena. For example, Richard Morrill wrote in <u>The Professional Geographer</u>: "What is special or unique about geography is simply that its object of analysis is the earth's surface, and that its purpose is to understand how that surface is structured or differentiated." [2]

The Association of American Geographers (<u>www.aag.org</u>) in its recent booklet entitled <u>Geography: Today's Career for Tomorrow</u> stated:

"Geographers play a crucial role in addressing national and global concerns like acid rain, nuclear war, hazardous waste, housing for low-income people, and world population growth. They study the characteristics of space, location, and place to understand how people interact with both physical and human environments."

Another way to view geography is to look at the various components that make up the discipline. These may include the following:

- Physical/environmental variables (climatology, biogeography, geomorphology, ...)
- Human factors (urbanization, population, political, cultural geography, ...)
- Technical aspects (cartography, geographic information systems, remote sensing, ...)
- Regional analysis (in depth study of various regions of the world)

Within this framework, geographers identify and analyze the local, regional, and global patterns that shape our everyday lives. As the world's nations become more interdependent, understanding other cultures may lead to better relations among all the people on our earth.

---

[1] STUDY GEOGRAPHY, Geography Department, SUNY-Oneota, 1993.
[2] Richard Morrill, "The Nature, Unity, and Value of Geography", <u>THE PROFESSIONAL GEOGRAPHER</u>, February 1983, Volume 35, #1, p. 5.

University of Iowa's Geography Department Web Page (www.uiowa.edu/~geog) gives the following view of geography:

"Geography is concerned with the "place" or "environment" and ongoing forces that promote change within and between human and physical systems. The discipline seeks to explain spatial organization and areal differentiation through detailed studies of significant patterns and processes. Geography is a composite science, requiring a broad base of knowledge from many related disciplines. It also is an analytical science that seeks answers to specific research questions from a distinctly geographic perspective.

Students of geography find that they develop insights and methods of inquiry that are particularly applicable to understanding many of the complex problems confronting societies. For instance, the distribution and consumption of natural resources, air and water pollution, processes and management of natural environments, the growth and development of urban areas, increasing populations, transportation problems, spatial inequalities, location of services, and conflicts between nations are some of the issues dealt with by geographers.

Studies in geography also provide students with concepts and methods for organizing urban areas, marketing regions, school districts, health service areas, drainage basins, and other areas of concern. Thus, geographers can make substantial contributions toward understanding the behavior of individuals and of societies and their relations with the environment.

Career opportunities for majors in geography exist in many branches of government and in business. In demand are persons capable of dealing with resource management, regional development, market area analysis, and problems in distribution and spatial interaction of physical, ecological, economic, social, and political phenomena.

Courses in geography are commonly required of students preparing to teach at the elementary and secondary school levels, those who want to work in urban and regional planning, and as a background for many related professions, including law, health care, environmental or transportation engineering, and business administration".

In a recent AAG Newsletter (Volume 35, #11, November 2000) Professor Alexander B. Murphy wrote that: "To understand fully geography's rising profile, it is also important to consider the interest the subject generates among those who expose it seriously. Despite the growing presence of geography in the pre-college curriculum, relatively few students arrive on college campuses declaring geography as a major. Yet a number of geography programs end up with a sizeable number of majors.                          This happens because students walk into geography classes for a variety of pragmatic reasons and then encounter issues and perspectives that help them make sense of the world in which they live. Their interest may be piqued by a physical geography class that allows them to understand why hurricanes are more likely to threaten the eastern seaboard of the United States than the western seaboard. They may be drawn to an environmental geography class that provides insights into how changes in land use can increase flood danger. Or they may be intrigued by a human geography class that sheds light on the ways in which changing patters of connectivity among people are affecting the place in which they live."

Professor Harm De Blij, a noted American geographer, writes about the field of geography in his recent book entitled "Why Geography Matters".* In this well written and well researched, scholarly book, De Blij stresses the traditions within the field of geography rather than giving a definition of the discipline. He states that the

- first, and in many ways the most important, is that geography deals with the natural as well as the human world.
- second is that geographers are especially well placed to assess the complex relationships between human societies and natural environments
- third is that geographers do research in, and try to understand, foreign cultures and distant regions
- fourth is the so-called location tradition, which is essentially a human-geographic (not a physical-geographic) convention.

Looking at the above statements on geography, is should be pretty clear that there is no short nor totally agreed upon definition of geography.

ASSIGNMENT #1          Name: _____

Find another definition of "GEOGRAPHY" and give SOURCE:

Name one job that geographers do.

What would be some of the things of interest to geographers in this aerial photograph of Washington, D.C. ?

## GEOGRAPHERS ARE SPATIAL

It may be easier to understand what geography is by looking at what geographers have been doing in the past decade. Modern geography is a changing field and the topics outlined below reflect some of the diversity of activity characterizing contemporary geographic research. The topics are selective and stress, for the most part, the social aspects of geography. They lead to better understanding of the location of things, the reasons for such location, and the public and government decisions influencing such spatial patterns.

1. SPATIAL  DISTRIBUTION AND INTERPRETATION (Spatial analysis)
   Where are things located?          Why are they located there?
   What are the resulting implications based on those locations ?
   Examples:  McDONALD'S RESTAURANTS;   AUTOMATED BANK TELLER MACHINES;
        CAPITAL CITIES OF STATES;     OIL FIELDS

2. URBANIZATION  -  cultural landscape;  city planning;  zoning;  housing

3. TRANSPORTATION  -  FAA; Washington, D.C. subway system; interstate road system

4. REGIONALIZATION  -  Africa; Latin America; Russia; Middle East; other regions

5. SPATIAL DIFFUSION  - Hispanic migration to the USA; origin and spread of a disease,
        like AIDS or Ebola; the start and growth of a particular music style

6. REGIONAL DEVELOPMENT AND ENVIRONMENTAL PLANNING  -  hazard perception and
        behavior; effects of acid drainage; depletion of world's rainforest

7. POPULATION GEOGRAPHY – understanding human migration, fertility, mortality;
        ethnicity; gerontology; the census

8. GEOPOLITICS and POLITICAL GEOGRAPHY  -  relations among the world's nation-states

9. HUMAN ECOLOGY and BIOGEOGRAPHY – the delicate balance between the environment
        and human activities

10. ECONOMIC and INDUSTRIAL GEOGRAPHY

11. PHYSICAL GEOGRAPHY  -  climatology; geomorphology; hydrology; oceanography

12. GEOGRAPHY OF RECREATION, TOURISM, AND SPORT  -  what would be the effect on a
    city, for example, which lost a major league team ?  What are the ten top rated golf
    courses in the United States and why ?  What are the major reasons for choosing a
    vacation location ?

In addition to the above examples, geographers also study topics such as Historical/Cultural Geography; Agriculture and Rural Land Use; Coastal and Marine Geography; Geographical Information Systems (GIS); and Medical Geography.

Geographers, like other social scientists, use a variety of investigative tools to help with their research.  Some of these major tools include:

\*\*\* quantitative techniques
\*\*\* field research methods
\*\*\* cartographic analysis
    - computer mapping (see map on the next page)
    - digitizing imagery
    - remote sensing - infrared scanning
    - air-photo interpretation
    - Geographic Information Systems (GIS)
    - Global Positioning System (GPS)

## GIS:    Geographic Information Systems

According to the U.S. Department of the Interior, GIS is a "computer system capable of the assembling, storing, manipulating and displaying geographically referenced information."  GIS can identify and manipulate data according to location and arrange it based on the needs of the researcher.

The GIS technology is used for scientific investigations, resource management, urban and regional planning, and for many other purposes.  For example, a GIS system could produce a map showing the best routes for garbage trucks to follow in collecting trash. Some other examples could show the residential location of hospital patients, distribution and exact location of particular retail outlets or show the emergency response times in the event of a natural disaster.

GIS can use information from a variety of sources in many different forms.
The primary requirement for the source data is that the locations for the variables be known. Locations may be given in longitudes, latitudes, and elevations or by such systems as ZIP Codes, bench marks or highway mile markers.  Any variable that can be located spatially can be used in GIS.

## GPS: Global Positioning System

This sophisticated satellite-dependent system was developed in the late 1970's by the U. S. Department of State. The worldwide radio-navigation system was formed from a constellation of 24 satellites and their ground stations. The receiver getting information from at least four satellites, can accurately determine the latitude, longitude and altitude of a place. Besides its obvious importance to the military, the system also benefits travelers, surveyors, law enforcement people, construction companies, farmers, 911 operators and others.
For additional information on the topic, check out the following sites:

www.garmin.com/aboutGPS
www.gps.gov

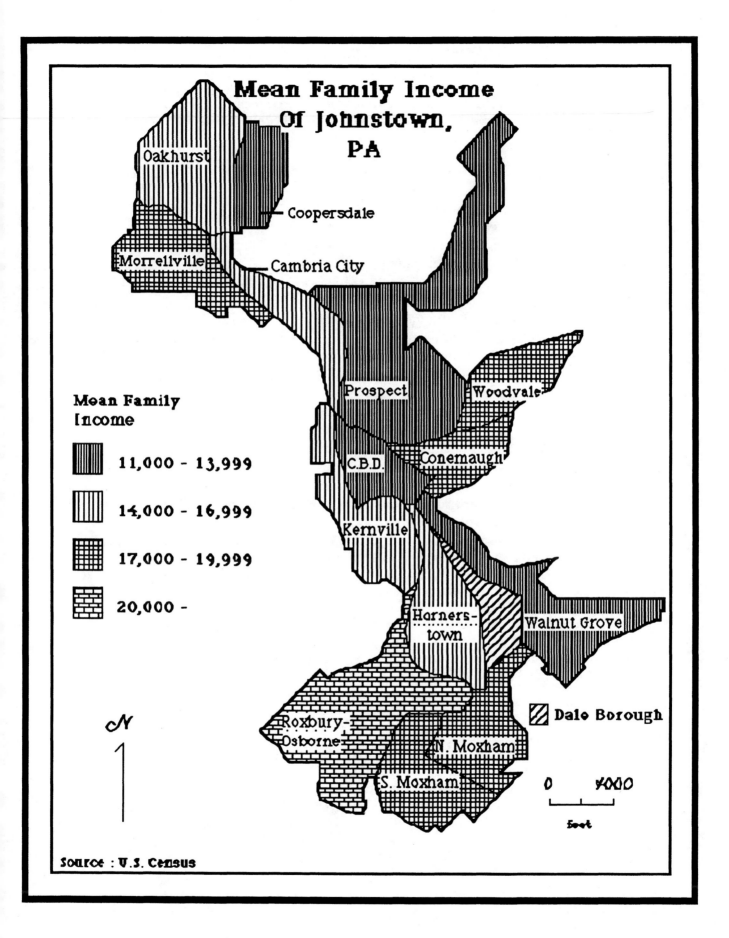

# Mean Family Income
# Of Johnstown,
# PA

Oakhurst

Coopersdale

Morrellville

Cambria City

**Mean Family Income**

| | |
|---|---|
| ▦ | 11,000 - 13,999 |
| ▦ | 14,000 - 16,999 |
| ▦ | 17,000 - 19,999 |
| ▦ | 20,000 - |

Prospect

Woodvale

C.B.D.

Conemaugh

Kernville

Horners-town

Walnut Grove

Dale Borough

Roxbury-Osborne

N. Moxham

S. Moxham

N

0        4000

feet

Source : U.S. Census

7

## USES FOR THE GLOBAL POSITIONING SYSTEM

Some GPS receivers can store data for use in GIS and map making. The instruments are getting more sophisticated and accurate with a variety of functional usages. First developed for military purposes, the technology has been used in a variety of non-military endeavors.

Listed below are just a few examples:

- During "Operation Desert Storm", some 10,000 GPS receivers were used by US and coalition forces
- More and more rental car companies are using GPS equipped vehicles that give directions to drivers
- Trucking companies are outfitting their trucks with GPS equipment for tracking purposes and in case of hijacking
- Ships use the equipment not only for location but also to track the depths of oceans
- Environmentalists use the equipment to track some species of wildlife
- A group of scientists used the GPS equipment to chart the paths and feeding grounds of elephants in central Africa
- Many emergency vehicles are using the equipments for a fast response to an event requiring immediate assistance
- Police departments throughout the country are relying more on the GPS systems to track criminals
- Scientists use the system to measure movements of arctic ice sheets and the earth's tectonic plates
- It has been used to detect volcanic activities
- GPS allows mine operators to navigate mining equipment safely, even when visibility is obscured
- During the construction of the "Chunnel" under the English Channel, British and French crews started digging from Dover, England and Calais, France. They relied on the GPS receivers outside the tunnel to check their positions to make sure that they would meet exactly in the middle while digging from the opposite directions.

The figure below shows the GPS constellation of 28 satellites orbiting 12,500 miles above the earth. It is designed to keep at least four satellites above the horizon anywhere on the planet. (Source: Global Positioning System; J. Spencer, B. Frizzelle, P. Page, J. Vogler; Blackwell Publishing; 2003; p. 28).

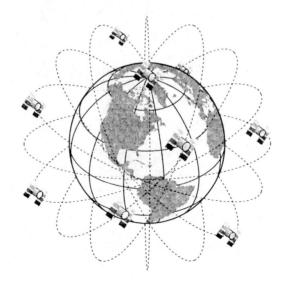

John Hunsinger

**Auto Insurance Premiums**

Launched in 1998 as a test pilot program, Progressive Auto Insurance equipped 1,000 vehicles in Houston with GPS devices that track the number of minutes customers drive as well as where and when. Called AutoGraph, driver's premiums are based on the actual driving time rather than the traditional flat rate. Now offered as an insurance program, AutoGraph collects miles driven, where and speed once a month in order to streamline insurance costs.

**Balloon Tracking**

The website, http://www.balloonfiesta.com, is one of two sites covering the annual Albuquerque Balloon Fiesta, the nation's largest hot-air and gas balloon meet. The festivities include a coast-to-coast balloon race, and this year the balloons are equipped with GPS units. The GPS coordinates of all the balloons are fed back to the website, so that when you click on the link to any particular racing team, the site's GIS application uses those coordinates to display a series of maps provided by MapBlast. The maps are centered on a marker pointing out the last known coordinates of the balloon.

**Business Logistics**

A growing number of companies like actra and Air-Trak that dispatch fleets of delivery or repair trucks are tracking their vehicles via GPS in order to monitor their employees' whereabouts and determine who to send to what job site.

**Farming**

In a program started by NASA's Jet Propulsion Lab (JPL) in partnership with NavCom Technology Inc., (a wholly owned subsidiary of Deere & Company) GPS sensors will be attached to tractors. These sensors will help with navigation at night and during periods of poor visibility. In addition, soil sensors and other monitors will also help pinpoint locations where changes in watering, fertilization or weed control are necessary in the farmers' fields.

**GeoCaching**

GeoCaching was launched May 3, 2000 as a way of celebrating the lifting of Selective Availability. This game, played worldwide, sends eager GPSers on the hunt for hidden treasure with a pair of coordinates as the only clue.

**Lost Pets**

Several companies sell implants for the family pet that, like the Digital Angel, track an animal's whereabouts and monitor its heart rate and temperature.

## II. CARTOGRAPHY: A GEOGRAPHIC TOOL

Cartography, along with computer cartography, remote sensing, air photo interpretation and other related topics, is an integral part of the field of geography. These sub-fields of geography help people to better understand and portray our physical and cultural world. Maps prepared by cartographers are useful, for example, in showing the exact depths of oceans, identifying diseased crops, highlighting the earth's population density, charting the spatial distribution of oil, examining political boundaries among various nation-states, or portraying the results of human misuse of the habitat.

Cartography may be simply defined as the art of drawing maps and charts. J.S. Keates, a British geographer, defines cartography as:

> "...the art, science, and technology of making maps...(It) is concerned with all stages of evaluation, compilation, design, and drafting required to produce a new or revised map document from all forms of basic data. It also comprises all stages of production of maps."

Since early times, humans tried to portray parts of our earth on some two-dimensional surface. Herodotus (see following map), Eratosthenes, Strabo, Ptolemy, and other geographers from the past, were pioneers in the art of map making. Ptolemy, in fact, is credited with being the first to compile a number of maps into an atlas, which was used in the second century.

With the development of usable paper by the Chinese in the first century A.D., maps became plentiful and, with time, more sophisticated. Today's maps are a far cry from the crude maps compiled by geographers from the past. It is, however, important to recognize the contributions of the early Greek, Roman, and Arab map makers. They set the foundation for the more sophisticated methods used in constructing maps of today.

Maps are produced for a variety of purposes and are used for a multitude of reasons. Numerous techniques are available for map construction, and the final product is used to convey specific ideas. THEMATIC MAPS, for example, usually present one category of information while CHOROPLETH MAPS divide data into a set of intervals and can show areas of high and low density. DOT MAPS are very useful for visual effect, while ISOLINE MAPS connect points of equal value.

TOPOGRAPHIC MAPS (contour maps), which connect points of equal elevation, serve as good examples of isoline maps. The United States Geological Survey (USGS) has produced a variety of topographic maps where elevation of the terrain is portrayed by contour lines. The most widely used USGS maps, which portray the whole of the United States, are the quadrangle maps with a scale of 1 to 24,000 and an area ranging from fifty to seventy square miles. The Geistown Quadrangle of Pennsylvania shows the area east of Johnstown.

Other examples of isoline maps include ISOBAR; ISOBATH; ISOHYET (see map); and ISOTHERM.

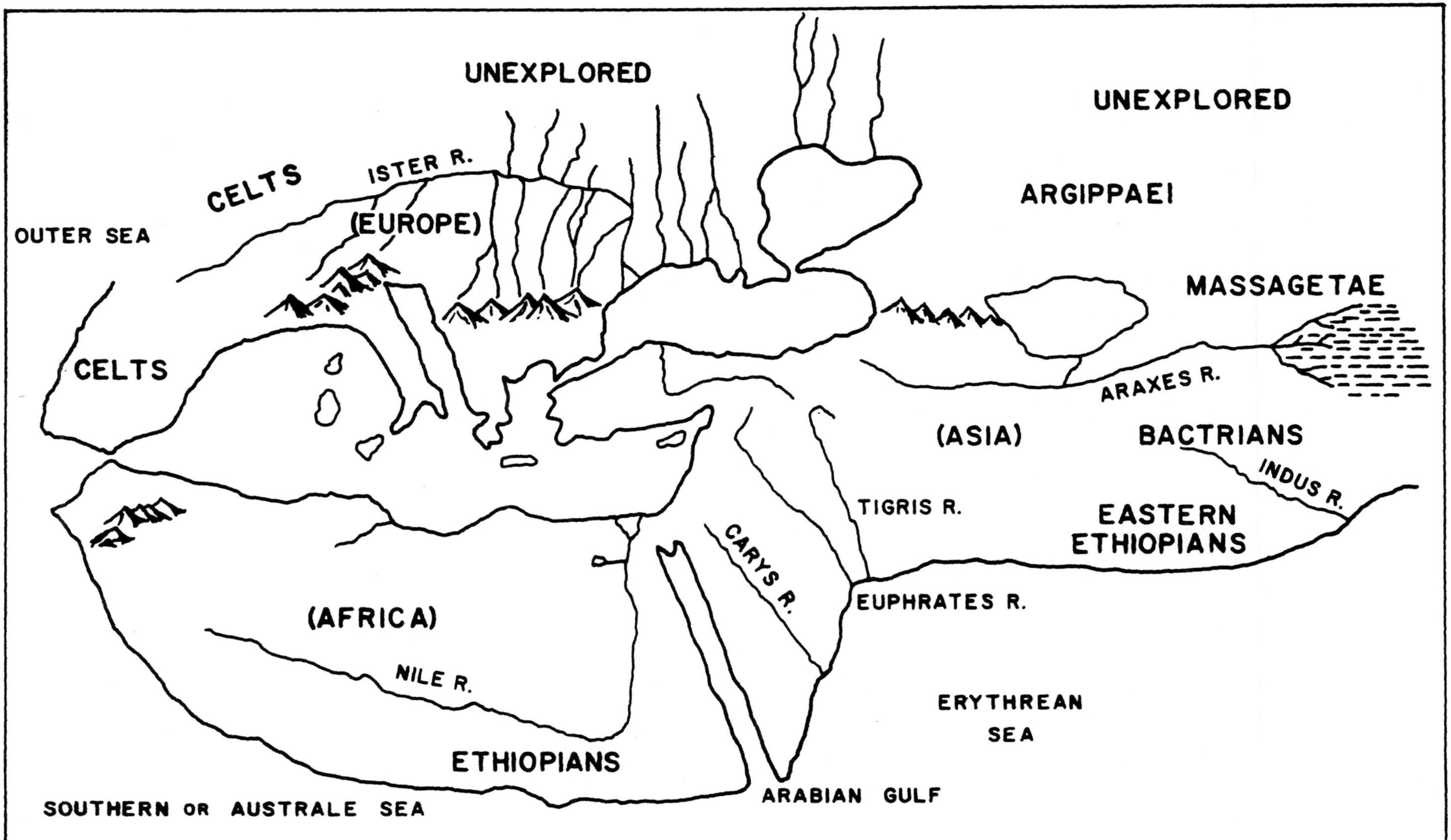

# THE WORLD ACCORDING TO HERODOTUS
## ABOUT 430 B.C.

UNEXPLORED

ARGIPPAEI

MASSAGETAE

ARAXES R.

BACTRIANS

INDUS R.

EASTERN ETHIOPIANS

(ASIA)

TIGRIS R.

EUPHRATES R.

ERYTHREAN SEA

ARABIAN GULF

CARYS R.

UNEXPLORED

CELTS

ISTER R.

(EUROPE)

CELTS

OUTER SEA

(AFRICA)

NILE R.

ETHIOPIANS

SOUTHERN or AUSTRALE SEA

UPJ – CARTOGRAPHY

NAME: _____

    A.  Define the terms and give source:

- Isobar:


- Isobath:


- Isohyet:


- Isotherm:



B.  Draw a simple Isoline map below:
        (include the five map essentials)

EXAMPLE OF AN ISOHYET MAP – Johnstown, Pennsylvania and Surrounding Area

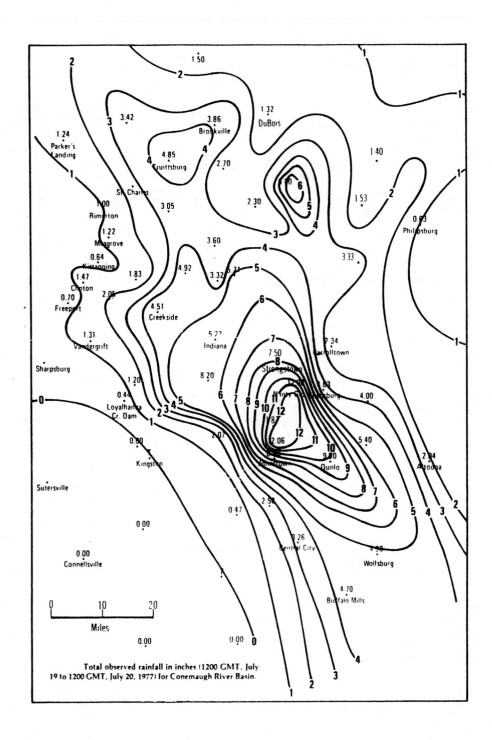

Total observed rainfall in inches (1200 GMT, July 19 to 1200 GMT, July 20, 1977) for Conemaugh River Basin.

Source: <u>Meteorological Analysis of the Johnstown, Pennsylvania Flash Flood, 19-20 July 1977.</u>; U.S. Department of Commerce, NOAA, Environmental Research Labs., Technical Report ERL40APCL43; October 1978.

Air-photos, such as the one shown below, are used by geographers, regional planners and others for a variety of land use (zoning, for example) purposes.

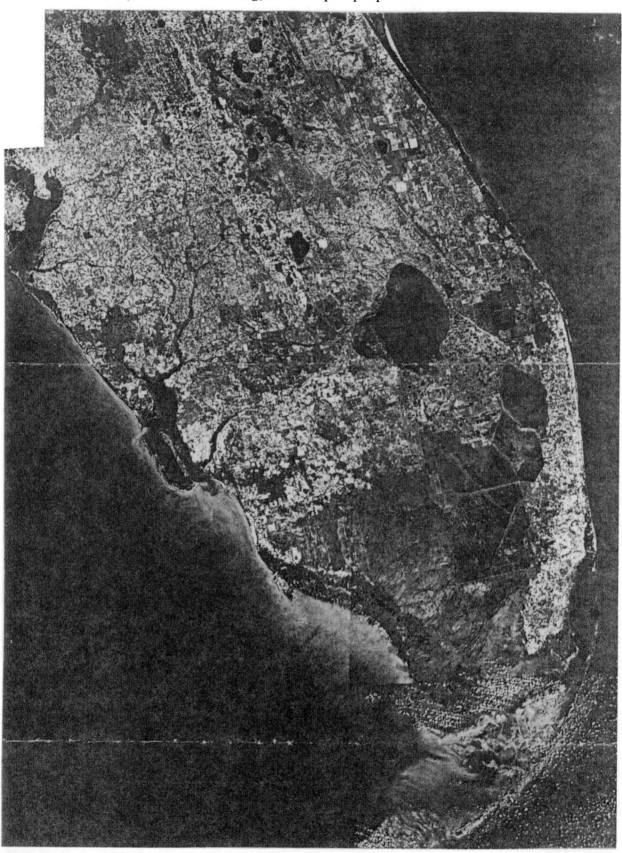

<u>MAP PROJECTIONS</u>
(To be used with Goode's <u>World Atlas</u> - newest edition)

Map projections are constructed to show parts of the earth's surface on a two dimensional, flat surface. There are dozens of map projections in use today. Each has been constructed for a specific task and all have some degree of inaccuracies. Some will distort true direction, others will exaggerate land area while still others will show incorrect distances. It is impossible to accurately portray our three-dimensional world on a two-dimensional map, and the larger the land area being shown, the more distortions will appear.

One of the best known map projections is the <u>Mercator Projection</u>. It was introduced in 1569 by a Flemish geographer Gerardus Mercator to serve as an aid to navigation (see following map). The <u>LONGITUDES</u> (MERIDIANS) and the <u>LATITUDES</u> (PARALLELS) on the Mercator projection are drawn perpendicular to each other, with the longitudes being parallel to each other. Because the longitudes do not converge at the poles, as they do on a globe, the latitudes have to be drawn farther and farther apart to maintain the correct relationship.

The Mercator projection distorts the shape and size of areas in the high latitudes. Greenland, for example, looks larger than South America where as in the real world, South America is nearly 8 1/2 times larger than Greenland. The advantage of using a Mercator projection is that it shows <u>true direction</u>. It was designed to help ship navigators in plotting correct course at sea.

The reliance on the Mercator Projection to portray our world has resulted in major distortions. Africa, for example, appears much smaller than Europe and North America, resulting in claims of pro-Europe bias. There have been attempts to picture the world in more equal-area way, and many new projections have been introduced over time. One of the more interesting has been the <u>PETERS PROJECTION</u> named after its author Dr. Arno Peters, a German historian (see following map). In this <u>orthogonal</u> projection, Peters placed the equator exactly in the middle of the map. In addition, he tried to show each nation on the map to be as close as possible to their size vis-à-vis other nations. Peters claimed that his map was accurate in the comparative size of nations and 50% more accurate than the Mercator projection map. One of Peters' concerns was that the MERCATOR maps perpetuated "Euro-centrism" by making Europe appear much larger on the map than it actually is in comparison to other regions. Mercator maps also showed the third world, and especially Africa, smaller than they are. Peters argued that the area distortion of regions had to be corrected and that his projection did the job.

In addition to Mercator and Peters projections there are many others which are used to show various facets of our world. Some of these include <u>ECKERT (equal area), CONIC, AZIMUTHAL, EQUIDISTANT, INTERRUPTED, and POLYCONIC</u>. The important thing to keep in mind is that all projections serve a purpose depending on the need of the user.

In the late 1980's, The National Geographic Society began to produce all of its world maps using the Robinson projection. This projection, the Society believed, shows the most realistic view of the world. It was introduced by Arthur H. Robinson in 1963, and minimizes distortion of size and shape of the world's regions.

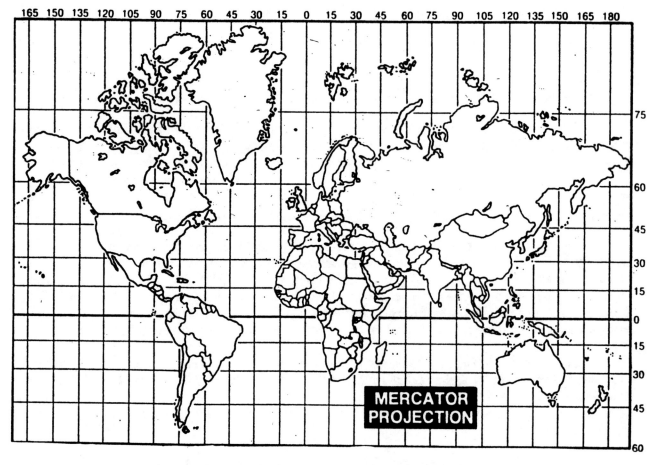

MERCATOR
PROJECTION

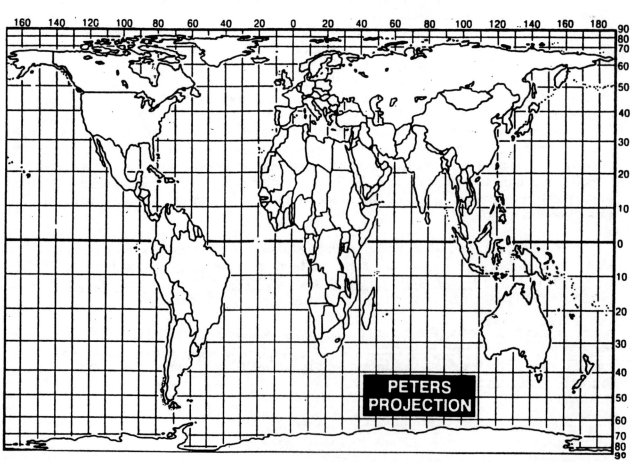

PETERS
PROJECTION

16

MAP ESSENTIALS

All good maps should be easily read and understood. They should have a number of standard items which are found on all well made maps. These "essential" items include a <u>title, direction, date, key, and scale</u>.

The title should be definitive and precise. The direction arrow should be pointing north, while the date should indicate when the map was made. The key, or legend, should explain what the symbols on the map represent. Different colors, for example, could represent various elevations, lines could show major roads, dots could depict houses or cities, and heavy broken lines may represent political boundaries.

The scale on a map shows to what degree an item on earth has been reduced on the map. The scale could be <u>fractional, linear, or descriptive</u>. A fractional scale of 1/20,000 means that one item on the map would be 20,000 times bigger in reality, while a descriptive scale of one inch equals one mile (1" = 1 mile) means that a measured inch on the map would equal a mile on land.
The one unique feature of the linear scale is that it remains correct even when the map changes size, e.g. through photocopying.

Maps with a very large scale (1/1,000 for example) show precise details with little exaggeration. The maps with a very small scale (1/1,000,000) show little detail and are sometimes referred to as the "atlas scale". In general, maps showing ground detail begin with a scale of 1/5,000. The U.S. Geological Survey generally uses a scale of 1/24,000 in its national topographic map series (see your Geistown Quadrangle map). These maps, showing contour intervals of 20 feet, cover an area of approximately 57 square miles.

The U.S. National Imagery and Mapping Agency uses a scale of 1/50,000 as do the French and German governments for their national map series. The U.S. Central Intelligence Agency (CIA) uses a number of fractional scales (for example, 1/400,000 for a map of Mauritius; 1/3,220,000 for a map of Egypt; and 1/4,070,000 for a map of Ethiopia). The National Geographic maps, which are of outstanding quality, also utilize a number of different fractional scales.

Converting a fractional scale to a descriptive scale is done by dividing the denominator of a fractional scale by the number of inches in a mile  (63,360" = 1 mile). For example, a fractional scale of 1/7,920,000 would equal a descriptive scale of 1" = 125 miles.

Scale can be defined as the proportion between land and its representation on a map. A fractional scale of 1/31,680, which can also be written as 1 to 31,680 or 1:31,680, means that one unit of measurement on the map equals to 31,680 units in reality. At this scale, one inch on a map would equal to half a mile on the ground.

Generally, a scale of less than 4 miles to an inch, is referred to as a large scale. Medium scale maps are 4 to 16 miles to an inch, and those over 16 miles to an inch are small-scale maps.

EARTH'S MOVEMENTS:
The earth has a slight wobble in addition to its major movements of Revolution and Rotation.
    <u>Revolution</u> – the earth orbits around the sun once every 365 1/4 days at the speed of
        approximately 18.5 miles per second or 66,600 miles per hour.
    <u>Rotation</u> – the earth spins on its imaginary axis in the easterly direction at the rate, at the
        equator, of 1,000 miles per hour.

    LATITUDES (Parallels): Latitudinal lines are parallel to the Equator and are shorter in distance as one proceeds north and south from the equator. The equator, which is the longest latitudinal line, is designated as 0 degrees latitude. The poles are marked 90 degrees north and 90 degrees south latitude.

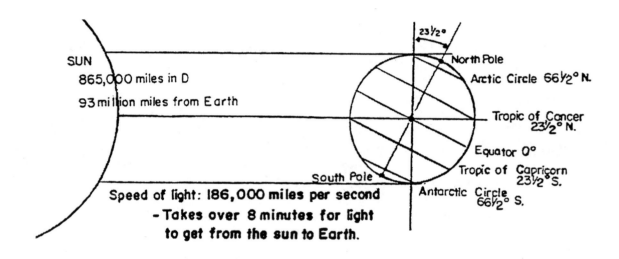

    As the earth revolves around the sun, its axis is inclined at an angle of 23.5 degrees and this axis of rotation remains inclined at the same angle throughout the earth's journey around the sun. Therefore, the direct rays of the sun fall on different parts of the earth at different times, causing the seasons.

    The above diagram shows the winter season in the northern hemisphere. At this time, the northern hemisphere receives the slanting or indirect rays of the sun, which have less heating power than direct rays. December 22, the <u>winter solstice</u> is the shortest day, receiving the least amount of daylight. Conversely, during the summer months in the northern hemisphere, the sun rays are more direct and have the greatest heating capacity. June 21st, the <u>summer solstice</u>, is the longest day in the northern hemisphere.

## II. LONGITUDES (Meridians)

Unlike the latitude lines, which become shorter in length as one moves north or south from the equator, the longitude lines are all equal in length, and run north and south from pole to pole. If the lines are all equal in length, how would the starting point, or 0 degree longitude, be determined? That line was chosen to run through GREENWICH (near London, England) at a conference held in 1884. The representatives from various nations to this conference, held in Washington, D.C., agreed on this location for the Prime Meridian. This allowed for all maps to be standardized regardless of where they were produced. (see the following page)

The longitudes are also used to demarcate time zones of the world (see following map). The earth rotates in the easterly direction through 360 degrees in about 24 hours. This equates to 15 degrees for each hour. When the sun is at its highest point (noon) at a given location, fifteen degrees west of that location the time will be 11 A.M. In the next time zone west, the time will be 10 A.M., in the next 9 A.M., and so on. To the east, the times will be 1 P.M., 2 P.M., and so forth. In other words, the time will be earlier in the west and later in the east.

As shipping and railroad transportation developed, it became necessary to establish rules on "time". At the 1884 conference mentioned above, 24 time zones were set up for the world, with Greenwich serving as the reference point (0 degrees longitude). Twelve zones are located east of Greenwich and twelve west of it. The zones lie next to each other and meet at an imaginary line called the International Date Line (see below).

The United States and Canada lie within eight standard time zones. These include ATLANTIC (centering on 60 degrees west longitude), EASTERN (75), CENTRAL (90), MOUNTAIN (105), PACIFIC (120), YUKON (135), ALASKA-HAWAII (150), and BERING (165). Russia has eleven time zones, while some of the smaller nations on earth only have one time zone. China chose to have only one time zone, the Beijing Time !

## INTERNATIONAL DATE LINE:

The International Date Line runs along the 180 degree longitude (east or west) where the date changes by one day when this line is crossed. The line is not rigidly followed, and some deviation to the rule is practiced to avoid confusion of dates on islands and land areas which are cut by the line. The date is one day earlier to the east of the line. A traveler crossing the date line westward, for example, would thus "lose" a day, advancing the calendar from Tuesday to Wednesday. Similarly, crossing the date line eastward gains a day, with the calendar being moved from Tuesday to Monday. This is because on a journey eastward from 0 degrees longitude (Prime Meridian) the time is advanced by one hour in each time zone until 180 degree line is reached. The time here, at the International Date Line (I.D.L.) is 12 hours ahead of Greenwich Time. Similarly, moving westward, the time in each zone will be earlier by one hour until the International Date Line is again reached. The time now is 12 hours behind the Greenwich Time. Thus, there is approximately 24 hour (one day) difference in time between two points placed just east and west of the International Date Line.

## Why Greenwich, England for the PRIME MERIDIAN?

At the request of President Arthur of the USA, 41 delegates from 25 nations met in Washington, D.C. in October of 1884 for the International Meridian Conference. Since it was advantageous to adopt a single "0" degree longitude to replace numerous ones in use to standardize all the maps, the discussion centered on what place to choose. Various delegates gave their reasons for choosing their nation for the honor. Great Britain was most persuasive and the Prime Meridian was awarded to pass through the Observatory in Greenwich overlooking the Thames River near London.

Prior to this time, the maps made in Russia had the Prime Meridian going through St. Petersburg, those made in Germany - through Berlin, the ones in France through Paris.

Needless to say, this caused a lot of confusion. The agreement to have a single Prime Meridian was an important and a needed step to advance the field of Cartography.

Prior to the agreement, the Prime Meridian went through Washington D.C. on a map made in the United states

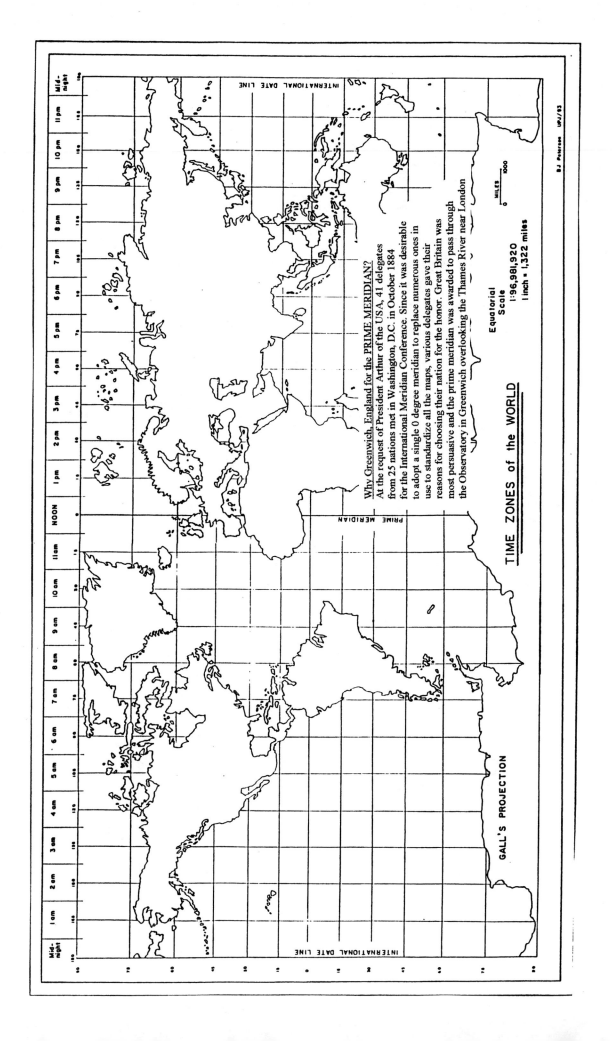

TIME ZONES of the WORLD

GALL'S PROJECTION

Equatorial
Scale
1:96,981,920
1 inch = 1,322 miles

MILES
0          1000

Why Greenwich, England for the PRIME MERIDIAN?
At the request of President Arthur of the USA, 41 delegates
from 25 nations met in Washington, D.C. in October 1884
for the International Meridian Conference. Since it was desirable
to adopt a single 0 degree meridian to replace numerous ones in
use to standardize all the maps, various delegates gave their
reasons for choosing their nation for the honor. Great Britain was
most persuasive and the prime meridian was awarded to pass through
the Observatory in Greenwich overlooking the Thames River near London

INTERNATIONAL DATE LINE

PRIME MERIDIAN

B.J Peterson  UPA/93

Mid-
night  1am  2am  3am  4am  5am  6am  7am  8am  9am  10am  11am  NOON  1pm  2pm  3pm  4pm  5pm  6pm  7pm  8pm  9pm  10pm  11pm  Mid-
night

21

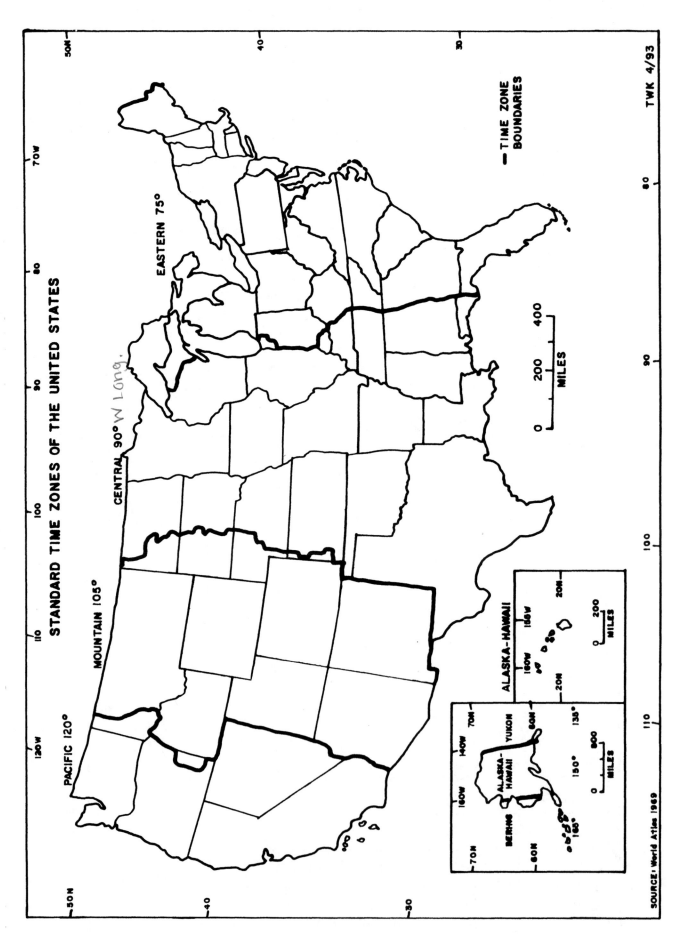

## STANDARD TIME ZONES OF THE UNITED STATES

EASTERN 75°

CENTRAL 90° W Long.

MOUNTAIN 105°

PACIFIC 120°

MILES
0    200    400

ALASKA-HAWAII

MILES
0    200

YUKON

ALASKA-HAWAII

BERING

MILES
0    500

TIME ZONE
BOUNDARIES

TWK 4/93

SOURCE: World Atlas 1969

22

## LENGTHS OF LATITUDES AND LONGITUDES

| Latitude (Degrees) | LENGTH OF 1° OF LATITUDE | | LENGTH OF 1° OF LONGITUDE | |
|---|---|---|---|---|
| | Statute Miles | Kilometers | Statute Miles | Kilometers |
| 0 | 68.704 | 110.569 | 69.172 | 111.322 |
| 5 | 68.710 | 110.578 | 68.911 | 110.902 |
| 10 | 68.725 | 110.603 | 68.129 | 109.643 |
| 15 | 68.751 | 110.644 | 66.830 | 107.553 |
| 20 | 68.786 | 110.701 | 65.026 | 104.650 |
| 25 | 68.829 | 110.770 | 62.729 | 100.953 |
| 30 | 68.879 | 110.850 | 59.956 | 96.490 |
| 35 | 68.935 | 110.941 | 56.725 | 91.290 |
| 40 | 68.993 | 111.034 | 53.063 | 85.397 |
| 45 | 69.054 | 111.132 | 48.995 | 78.850 |
| 50 | 69.115 | 111.230 | 44.552 | 71.700 |
| 55 | 69.175 | 111.327 | 39.766 | 63.997 |
| 60 | 69.230 | 111.415 | 34.674 | 55.803 |
| 65 | 69.281 | 111.497 | 29.315 | 47.178 |
| 70 | 69.324 | 111.567 | 23.729 | 38.188 |
| 75 | 69.360 | 111.625 | 17.960 | 28.904 |
| 80 | 69.386 | 111.666 | 12.051 | 19.394 |
| 85 | 69.402 | 111.692 | 6.049 | 9.735 |
| 90 | 69.407 | 111.700 | 0.000 | 0.000 |

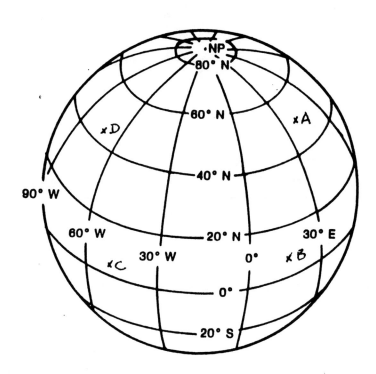

Draw and label the following lines on the globe above:
Tropic of Cancer; Tropic of Capricorn; Arctic Circle; Equator; 42 degrees N; 32 degrees W.
Identify the points from the globe to the nearest degree:

A: _____ ; B: _____ ; C: _____ ; D: _____

## LOCATING PLACES

Latitudinal and longitudinal lines are used to locate places on maps and globes. For example, Johnstown, Pennsylvania is located at approximately 40 degrees north latitude and 79 degrees west longitude. Because distances on earth are so great (one degree at the equator is equal to approximately 69 miles), each degree (°) is subdivided into smaller units. There are 60 minutes (') in each degree, and 60 seconds (") in each minute. Even a second can be subdivided into decimals for greater accuracy, making it possible to identify any place on the face of the earth, no matter how small. A single house in Johnstown, for example, might be located at 40°16'22.367" north latitude and 78° 51'56.874" west longitude.

Global Positioning System (GPS) is used to give precise location of places in latitudes and longitudes. To get from point A to point B on the earth surface, one uses <u>directions</u> (north, south, east, west or any combination of these) and can measure the distances in units such as miles or kilometers. The words up and down refer to elevation and should not be used to describe directions. The chart below shows both distances and elevations between two points in the Geistown Borough of Pennsylvania.

This profile was constructed by P. Riddle

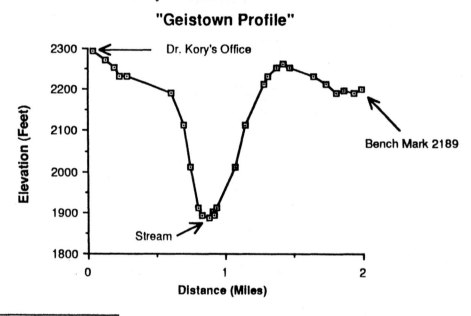

ASSIGNMENT #3: Locate the following cities to the nearest degree:

1. PHILADELPHIA ~
2. LOS ANGELES ~
3. ANCHORAGE ~
4. MIAMI ~
5. MEXICO CITY ~
6. MOSCOW ~
7. CAIRO ~
8. MONROVIA ~
9. CAPE TOWN ~
10. BUENOS AIRES ~
11. SYDNEY ~
12. LONDON ~
13. LIMA ~
14. TOKYO ~
15. NAIROBI ~
16. VLADIVOSTOK —

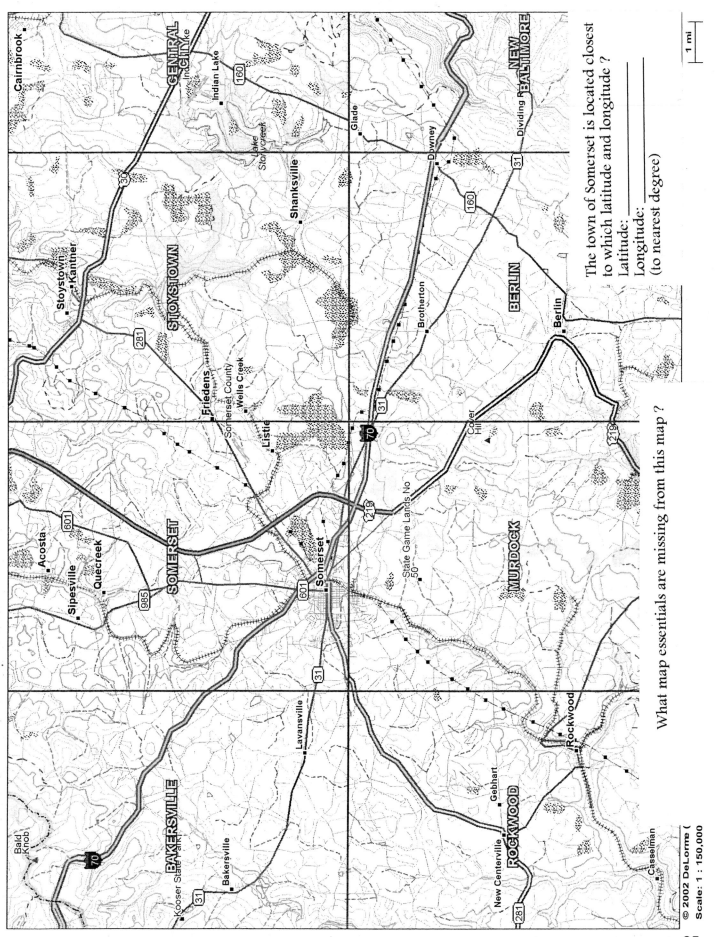

The town of Somerset is located closest to which latitude and longitude?

Latitude: _____
Longitude: _____
(to nearest degree)

What map essentials are missing from this map?

© 2002 DeLorme (
Scale: 1 : 150,000

1 mi

25

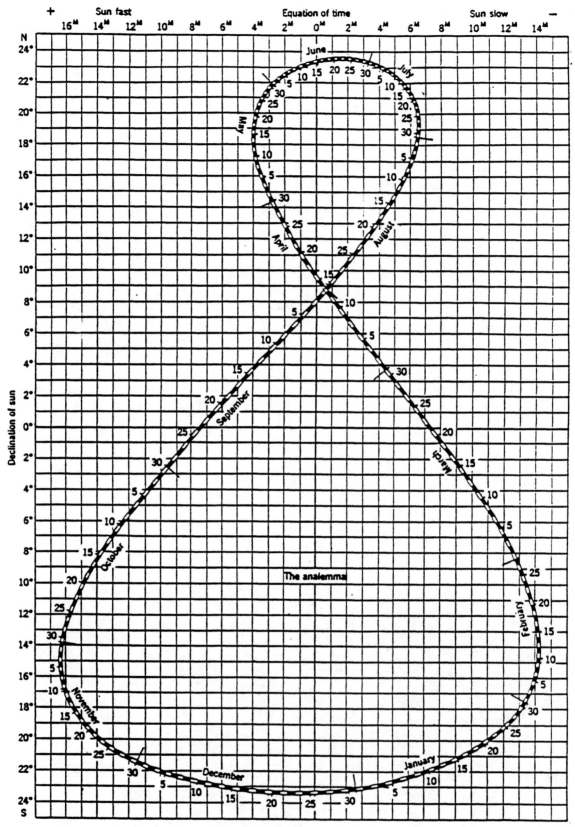

The analemma gives the declination of the sun and the equation of time for each day in the year.
From U.S. Coast & Geodetic Survey.

DISTANCE and ELEVATION

Distance on earth is measured in miles, kilometers or in other units, and usually follow some linear direction (north-south, east-west, northwest-southeast). Geographers never refer to direction on a map as being up or down. Those terms are used to describe elevation (height) on the earth's surface.

Earth's elevations can be shown on maps in a number of ways. There are *raised relief* maps, maps which use *color* for different elevations, and *topographic maps*, which show elevations by using the contour lines.

TOPOGRAPHIC MAPS: A topographic map shows the shape of the earth's surface, specifically the area's elevations. The numbered, circular lines on a topographic map are called contour lines. All points on a contour line have the same elevation. For example, a line labeled "200" on the map below connects all points located 200 feet above sea level.

The map of the ROCK RIVER CANYON (contour map #2) shows the elevation of an area using the contour lines. Points "A" and "B" are the highest on the map with the elevations decreasing to the south-east. Using that map, answer the questions below:

ASSIGNMENT #4
1. What is the elevation of point A? _____
2. What is the elevation of the contour line next to A? _____
3. What is the elevation of point B? _____
4. What is the elevation of the contour line next to B? _____
5. What is the highest elevation on the map ? _____
6. What is the difference in elevation between any two contour lines on the map?
_____

TOPOGRAPHIC PROFILES: It is sometimes difficult to see terrain features such as hills and valleys, because they do not project above or below the surface of the flat topographic map. Topographic profiles help to visualize the elevations shown by contour lines. A topographic profile is a side view of a portion of the earth's surface along a line drawn between two points on a map.

The map below (contour map #1) shows a profile (lower portion) constructed from a contour map (upper portion):
Contour map #1:

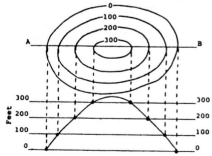

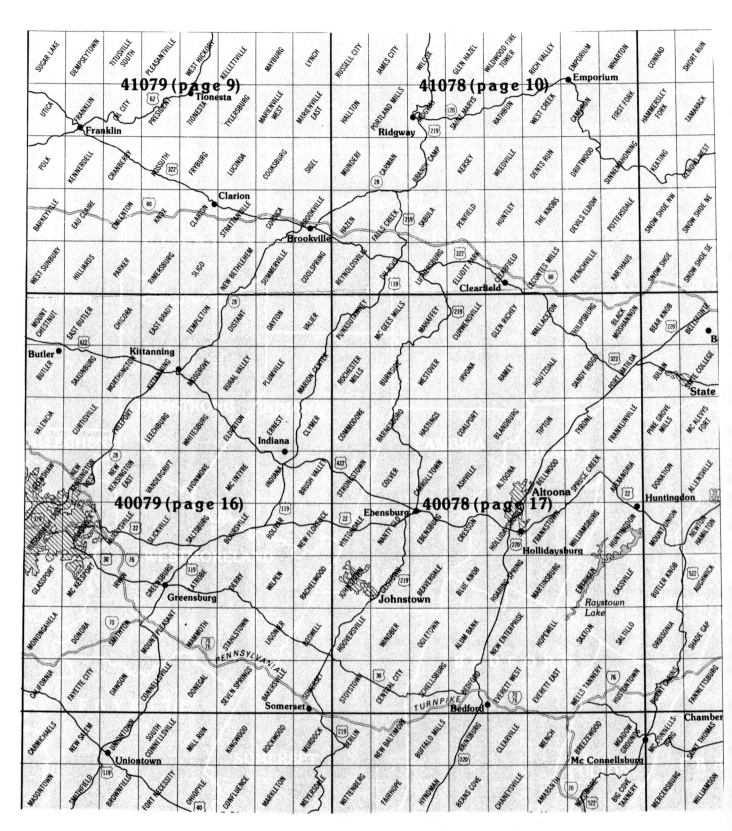

www.nationalmap.usgs.gov

28

## DIRECTIONS FOR CONSTRUCTING A PROFILE FROM THE "ROCK RIVER CANYON" MAP

1. Tear out the ROCK RIVER CANYON map from the book.

2. Look at the map and check for the five map essentials:

title: _____

date: _____

direction: _____

key: _____

scale: _____

3. Measure the distance from point "A" to point "C" _____

4. Measure the distance from point "A" to point "B" _____

5. RULER FOR PROFILE CONSTRUCTION

6. CONSTRUCT A PROFILE FROM POINT "A" TO POINT "B" ON THE GRAPH BELOW THE MAP

_____
_____

Assignment #5: On a separate sheet of paper construct a graph and
draw a profile from point "A" to point "C" of Rock River Canyon.

What would be the highest point in this profile (A to C)? _____
How high is it ? _____

What would be the lowest point in this profile (A to C)? _____
How high is it ? _____

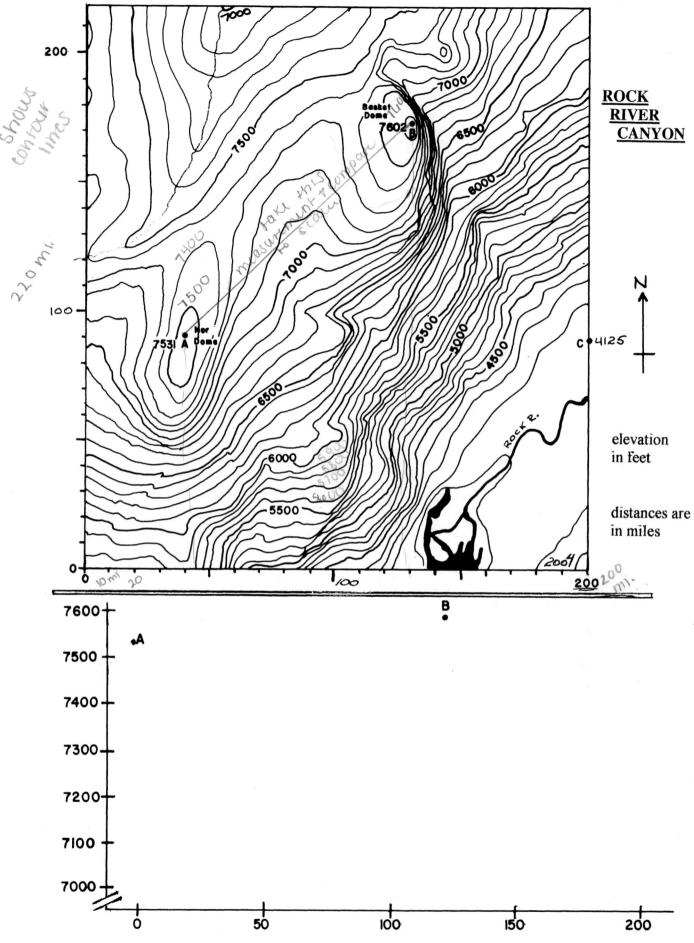

ROCK
RIVER
CANYON

elevation
in feet

distances are
in miles

Shows contour lines

220 mi.

Basket Dome 7602 B

7531 A Nor Dome

Rock R.

C 4125

N

30

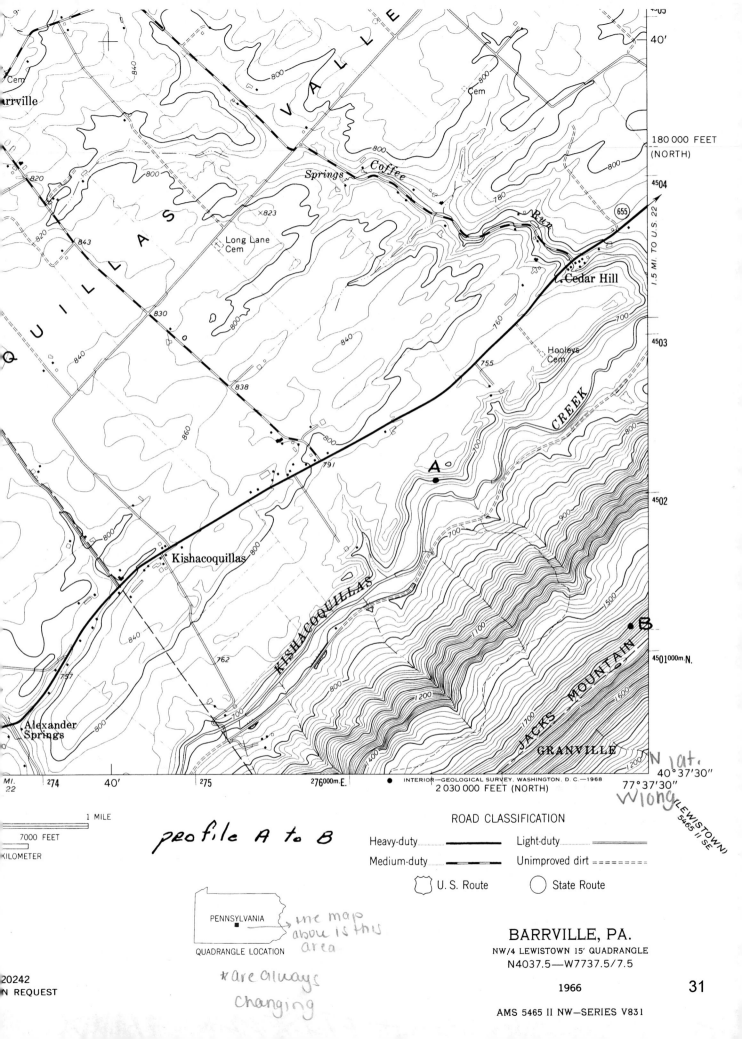

profile A to B

ROAD CLASSIFICATION

Heavy-duty ———————  Light-duty ═══════

Medium-duty —·—·—·—  Unimproved dirt ========

U. S. Route    State Route

PENNSYLVANIA

→ the map above is this area

QUADRANGLE LOCATION

*are always changing

**BARRVILLE, PA.**

NW/4 LEWISTOWN 15' QUADRANGLE

N4037.5—W7737.5/7.5

1966

31

AMS 5465 II NW—SERIES V831

20242
N REQUEST

N lat.
Wrong

(LEWISTOWN)
5465 II SE

## III. GEOGRAPHER'S VIEW OF THE WORLD

Geographers study the relationships among the <u>physical, cultural</u> and <u>human</u> phenomena on earth.  They observe the physical features, examine the cultural landscapes, and investigate the human aspects of various places, in order to understand and explain regional patterns on the earth.  Geographers look at what **people** (human geography) have done to the **land** (physical geography) to create various landscapes and social organizations (cultural geography).  Thus, we can better appreciate any place on earth if we understand the human, cultural and physical characteristics of that place. The approach to comprehending geographical phenomena can be either <u>topical</u> or <u>regional</u> but the end result should be an unbiased vision of the world's regions occupied by a variety of people.

Some Examples of:

| Human Geography | Cultural Geography | Physical Geography |
|---|---|---|
| 1. Population Growth | 1. Geopolitics | 1. Climatology |
| 2. Geodemography | 2. Urbanization | 2. Oceanography |
| 3. Gerontology | 3. Agricultural patterns | 3. Geomorphology |
| 4. Ethnicity | 4. World's Religions | 4. Hydrology |
| 5. Human Migration | 5. Economics | 5. Pedology |
| 6. Fertility patterns | 6. Rural landscapes | 6. Flora |
| 7. Mortality patterns | 7. World's language patterns | 7. Diastrophic Forces |

## <u>UNDERSTANDING A PLACE = KNOWING ITS HUMAN, CULTURAL, AND PHYSICAL VARIABLES</u>

Much has been written about geographic ignorance of the American public.  For example, 42% of geography students surveyed at the University of Miami could not find London on a map, and 9% could not identify the Atlantic Ocean.  Nearly one third of the students at the University of Kentucky could not locate Lexington on the map of Kentucky, and 97% of UPJ students surveyed, placed Jonestown, Guyana (the place of mass religious suicide) in Africa.

Geographic ignorance is wide spread and is found among all segments of our society. An American ambassador to the United Nations, Warren Austin, suggested in 1948 that Jews and Arabs should resolve their differences "**in a true Christian spirit**"!!!

Why should we know about various places and people who inhabit our earth?  One of the reasons is that we are living in an interdependent world, and international trade is growing.  The United States, for example, imports half of its oil needs from other nations, and total imports and exports account for over 30% of USA's GDP. In addition, the United States is involved with various nations through its foreign aid program, political alliances, cooperative projects in the fight against terrorism and in other ventures. Americans are also linked to citizens of other nations through their involvement in global issues such as air and water pollution, soil conservation, population control and nuclear proliferation. There is a need to understand how other societies view these and other issues in order to deal with them in an effective and efficient manner.

We can not afford another generation of leaders who are ignorant about basic geographic knowledge.  Their decisions in the international arena affect all of us.

On July 24, 1987, President Reagan signed into law a new act designating the third week in November as the <u>Geography Awareness Week</u>. The joint resolution was introduced in March of 1987 by the New Jersey senator Bill Bradley, Vermont's senator Robert Stafford, and California's representative Leon Panetta. The resolution focused national attention on the importance of geography in an increasingly interdependent and interconnected world. That week was observed nationwide with a series of lectures, exhibits, symposia, and scholarly presentations on all aspects of geography. The event continues to be a standard practice each November, and the media coverage should help to give much needed exposure to the field of geography.

We must guard, however, against the notion that Geography is a study of memorizing place names. It is not !!! Just because a person knows the names of the countries of Africa, for example, does not make that person a geographer; any more than a person who can write a letter would be considered a novelist.

There are many approaches to the study of Geography. Recently, the National Council for Geographic Education and a number of State Geographical Alliances developed and emphasized the following five themes for a better understanding of the world in which we live. These included:

1. <u>LOCATION</u>-        examples: Where is the country located (latitude and longitude)?
                             What countries does it border?

2. <u>PLACE</u>-         examples:  What are the major physical features of the country?
                             What is its major climate?

3. <u>HUMAN-ENVIRONMENTAL INTERACTION</u> – examples:
                             Is the major portion of the country's land used for agriculture?
                             What are the major industries in the country?
                             What percent of the population is urban?

4. <u>MOVEMENT</u>-       examples:  How are the major goods exported?
                             Who are the country's major trading partners?
                             What is the rate of emigration and why?

5. <u>REGION</u>-        examples:  what is the country's primary language?
                             What are its internal political divisions?
                             What is its major religion?

Take any country and give one example of the above themes: _____
1.

2.

3.

4.

5.

## Regional Geography

Regional geography deals with an in-depth study of a specific portion of our planet. The part to be studied may be a continent, a country, a number of countries having some common variable, or some other sub-division of our earth. These geographical realms may also be delineated based on common cultural traits (similar language, same religion); economics (capitalist system, socialist system); physical (climate, soils, vegetation, geomorphology); or political (democracy, dictatorship).

### One World - Divided

As mentioned above, there are a number of ways to divide our world. The economic, cultural, political and other variables used for this purpose all have limitations and drawbacks. Two nations, for example, with similar economies, may have different political systems, while two nations with the same official language may have different economic structures.

One frequently used method has been to divide the world into the "DEVELOPED" and "UNDERDEVELOPED" categories. The terms should be used only when comparing the level of technology of a nation, and not to rank cultures. Japan, for example, would be developed, while Afghanistan would be underdeveloped, based on the level of technology in the two nations.

It is, however, difficult to place all the nations of the world into the two categories outlined above. Obviously, the United States, Japan, France, Germany, and Great Britain would fit into the "Developed" group, while Ethiopia, Uganda, Liberia, and Sri Lanka would be in the "Underdeveloped" group. But where, for example, would Portugal or Argentina fit?

One of the ways to resolve this issue would be to rank all the nations from the most developed to the least. A number of variables, such as literacy rates, percent of people living in urban areas, infant mortality rates, or life expectancy, could be used for the ranking of nations. If, for example, we use urbanization as the criteria and state that the most developed nations are also the most urbanized, we can see where all the nations are ranked in relation to all others (see below). Thus, if a nation is 79% urban (like the USA), it is more developed, by our criteria, than a nation which is 28% urban (like India). An arbitrary figure (50%, for example) can be used to separate the developed nations from underdeveloped.

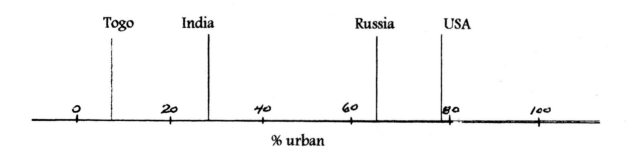

% urban

## V. GEOPOLITICS

Geopolitics is a subfield of **Political Geography**. The latter may be defined as the study of interaction between political processes and geographic location and functions of nation-states. The nation-state is the major focus in the study of Political Geography and Geopolitics.

Geopolitics was developed in Germany in the 19th century. The nazis later used the concept to justify their aggression and conquest of much of Europe in World War II. Today, geopolitics as a political theory, is not widely accepted in the scholarly community.

NATION-STATE: Harm J. DeBlij, a noted political geographer, defines a nation-state as: "a desirable political unit where the nation part of the word is roughly equivalent to the term "people" and the state part roughly equivalent to the term "country" wrapped around the people".

Although all countries of the world aspire to become nation-states, few come close to achieving the goal. Most nations have minorities - ethnic, racial, religious, or linguistic - who reside within their boundaries making the population less homogeneous. Some countries like POLAND, BULGARIA, ARMENIA and NORWAY have a high degree of population homogeneity, thus putting them closer on a scale to a true nation-state. On the other hand, nations like NIGERIA, GHANA, LIBERIA and UGANDA, whose population is very heterogeneous, are a long way from becoming nation-states.

It is important not only to understand how nation-states function, but also how they interact and align themselves with one another. The alliances may be based on economic, political, military, or other common interest. Nations do join together to form cartels and international organizations based on one or more of the above-mentioned variables. Some examples of international organizations are discussed below.

## INTERNATIONAL ORGANIZATIONS

Many countries of the world are members of one or more international organizations. These organizations may be based on military, political, economic or other criteria. The EUROPEAN UNION, for example, is an important political/economic block which is comprised of twenty-seven (2010) member countries.

The North Atlantic Treaty Organization (NATO) was founded after World War II (on 9/17/1949) to restrain Communist expansion in Europe. It was led by the United States and was primarily a military organization whose purpose was to curb the influence and military ambitions of a powerful State – The UNION OF SOVIET SOCIALIST REPUBLICS (USSR). Even after the USSR disintegrated as a country in 1991, NATO continued to grow in membership. In April of 2004, seven new nations – Bulgaria, Estonia, Latvia, Lithuania, Romania, Slovakia and Slovenia – became new members of the organization. All were either former Republics of the USSR or allies of the USSR which opposed NATO. Thus, the original purpose for NATO's creation – curbing the expansion of communism in Europe – no longer applies ! Today, as one opponent of NATO stated, it is an organization "in search of an enemy".

Of the 28 counties which are members of NATO (2010), three (the United States, Canada and Turkey) are located outside Europe. The two newest members, admitted in 2009, were Albania and Croatia.

Entrance to NATO Headquarters in Brussels, Belgium

## OTHER INTERNATIONAL ORGANIZATIONS

There are numerous other international organizations. A few selected ones are listed below.

- **The Organization of Petroleum Exporting Countries (OPEC)** – this twelve member economic organization is comprised of seven Arab states – ALGERIA, IRAQ, KUWAIT, LIBYA, QUATAR, SAUDI ARABIA and UAE – in addition to IRAN, ANGOLA, NIGERIA, ECUADOR and VENEZUELA. The main purpose of the organization is to regulate the production of oil based on the demand for petroleum products in the world.

- **The Commonwealth of Independent States (CIS)** – this organization is comprised of 11 members of the former Republics of the USSR. Georgia, Estonia, Latvia and Lithuania are not members of the organization.

- **The Arab League** – this 22 member organization focuses on issues which are of importance to the Arab population of the world.

- **Organization of African Unity** – encompasses the nations of the continent of Africa to deal with issues of concern in that part of the world.

- **Organization of American States** – comprised of nations of North, Central and South America.

- **The Commonwealth of Nations** – this organization, led by Great Britain, brings together the nations which were colonies of Great Britain.

- **Association of Southeast Asian Nations (ASEAN)** – comprised of Brunei, Cambodia, Indonesia, Laos, Malaysia, Myanmar, Philippines, Singapore, Thailand and Vietnam, the purpose of the organization is for mutual respect, peace and shared prosperity for its members. In addition, the basic aim of ASEAN is the general economic cooperation among all Asian-Pacific nations.

- **The World Trade Organization** – established in 1995 and headquartered in Geneva, Switzerland, it is the only international organization dealing with rules of trade among the world's nations. Its goal is to help promote trade and help exporters and importers conduct their business with technical assistance. The membership is approaching 150.

- **International Atomic Energy Agency** – with over 130 members, the organization serves as a global focal point for nuclear cooperation.

- **International Maritime Organization** – the main purpose of IMO is to regulate and improve safety at sea for its nearly 170 members.

- **Organization for the Prohibition of Chemical Weapons** – as the name implies, the organization strives to rid the world of chemical weapons.

- **International Organization for Migration (IOM)** – the organization assists the growing number of people who are migrating in search of better living conditions, employment, education, political freedom and safety from persecution and violence. Since its creation, IOM has assisted nearly 14 million refugees and migrants to settle in over 125 countries. Nearly 100 nations are members of the organization.

These are just a few international organizations which exist in the world. There are many others, focusing on virtually any issue facing the world.

THE UNITED NATIONS
www.un.org

The most important and the most visible of all international organizations is the UNITED NATIONS (UN), with its headquarters in New York City. The UN came into being on October 24, 1945, when its charter was drawn up and signed in San Francisco by 51nations. The membership of the organization has almost quadrupled and now stands at 192. Switzerland and Timor-Leste (2002) and Montenegro (2006) were the last countries to join the organization.

The United Nations is divided into a variety of agencies and councils with two of the most important being the General Assembly and the Security Council. The organizational chart is shown on the next page.
The GENERAL ASSEMBLY meets annually from September to December and every member country has a vote. The SECURITY COUNCIL is comprised of 5 permanent members, including USA, UNITED KINGDOM*, FRANCE, PEOPLE'S REPUBLIC OF CHINA, and RUSSIA (replaced the Soviet Union** in 1992) and ten rotating members. Each permanent member of the Security Council has a veto power on any issue brought before that body. The rotating members are chosen for a two-year term, with 5 new members elected every year.

* The UNITED KINGDOM is comprised of Great Britain (England, Scotland, and Wales) and Northern Ireland. The British Isles include the United Kingdom and the Republic of Ireland.

** The breakup of the Union of Soviet Socialist Republics (USSR) in 1991 was a particularly significant event as the 15 former Republics of the Union each joined the UN within a year. Ukraine and Belarus were members before the collapse of the Soviet Union and Russia took the place of the USSR. The other 12 new members include Moldova; the Baltic republics of Estonia, Latvia and Lithuania; the Republics located in the Caucasus Mountains: Armenia, Georgia and Azerbaijan; and the former Soviet Republics with the majority Asian population - Kyrgyzstan, Kazakhstan, Tajikistan, Turkmenistan, and Uzbekistan.

*************************************************************************
The Charter of the United Nations states:

"WE THE PEOPLES OF THE UNITED NATIONS DETERMINED
- to save succeeding generations from the scourge of war, which twice in our lifetime has brought untold sorrow to mankind, and
- to reaffirm faith in fundamental human rights, in the dignity and worth of the human person, in the equal rights of men and women and of nations large and small, and
- to establish conditions under which justice and respect for the obligations arising from treaties and other sources of international law can be maintained, and
- to promote social progress and better standards of life in larger freedom,
AND FOR THESE ENDS
- to practice tolerance and live together in peace with one another as good neighbors, and

- to unite our strength to maintain international peace and security, and
- to ensure, by the acceptance of principles and the institution of methods, that armed force shall not be used, save in the common interest, and
- to employ international machinery for the promotion of the economic and social advancement of all peoples,

HAVE RESOLVED TO COMBINE OUR EFFORTS TO ACCOMPLISH THESE AIMS

Accordingly, our respective Governments, through representatives assembled in the city of San Francisco, who have exhibited their full power found to be in good and due form, have agreed to the present Charter of the United Nations and do hereby establish an international organization to be known as the United Nations."

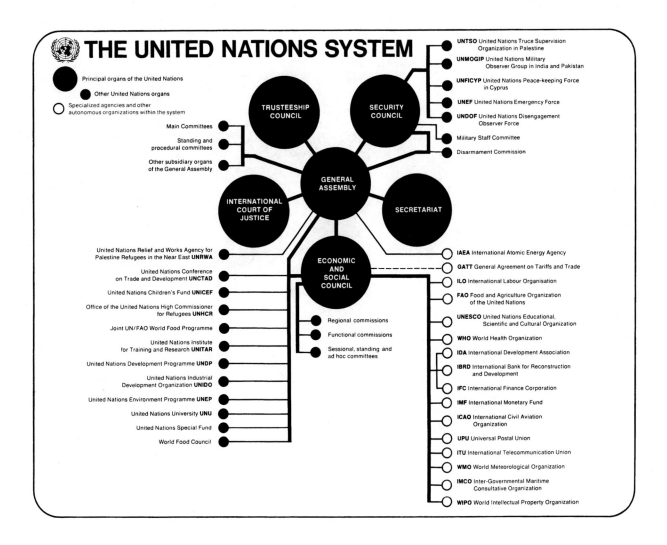

## UNITED NATIONS FUNDING

The United Nations is financed by contributions from its member countries, which are assessed annually. The funds are used to support the agencies listed on the previous page and for a variety of other purposes.

Article 17 of the U.N. charter specifies the amount to be contributed by member states. The United States is assessed the maximum, or 22% of the total regular budget, while over ninety members (from less developed part of the world) pay a minimum of 0.01%. In 2010, UN's budget was a little over two billion dollars with the United States contributing nearly $450 million.

| Top 10 donators to the UN budget, 2009 | |
|---|---|
| **Member state** | **Contribution** (% of UN budget) |
| United States | 22.00% |
| Japan | 16.624% |
| Germany | 8.577% |
| United Kingdom | 6.642% |
| France | 6.301% |
| Italy | 5.079% |
| Canada | 2.977% |
| Spain | 2.968% |
| China | 2.667% |
| Mexico | 2.257% |
| Other member states | 23.908% |

The signing of the UN Charter in San Francisco, 1945.

The above ten nations contribute nearly 80 percent of the total budget of the UN. The organization employs over 50,000 people, with nearly 5,000 working at the UN's New York City Headquarters.

The United States of America, whose citizens hold more jobs in the United Nations than any other member nation, derives additional benefits from its contributions. For example, for every dollar the US contributes to the New York based UN Development Program, American companies get back more than $2 in the procurement orders.

The budget for UN's core functions is about $2 billion per year. That is about 8% of New York City's annual budget and some $3 billion less than the annual budget of New York's state University system. USA's share of UN's regular budget is slightly over $1 per American.

## Additional Facts about the United Nations

*The UN has no army. The five permanent members of the Security Council authorize military action and various governments voluntarily supply troops and other personnel to the region.

*The yearly average cost for all UN peace-keeping operations – in the former Yugoslavia and a dozen other places – was about $3 billion. That was equivalent to 1% of the US military budget (not including the Iraq conflict).

*All member States share the responsibility of maintaining peace and security throughout the world. Since its founding, over 1,300 UN peace-keepers lost their lives in the performance of their duties. Less than three percent were Americans.

*The UN's agencies and diplomatic and consular corps contribute over $3 billion every year to the economy of New York City. That generated over 30,000 jobs for the city.

*Ban Ki-moon of South Korea is the Secretary General of the United Nations. He was elected in 2007 for a four year term and is eligible for reelection in 2011.

*The official languages in the United Nations are: Arabic, Chinese, English, French, Russian, and Spanish.

*The International Court of Justice in headquartered in the Hague, Netherlands.

*In the 65 years of its existence, over 80 nations obtained their independence from colonial powers.

*Kosovo, Taiwan and Vatican City are three places which are not members of the United Nations. Why?

### Kosovo
This province located in southern Serbia and populated by ethnic Albanians declared independence from Serbia on February 17, 2008 but has not gained international recognition to allow it to become a member of the United Nations.

### Taiwan
In 1971 the People's Republic of China (mainland China) replaced Taiwan (also known as the Republic of China) in the United Nations. China has blocked all attempts by Taiwan to join the UN claiming that Taiwan is an integral part of China.

### Vatican / The Holy See
This independent papal state of 771 people (including the Pope) was created in 1929. They have not chosen to become part of the international organization.

visit the
united
nations

UNITED NATIONS, NEW YORK

TWO FAMOUS EXAMPLES OF BOUNDARIES:

BOUNDARIES constitute an important concept in Geopolitics. They separate the sovereignty of one nation-state from another. The Great Wall of China (left) was built in the 3$^{rd}$ century, B.C. to protect China against invaders. It stretches    1,500 miles.

North and South Korea are separated by the 38$^{th}$ parallel. The peninsula was divided after W.W. II with the USSR controlling the north and the USA the south. Efforts to unite the communist N. Korea with the capitalist S. Korea have failed, so far.

*The Great Wall*

43

## VI. WEATHER AND CLIMATE

A DIRECTORY OF GEOGRAPHY defines weather and climate as follows:

<u>WEATHER:</u> The condition of the atmosphere at a certain time or over a short period, as described by various meteorological phenomena including atmospheric pressure, temperature, humidity, rainfall, cloudiness, and wind speed and direction.

<u>CLIMATE:</u> The average weather conditions of a place or region throughout the seasons. It is governed by latitude, position relative to continents and oceans, and local geographic conditions.

The word <u>weather</u>, therefore, is applied to describe the state of the atmosphere during short intervals, while the term <u>climate</u> describes the atmospheric condition over an extended period of time. Since a large number of processes combine to produce a variety of climatic types, many systems exist to classify the climates of the world. These systems group together locations on our earth which share common climatic characteristics.

One such climatic classification was designed by a German scientist, who died in 1940 at the age of 94. His name was Vladimir Koppen and he worked most of his life, both in Germany and Russia, examining various associations of natural vegetation with atmospheric elements on our planet. These associations, along with temperature, moisture conditions, and a number of other variables form the basis for his classification which, with slight modification, are still used today. (Goode's p. 14 – 15)

Koppen identified <u>FIVE</u> principle groups of world climates, which are intended to correspond with principle vegetation groups of the world. These groups, each designated by a capital letter, are:

| | | |
|---|---|---|
| A | = | tropical rainy climate with no cool season |
| B | = | dry climate |
| C | = | middle-latitude rainy climate with mild winters |
| D | = | middle-latitude rainy climate with severe winters |
| E | = | polar climate with no warm season |

Each of these major categories are further subdivided, based primarily on temperature and the amount of precipitation, as shown below:

### "A" CLIMATES

In order to be placed in this category, the area must have an average temperature of its coolest month above 18 degrees C. (64.4 degrees F.) *[handwritten: monthly]*

Af: <u>tropical rainforest climate.</u> Annual rainfall measures about 90".
   f: rainfall in the driest month here is at least 2.4"
Aw: <u>tropical savanna climate.</u> Annual rainfall measures about 50".
   w: distinct dry season in the "winter" (low sun period).
Am: <u>tropical monsoonal climate.</u> Annual rainfall measures about 200".
   m: short dry season and a longer wet season.

INTERTROPICAL CONVERGENCE ZONE (ITC) – an example of ITC in West Africa is shown on the following two pages.

<u>COMFORT INDEX</u> = Temperature (in degrees F) + Humidity (in %)

# INTERTROPICAL CONVERGENCE ZONE (ITC)

The Intertropical Convergence Zone is the region along the equator where the north-eastern and southeastern tradewinds converge, creating a belt of low pressure cells.

## AFRICA

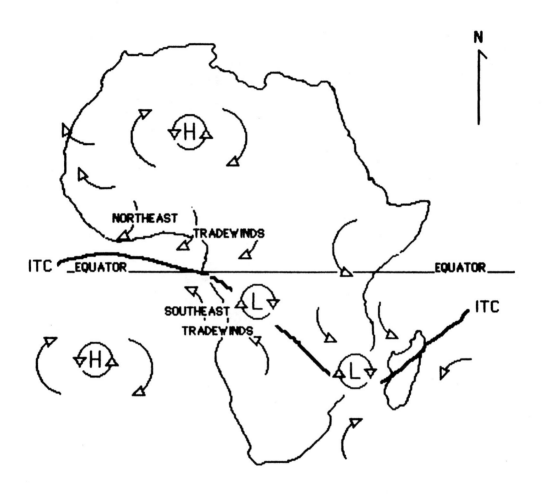

NOTE: This map depicts the movement of air masses in the winter months (December, January, and February).

0        1000
miles

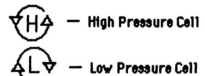

(H) — High Pressure Cell

(L) — Low Pressure Cell

— Movement of Air Masses

SOURCE: *Our Environment,* by Fellows, Donald Keith, p.116.

R. O. H. - 90

# INTERTROPICAL CONVERGENCE ZONE OF AFRICA
## IN THE SUMMER MONTHS

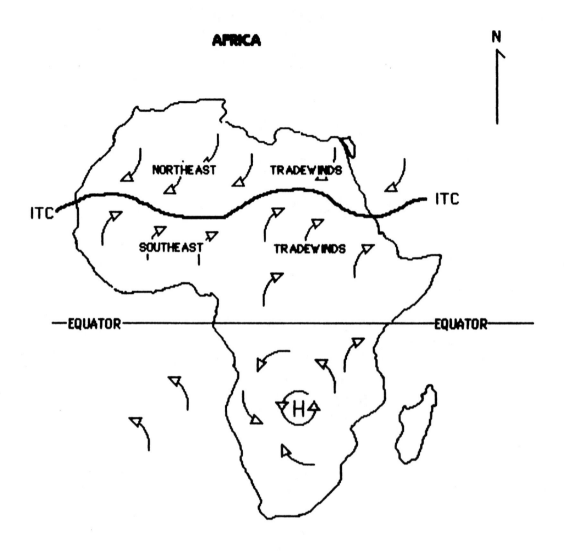

AFRICA

N

NORTHEAST     TRADEWINDS

ITC                                    ITC

SOUTHEAST     TRADEWINDS

—EQUATOR————————————————EQUATOR—

H

NOTE: This map depicts the movement of air masses in the summer months (June, July, and August).

0                    1000
miles

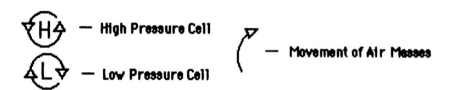

H  — High Pressure Cell          — Movement of Air Masses

L  — Low Pressure Cell

SOURCE: *Our Environment,* by Fellows, Donald Keith, p.116.

R. O. H. - 90

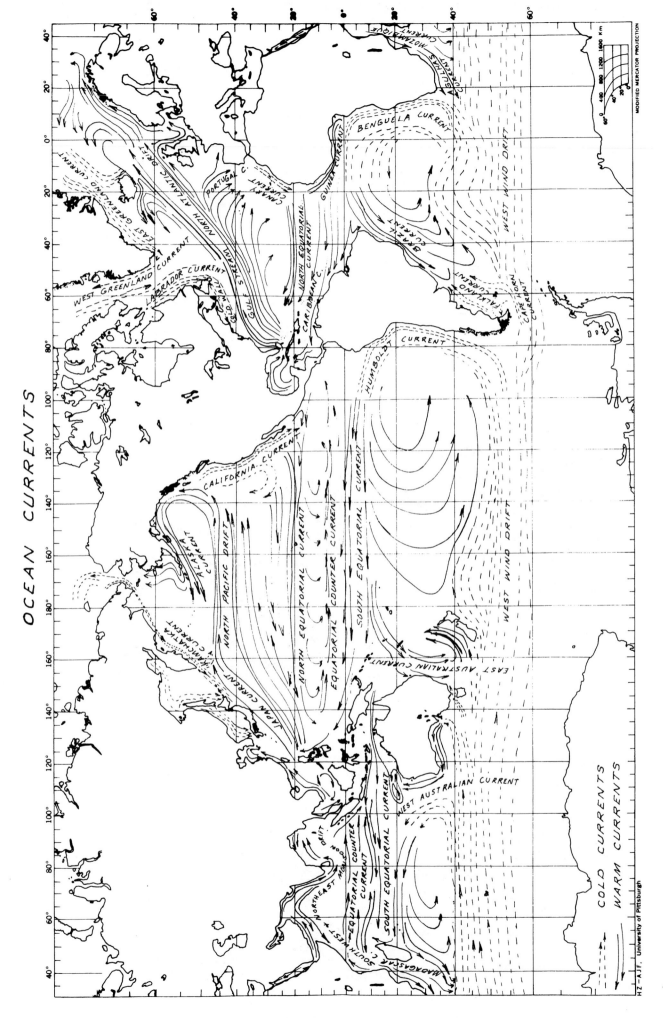

# OCEAN CURRENTS

GULF STREAM • NORTH ATLANTIC DRIFT • PORTUGAL C. • CANARIES CURRENT • NORTH EQUATORIAL CURRENT • GUINEA CURRENT • BENGUELA CURRENT • BRAZIL CURRENT • WEST WIND DRIFT • AGULHAS CURRENT • MOZAMBIQUE CURRENT • CAPE HORN CURRENT • FALKLAND CURRENT • HUMBOLDT CURRENT • EAST GREENLAND CURRENT • WEST GREENLAND CURRENT • LABRADOR CURRENT • COLD WALL • CARIBBEAN C. • CALIFORNIA CURRENT • ALASKA CURRENT • NORTH PACIFIC DRIFT • KAMCHATKA CURRENT • JAPAN CURRENT • NORTH EQUATORIAL CURRENT • EQUATORIAL COUNTER CURRENT • SOUTH EQUATORIAL CURRENT • EAST AUSTRALIAN CURRENT • WEST AUSTRALIAN CURRENT • WEST WIND DRIFT • NORTHEAST MONSOON DRIFT • SOUTHWEST EQUATORIAL COUNTER CURRENT • SOUTH EQUATORIAL CURRENT • MADAGASCAR C.

COLD CURRENTS
WARM CURRENTS

MODIFIED MERCATOR PROJECTION

480  880  1200  1600 Km

HZ - AJF, University of Pittsburgh

47

## "B" CLIMATES

Dry climates are classified as those in which **evaporation** exceeds **precipitation**. No surplus of water remains and <u>permanent</u> streams cannot originate here.

There are two main types of B climates: BW (W from the German "wuste" meaning desert) and BS (S from "steppe" meaning grasslands). Temperature range in the B type climate is greatest in the 24 hour period.

BW: <u>arid climate or desert</u>. Annual rainfall measures under 10 inches. The two major types of deserts in the world are: <u>ERG</u> - the sandy desert and the <u>HAMADA</u> - the rocky desert with some vegetation.

BS: <u>semiarid climate or steppe</u>. Annual rainfall measures between 10" and 18".

SUBDIVISIONS:

h = "hot" desert. Average annual temperature over 64.4 degrees F (18 degrees C); low-altitude or tropical deserts.

k = "cold" desert. Average annual temperature is below 64.4 degrees F. mid-latitude deserts.

s = summer drought;   w = winter drought;   n = frequent fog

An example of an area with BWkw climate would be a portion of the Gobi Desert in Mongolia.

A <u>xerophyte</u> plant can survive in a desert with little availability of water or moisture. <u>CACTI</u> plants like the saguaro (picture below) live for 200 years and grow to 50 feet in height.

<u>"C" CLIMATES</u> are sometimes referred to as the MEDITERRANEAN TYPE CLIMATES.
These are warm-temperate rainy climates with average temperature of the coldest month being below 64.4 degrees F. and the average temperature of the warmest month being over 50 degrees F.

    SUBDIVISIONS:

       f =   no distinct dry season; driest month of the summer receives over 1.2 inches of rain (3 cm.)

     w =   dry winters; two characteristic locations include elevated sites in low latitudes and monsoon lands in mid-latitudes.

      s =   dry summers, with the driest month receiving under 1.2 inches of precipitation. The wettest month (in winter) receives at least 3 times more rain than the driest month (in summer).

    OTHER SYMBOLS:

a = hot summer. Average temperature of the warmest month is over 71.6 degrees F.

b = cool summer. Average temperature of warmest month is under 71.6 degrees F.

c = cool short summer. Less than 4 months in a year average over 50 degrees F.

Found in the nations surrounding the Mediterranean Sea, in southern California, southeastern United States, central parts of South America and elsewhere, these regions produce citrus fruits, grapes for the wine producers and a variety of other crops.

## "D" CLIMATES

These are cold, snowy climates. Average temperature of the coldest month is below 26.6 degrees F. Average temperature of the warmest month is above 50 degrees F.

SUBDIVISIONS:
  f =  cold climates with humid winters. Johnstown is a good example.
  w =  cold climates with dry winters. These climates are found in the higher latitudes and include northern Russia and northern Canada.
  s =  dry summers.

Most of north-eastern United States and southern Canada have this type of climate.

In the northern parts of the D type climate, especially in Canada and Russia, one finds a vast extent of the evergreen, needle leaf forests called the TAIGA.
Much of the pulp used for newspapers printing comes from the wood of these trees.

## "E" CLIMATES
These are the POLAR climates found near the poles of the earth.

SUBDIVISIONS:
ET =   TUNDRA climate. The average temperature of the warmest month is
        below 50 degrees F.
EF =   ICE CAP climate. The average temperature of the warmest month is
        below 32 degrees F.

Antarctica, where the penguins and the killer whales share the coastal areas, is a good example of the "E" type climate.

## VERTICAL ZONATION

Vertical Zonation refers to the change in climate and vegetation as one ascends a high mountain. These vegetation and climatic zones are especially distinctive on mountains located near the equator. In fact, the zones encountered from the foot of a mountain to its peak are strikingly similar to the climatic zones found from the equator to the poles of the earth.

In Latin America, the zones of the mountains are given specific names. From the base of the mountain to about 3,000 feet, the zone is called <u>tierra caliente,</u> the next zone to about 6,000 feet is called <u>tierra templada,</u> and the zone to about 11,000 feet is called <u>tierra fria</u>. At about 14,000 feet, the vegetation zone is replaced by permanent snow and ice.

Mt. ORIZABA (about 18,000 feet in elevation), located in the southern part of eastern Sierra Madre, between Mexico City and Veracruz, is a good example of the above. Another mountain near the equator with Vertical Zonation is Mt. Kilimanjaro, the highest mountain in Africa of over 19,000 feet and located in northern Tanzania.

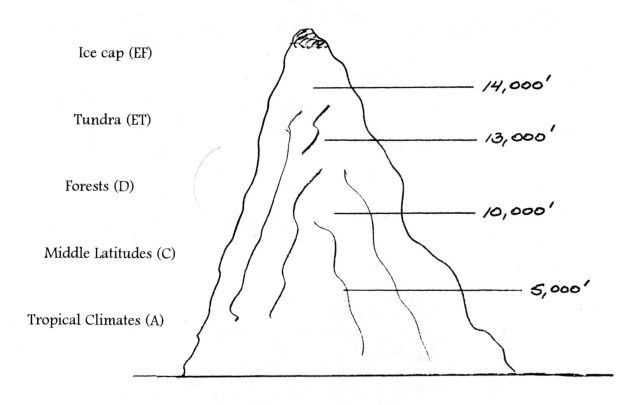

Ice cap (EF)

Tundra (ET)

Forests (D)

Middle Latitudes (C)

Tropical Climates (A)

14,000'

13,000'

10,000'

5,000'

Mountain near the equator
Vertical Zonation

52

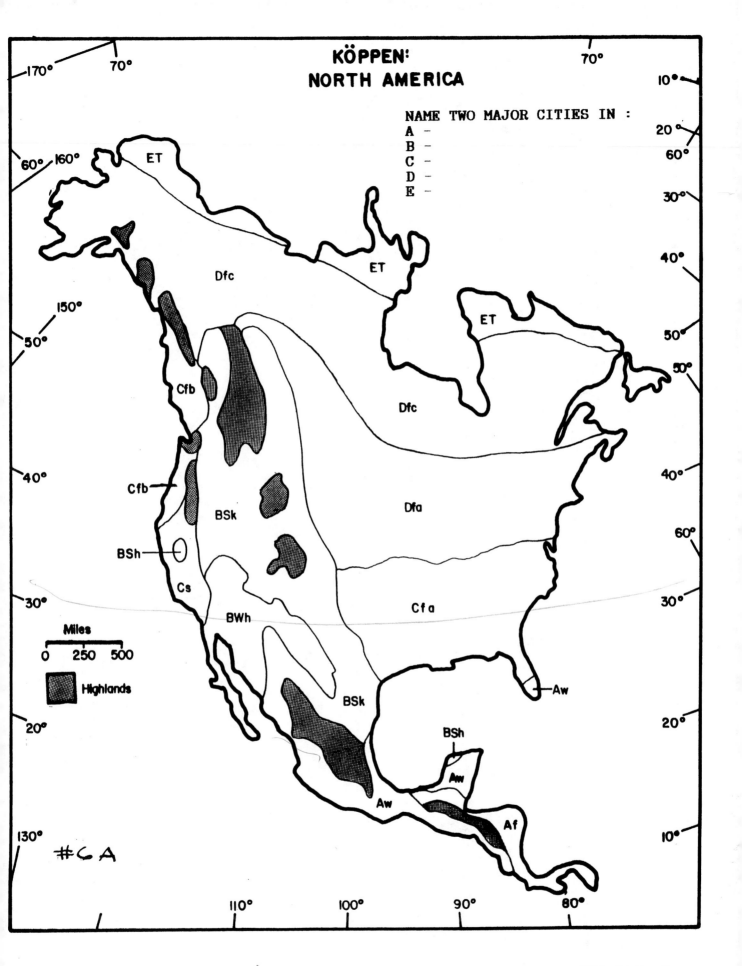

# KÖPPEN:
# NORTH AMERICA

NAME TWO MAJOR CITIES IN :
A –
B –
C –
D –
E –

ET

ET

ET

Dfc

Dfc

Cfb

Cfb

BSk

BSh

Cs

Dfa

Dfa

Cfa

BWh

Aw

BSk

BSh

Aw

Aw

Af

Miles
0   250   500

Highlands

#6A

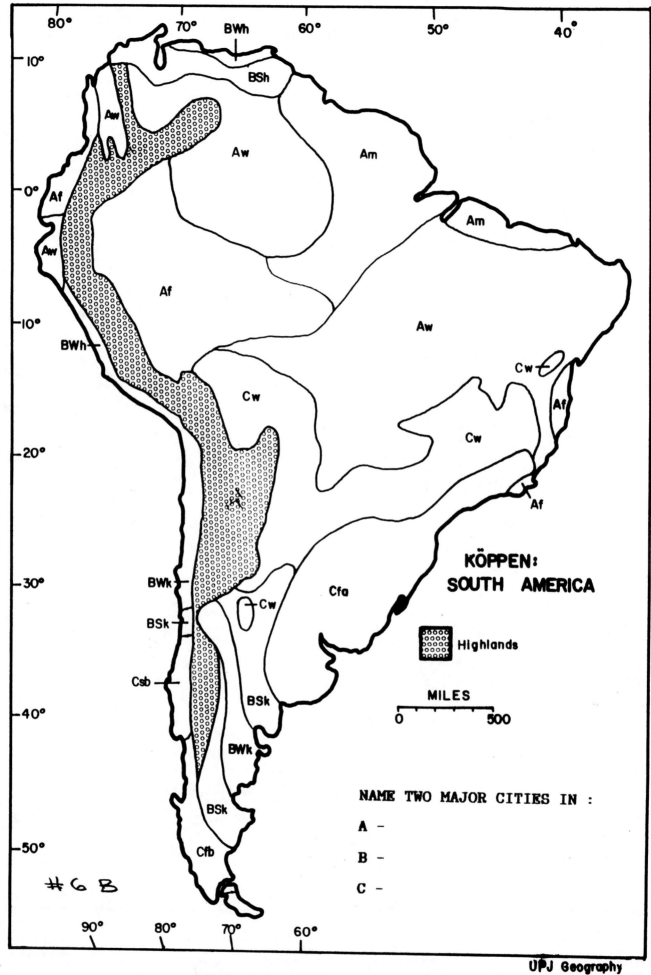

KÖPPEN:
SOUTH AMERICA

[] Highlands

MILES
0          500

NAME TWO MAJOR CITIES IN :

A -

B -

C -

# 6 B

54

## THE FORCES OF NATURE

The satellite photo below shows the lingering storm which dropped over eleven inches of rain on the city of Johnstown from July 19 to 20, 1977. The flooding which followed, killed 77 people and demolished over 6500 homes. An even more devastating flood on May 31, 1889 killed over 2,200 people in Johnstown and caused $17 million of damage to the city.

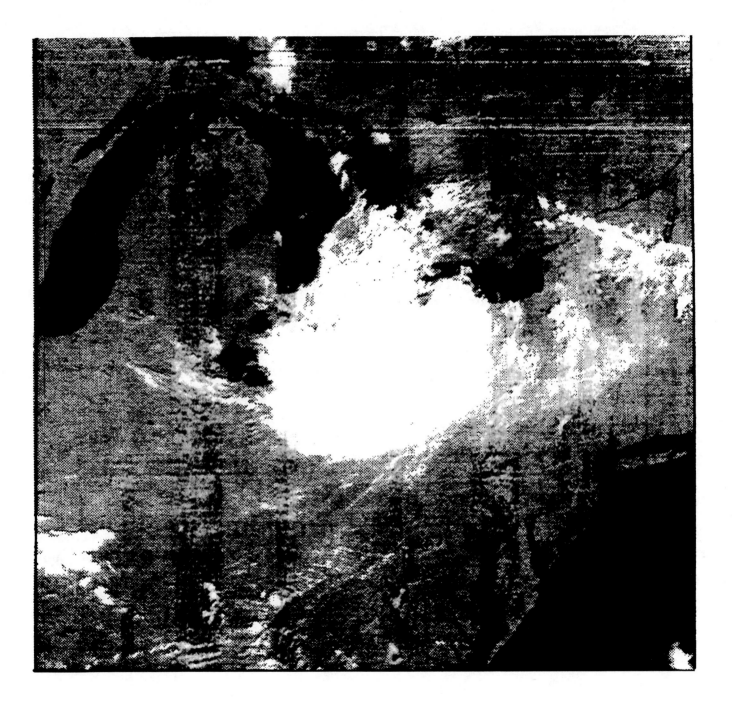

## VII. PHYSICAL GEOGRAPHY

Physical Geography may be defined as the branch of geography which deals with the physical features of the earth, including land, water, and air. The land, or the solid crust of the earth, is called the LITHOSPHERE, the water on the earth's surface is the HYDROSPHERE, and the air above the earth is the ATMOSPHERE. These three ZONES of the earth comprise the earth's physical environment. The study of physical geography is complementary to the study of cultural and human geography, and should result in the better understanding of our planet.

Sub-fields of physical geography include, among others, geomorphology (study of landform); hydrology (study of earth's water); meteorology (study of weather); pedology (study of soils); and climatology.

The influence of the world's climates on human societies have been debated for centuries by geographers and other scholars. Aristotle suggested in his writings over 2200 years ago that people living in very cold climates were not suited for ruling other people, while those living in very hot climates could be dominated and enslaved. Some three centuries later, a Greco-Roman geographer Strabo like Aristotle, believed that his homeland had the "ideal" climate (Mediterranean - C type) and thus the people living there had the best government and, by implication, were superior to others.

These deterministic views were perpetuated by people like Montesquieu, a 17th century French writer who emphasized the role of climate in creating different governmental systems, and by German geographers Carl Ritter (late 19th century) and Friedrich Ratzel (1844-1904). Ellen Churchill Semple, a student of Ratzel, introduced Ratzel's views to the United States, and later, geographers like Ellsworth Huntington (1876-1947) suggested in his writings that people living in the temperate zones were more progressive and energetic than the people living in the tropics. These views resulted in a doctrine referred to as the ENVIRONMENTAL DETERMINISM; a geographical theory which was popular in the first few decades of the 20th century. The theory basically states that the physical environment, and especially climate, determines human behavior of individuals and whole societies. It further suggests that the best climatic conditions for progressive cultural innovations are found in the mid-latitudinal regions of the world. The people living in areas with tropical or cold climate, the theory continues, would never achieve a degree of progress and innovation developed by the population residing in more temperate climate.

As geographers studied and debated the theory of Environmental Determinism, it became apparent that the theory had major flaws. First, people could modify their environment. As technology advanced, the environment's influence declined. In addition, there is no scientific evidence that a particular climatic region is tied to a particular form of government. Today, the theory is no longer widely accepted by geographers and has been replaced by POSSIBILISM and PROBABILISM. The former states that a society can modify the environment and make those modifications possible based on the level of their technology. The group that subscribes to the latter option feels that the Possibilists have gone too far from the realistic influence of the environment on the society and that natural environment probably influences certain human behavior.

## EARTH'S DIMENSIONS – GEODESY

Our earth is made up of a series of layers of material and covers a surface area of 196.8 million square miles. The earth's solid inner core is surrounded by a liquid outer core which is comprised of molten iron and nickel. The temperature at this core is over 12,000 degrees Fahrenheit.

The circumference of the earth, at the equator, is nearly 25,000 miles, and approximately 70% of the earth's surface is covered by water. The four major bodies of water (oceans) include:

PACIFIC OCEAN  -  64 million sq. miles, with an average depth of 12,900 ft.
ATLANTIC OCEAN -  33 million sq. miles, with an average depth of 11,700 ft.
INDIAN OCEAN  -  28 million sq. miles, with an average depth of 12,600 ft.
ARCTIC OCEAN  -  5 million sq. miles, with an average depth of  3,400 ft.

The largest lakes on earth are Caspian, which measures 143,240 sq. miles and is made up of salt water, and Superior (fresh water) measuring 31,700 sq. miles.

The earth's land surface, comprising about 30% of the earth's total surface, has an average elevation of about 0.5 miles above sea level. This land area is made-up primarily of:
  1. SEDIMENTARY ROCK MATERIAL (such as limestone, shale and sandstone)
  2. IGNEOUS ROCK MATERIAL (such as granite, basalt and rhyolite)
  3. METAMORPHIC ROCK MATERIAL, which is sedimentary or igneous rock changed to a new state as a result of a great amount of heat and pressure. For example, limestone turns to marble, sandstone to quartz, and granite to gneiss when enough heat and pressure is applied.

Identifying the physical properties of landforms, including the various rock formations, is the task of physical geographers. They examine the color, luster, hardness, specific gravity, magnetism and other properties to classify the material. Physical geographers also deal with locating and identifying mineral resources ranging from coal to asbestos.

The following charts give examples of composition and characteristics of some of the rocks found on earth.

Chart 1: Some examples of METAMORPHIC rocks

Slate; Composition - clay materials; Characteristics – formed from shale, red or gray in color
                 splits into smooth, flat surfaces.
Marble; Composition – lime carbonates (calcite) or magnesium carbonates (dolomite);
                 Characteristics – white or gray – sometimes streaked with colors due
                 to the presence of impurities like iron and carbon. Crystalline and
                 granular. Dolomite marble will bubble when sufficiently heated.
Anthracite Coal; Composition – between 90-99 percent carbon, of plant remains;
                 Characteristics – made from bituminous coal, does not crumble,
                 Hard and shiny.
Quartzite; Composition – quartz sand particles;
                 Characteristics – formed from sandstone, hard, dense and crystalline

Chart 2: Some examples of SEDIMENTARY rocks

Sandstone; Composition – cemented sand grains, mostly quartz; Characteristics – various
           colors including grey and red, porous and usually in layers
Shale; Composition – compact mud or clay particles; Characteristics – has mostly irregular
           surface, earth odor when moist, brittle and porous
Limestone; Composition – grains of calcium carbonate; Characteristics - gray to white in
           color, impervious
Chalk; Composition – compact microscopic shells of marine animals; Characteristics – very
           fine texture, soft and porous
Coral; Composition – coral remains of skeletons; Characteristics – pink to gray color, coral
           fragments
Bituminous Coal – Composition - carbonized plant remains/some 75% carbon;
           Characteristics – brittle, often shows layers with fossils
Rock Salt – Composition – halite from evaporation; Characteristics – salty taste

---

Igneous Rock is formed by MAGMA (molten rock) which cools and becomes solid. Over 700 types of igneous rocks have been identified, most forming beneath the earth's crust.

Chart 3: Some examples of IGNEOUS rocks:

Basalt is usually grey to black and fine-graded due to rapid cooling of lava at the surface of a planet. It may contain larger crystals in a fine matrix. On earth, most basalt rocks have formed by melting of the earth's mantle. Basalt has also formed on the moon and Mars.

Basalt Formation in Yellowstone Park.

Granite is a common igneous rock known to many for decorative kitchen countertops. It has a medium to coarse grain texture and can be pink to dark gray – sometimes even black.
Granite is currently known only on Earth where it forms a major part of continental crust.
It is the most abundant rock that underlies the relatively thin sedimentary veneer of the continents.

## EARTH'S LAND MASSES

The major land masses (continents) on the earth include:

| | |
|---|---|
| EURASIA | ~ 21 million sq. miles  Europe + Asia |
| AFRICA | ~ 12 million sq. miles |
| NORTH AMERICA | ~ 9.5 mill. sq. miles |
| SOUTH AMERICA | ~ 7 million sq. miles |
| ANTARCTICA | ~ 5.5 mill. sq. miles |
| AUSTRALIA | ~ 3 million sq. miles |

The world's major islands include:

| | |
|---|---|
| Greenland | ~ 840,000 sq. miles |
| New Guinea | ~ 306,000 sq. miles |
| Borneo | ~ 280,100 sq. miles |
| Madagascar | ~ 226,658 sq. miles |
| Baffin | ~ 195,928 sq. miles |
| Sumatra | ~ 165,000 sq. miles |

## EARTH'S HIGHEST POINT

The relationship between distance and elevation was discussed earlier in the book. Keep in mind that the circumference of the earth is approximately 25,000 miles, while the highest mountain on the earth, Mt. Everest, is only 5.5 miles (29,028 feet) high. This height is only 0.02% of the earth's distance around the equator.

Mt. Everest is located in the Himalayas, a mountain system in Asia which forms a broad arc of some 1,600 miles along the northern fringe of the Indian subcontinent. The Himalayas form the earth's highest mountain region and contain 9 of the worlds 14 highest peaks. Mount Everest in located on the Nepal-Tibet border.

This mountain system developed in stages 30 to 50 million years ago as the Indian and Eurasian plates pressed against each other. Even today, the ranges continue to change and earthquakes occur frequently in the area.

The mountain ranges influence the climate of the Indian subcontinent by blocking the cold air masses of Central Asia. Himalayas also exert a major influence on monsoon and rainfall patterns. The temperature in the region ranges from about 86 degrees Fahrenheit in the subtropical southern foothills to a cold alpine climate in at higher elevations, where winters are severe. At elevations above 16,000 feet, the climate is below freezing and the area is permanently covered with snow and ice.

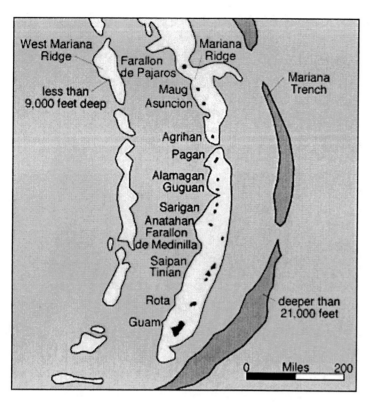

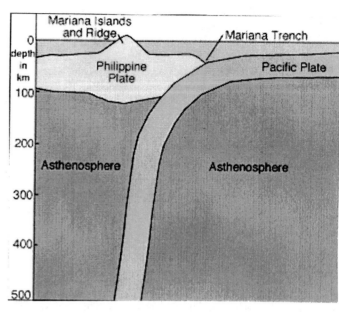

## The MARIANA TRENCH

The Mariana Trench is the lowest region on the earth's surface or the deepest part of the sea floor. It is 500 miles long, with the deepest gorge (called the <u>Challenger Deep</u> - being 36, 210 feet below sea level.

The Trench is located in the eastern part of the Pacific Ocean, about 200 miles east of the Mariana Islands.

Compared to Mt. Everest, the highest point on the earth's surface, Challenger Deep is over 7,000 feet deeper that the mountain is high. As the Pacific and Philippine Plates continue to rub against each other causing turbulence and instability, the depth of the trench may increase.

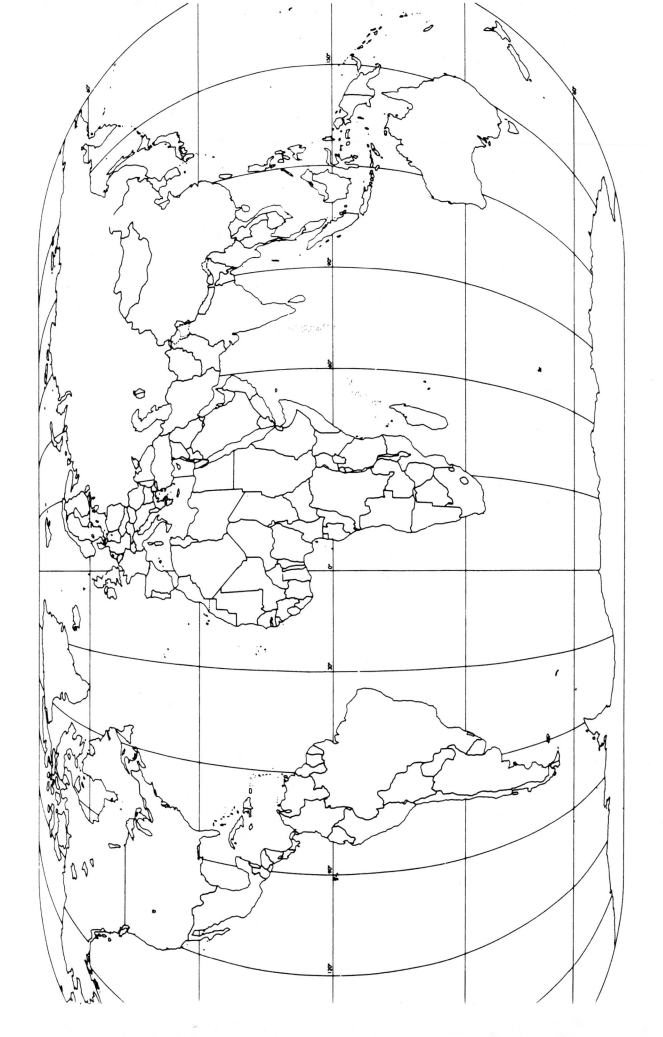

61

# EARTH'S FORCES

Our earth is in a state of constant change. A number of forces are at work to alter the appearance of earth's surface, both from within and from without. The forces within the earth are called the <u>DIASTROPHIC FORCES</u>, while the latter are called the <u>HYDROSPHERIC FORCES</u>.

I.  <u>DIASTROPHIC FORCES</u>. These include <u>folding, faulting, earthquakes, and volcanoes</u>. When a moving plate of land (mainly granite) meets an ocean-bearing plate (consisting of dense, less buoyant basalt), it rides over the ocean plate scraping up sediment deposits on the sea floor along the edge of the land, forming mountain ranges. The ocean bearing plate melts from the heat of friction forming underground pockets of white-hot lava. The trapped lava is forced up through crevices, erupting on the surface as inland <u>volcanoes</u>. The collision, separation, and shearing of the plates also create seismic distribution disturbances which result in <u>earthquakes</u>.

The major plates of the earth are shown on the map below:

<u>World's Major Plates</u>

The double lines on the map indicate spreading centers on plate boundaries. Single lines show transform boundaries. The heavy lines with small black triangles show converging boundaries. The famous San Andreas fault of California can be seen on the eastern edge of the Pacific Plate.

Source: W. Hamilton, <u>US Geological Survey</u> and Plummer/McGeary, <u>Physical Geology</u>

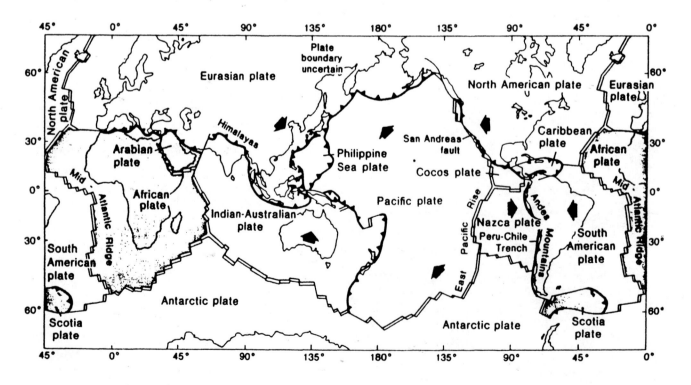

## TSUNAMI

One of the resulting consequences of submarine earthquake or volcanic action may be a tsunami, popularly known as the "tidal wave". This destructive wave can cause considerable damage thousand of miles from its point of origin. Deadly eruptions like the ones occurring on Krakatoa and Pelee were accompanied by tsunamis with its high waves inundating the surrounding lowland and drowning thousands of people.

In December of 2004, a 9.3 magnitude earthquake centered off the north-west coast of Indonesia unleashed a series of tsunamis which crashed into fishing villages, costal town and tourist resorts as far west as Somalia, some 3,000 miles from the epicenter. Waves, as high as 30 feet, slammed onto the land causing unimaginable destruction and resulting in 300,000 deaths. It was the world's strongest earthquake in 40 years and the third most powerful since 1900. The photos below, released by DigitalGlobe, show the shoreline of Banda Aceh in Indonesia before and after the tsunami hit the area.

# THE DIASTROPHIC FORCES

The Dictionary of Geography defines the four major Diastrophic Forces as follows:

## 1. FOLDING (or Folded Mountains)

These are mountains which have been thrown up into a massive *fold* or ridge by earth movements. Often the mountains form an *Anticline*, and the adjacent valleys are *Synclines*. Most of the important mountain ranges consist of folded mountains, including Himalayas, the various Alpine chains, and the Pyrenees.

## 2. FAULTING (or Fault)

It is a fracture in the earth's crust along which movement has taken place. Although the movement is usually vertical, a fault may take place in any direction. There are a number of recognizable faults on earth, including the famous St. Andreas Fault in California and the Great Rift Valley Fault in East Africa.

## 3. EARTHQUAKE

A movement or tremor of the earth's crust which originates naturally and below the surface. An earthquake may be produced by a volcanic explosion, and often precede or accompany eruptions. It is more likely, however, to be of *Tectonic* origin, and probably due to the existence of a *Fault*. The three regions where earthquakes occur most frequently are (1) the west coast region of North and South America, (2) the western side of the Pacific Ocean including Japan, (3) a belt across southern Europe and southern Asia. Of the thousands of earthquakes recorded annually, only a few cause great damage.

## 4. VOLCANOES

These are vents in the earth's crust caused by *Magma* forcing its way to the surface. Molten rock, or *Lava*, is ejected, sometimes with explosive force. The emissions of lava often causes the volcano to take the form of a conical hill or mountain which are built up of ejected material. Volcanoes are situated along the lines of weakness in the earth's crust, one of which runs around the edges of the Pacific Ocean and known as the "PACIFIC RING".

One of the most violent recorded eruptions occurred in 1902 on the island of Martinique, when Mt. Pelee exploded killing over 28,000 inhabitants.

**Illustration: epicenters of earthquakes along a portion of the Pacific Ring**

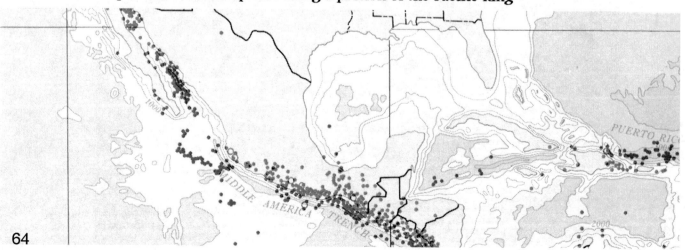

DISASTER IN HAITI

In January 2010, a devastating earthquake with a magnitude of 7.0, struck the nation of Haiti. Its epicenter was some 15 miles west of the capital city of Port-au-Prince and the destruction was catastrophic. Over a quarter million people were dead, nearly a third of a million injured and another million people were left homeless. This poorest and least developed nation in the western hemisphere had its share of natural disasters. The latest, before the quake, occurred in the summer of 2008 when three hurricanes hit the island causing over 800 deaths.

The 2010 quake occurred at the boundary of the Caribbean plate and the North American plate as the former shifted eastward in relation to the later. Eight aftershocks were recorded within a couple of hours after the main quake, measuring (on average) a magnitude of about 5. Thousands of structures collapsed, burying people within their confines. An estimated 30,000 commercial properties and nearly 300,000 residences were destroyed or severely damaged. Hospitals, schools, churches (including the main Roman Catholic cathedral in the capital), governmental buildings (including the President's gleaming white National Palace – see picture below), all were no match to the destructive power of the earthquake.

Earthquake in Chile

A month after the Haiti disaster, Chile was hit by an 8.8 magnitude earthquake. More than 1.5 million people were displaced by the quake and hundreds died. Although the quake in Chile was of a higher magnitude than Haiti's, the damage and death tolls were much lower than in Haiti. Chile's building codes are much stricter than Haiti's, it is a much more developed country and the government's response teams were better equipped and trained to deal with the disaster.

The chart on the following page shows the deadliest earthquakes on record.

Deadliest earthquakes on record

| Rank | Name | Date | Location | Fatalities | Magnitude | Comments |
|---|---|---|---|---|---|---|
| 1 | "Shaanxi" | January 23, 1556 | Shaanxi, China | 830,000 | 8.0 | Estimated death toll in Shaanxi, China. |
| 2 | "Tangshan" | July 28, 1976 | Tangshan, China | 255,000 | 7.5 | Estimated death toll as high as 655,000. |
| 3 | "Gansu" | December 16, 1920 | Ningxia–Gansu, China | 234,117 | 7.8 | Major fractures, landslides. |
| 4 | "Haiti" | January 12, 2010 | Haiti | 233,000 | 7.0 | Provisional estimate one month after the earthquake. |
| 5 | "Indian Ocean" | December 26, 2004 | Sumatra, Indonesia | 230,210 | 9.3 | Deaths from earthquake and resulting tsunami. |
| 6 | "Aleppo" | October 11, 1138 | Aleppo, Syria | 230,000 | 8.5 | Death toll disputed as first mention of 230,000 dead was in the 15th century. |
| 7 | "Great Kantō" | September 1, 1923 | Kantō region, Japan | 142,000 | 7.9 | Caused the Great Tokyo fire. |
| 8 | "Ashgabat" | October 6, 1948 | Ashgabat, Turkmenistan | 110,000 | 7.3 | |

The highest magnitude earthquake ever recorded was 9.5 in 1960 in Chile. The localized tsunamis battered the Chilean coast and raced across the Pacific Ocean devastating parts of Hawaii. Thirty-five feet waves were recorded in Japan, some 6,000 miles away. The death toll was estimated at nearly 6,000.

The highest recorded magnitude (9.2) for an earthquake in the USA occurred in 1964 in Prince William Sound just southeast of Anchorage, Alaska. Some 130 people died in Alaska and the ensuing tsunami caused damage in Hawaii and Japan.

# CONTINENTAL DRIFT

The Continental Drift Theory, first postulated in the 1920's by a German scientist named Alfred Wegener, states that the earth's crust is made up of several plates (six major ones and a number of minor ones) comprised of rock 40 to 60 miles thick floating on hot mantle beneath them. Land and ocean surface rests on these plates and at one time, all land surface was welded together in one super continent called <u>PANGAEA</u> (Greek for "all lands"). 200 million years ago (the earth is believed to be 4.5 billion years old) the continents began to separate and flow away from one another (see map). The first break created <u>LAURASIA</u> (land comprising North America, Europe, and Asia) and <u>GONDWANALAND</u> (land comprising Africa, South America, Australia, Antarctica and India). Later, Laurasia and Gondwanaland separated into their respective components.  (see following map)

North America separated from Eurasia and moved north-west, while Eurasia is twisting 20 degrees clockwise to the north. Africa moved north, South America west, while Greenland parted from Northern Europe. Australia and Antarctica split from each other. India broke away from East Africa and traveled 5,500 miles in 180 million years to collide with southern Asia creating the Himalayan mountains. Climbers on top of Mt. Everest stand on what was formerly an ocean floor!

In the future, the Atlantic Ocean will widen while Pacific Ocean will shrink. Africa will join with Europe obliterating the Mediterranean Sea. India will slice off Asia and move eastward. Australia, moving north at 2 inches per year, will sideswipe Asia. California coast, west of San Andreas fault, will tear away and move in north-westerly direction.

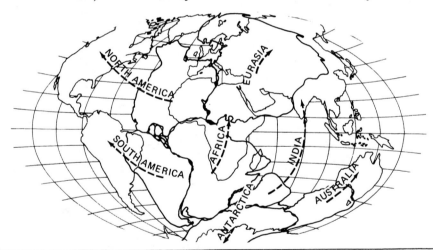

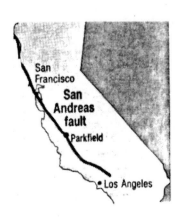

# CONTINENTAL DRIFT

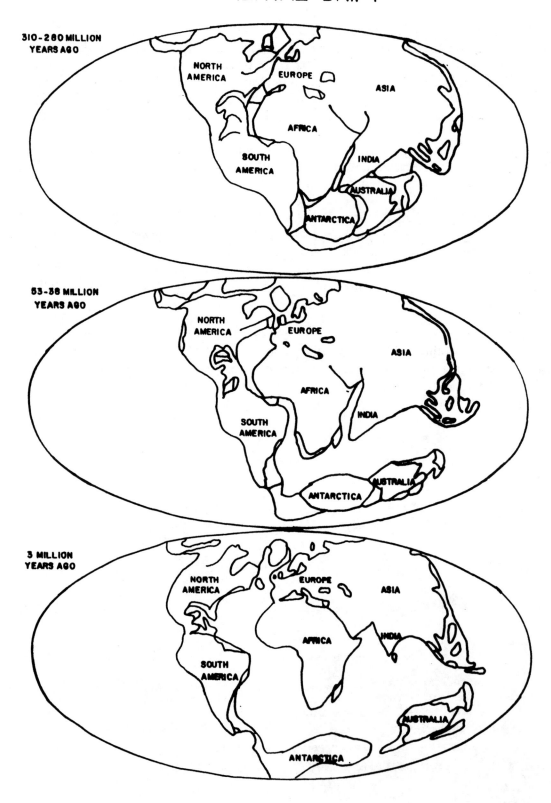

310-280 MILLION YEARS AGO

NORTH AMERICA
EUROPE
ASIA
AFRICA
SOUTH AMERICA
INDIA
AUSTRALIA
ANTARCTICA

53-36 MILLION YEARS AGO

NORTH AMERICA
EUROPE
ASIA
AFRICA
SOUTH AMERICA
INDIA
AUSTRALIA
ANTARCTICA

3 MILLION YEARS AGO

NORTH AMERICA
EUROPE
ASIA
AFRICA
SOUTH AMERICA
INDIA
AUSTRALIA
ANTARCTICA

HYDROSPHERIC FORCES: weathering, leaching, and erosion.

**Weathering** is caused by the decay and disintegration of rock materials on the earth's crust by exposure to the atmosphere. CHEMICAL WEATHERING occurs when various chemicals in the rain water react with chemicals in the rocks and disintegrates or breaks down the rocks. MECHANICAL WEATHERING is due to either great heat or cold. The heat of the sun causes rocks to expand and the subsequent cooling causes them to contract; the alternating expansion and contraction causes the breaking of the rocks near the surface. This effect is most noteworthy in the hot deserts (BW Climate), where the temperature changes are usually rapid. In the D climates, frost is a more powerful agent. Rain water fills the cracks and pores of the rocks and expands on freezing, exerting great pressure on the rocks. The alternating thawing and freezing will eventually break up the rock.   (see following page)

**Leaching** is the process by which soluble substance such as organic matter (underline humus) and mineral salts are washed out of the upper layer of soil into a lower layer (zone) by percolating rain water. It is particularly evident in the **Af and Am type climates** where the rainfall is heavy. The resulting top layer of soil is of poor quality and takes on a reddish coloration.

**Erosion** is the wearing away of the land surface by natural agents like <u>water</u> (rain, sea, or river), <u>ice</u>, and <u>wind</u>.

SOIL HORIZONS
All soils have stages or "horizons" made up of various material. Top soil is the richest soil for agriculture since it is made up of **humus** (the dark organic part of soil formed from decaying matter). This horizon can vary in depth from a few inches in the A type climate to a yard or deeper as in the mid-west of the United States.
The <u>A-horizon</u> is a zone of leaching, most notably in the A-type climate.
The <u>B- horizon</u> is a zone of accumulation of soluble minerals which have been pushed down from the A-horizon by heavy rains, especially in areas with the Am type climate.
The <u>C-horizon</u> is a zone of coarsely broken-up bedrock.
The <u>D-horizon</u> consists of bedrock

soil horizons:

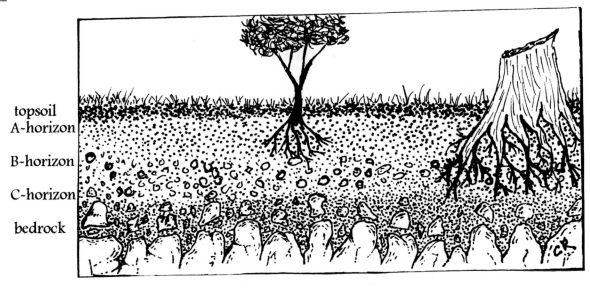

topsoil
A-horizon

B-horizon

C-horizon

bedrock

above: a street in Richland Township

1. A crack develops in the pavement near joints. Water enters crack area; freezes; expands crack area, knocking small piece loose.

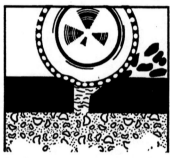

2. Car wear continues to enlarge the crack area. More water enters and the cycle repeats.

3. Water eventually leaks into sub-base, freezing below the surface area. Expansion forces larger pieces to become dislodged.

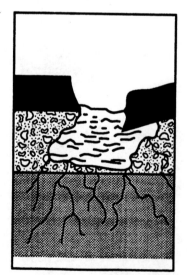

4. As ice thaws, whole sections of the road surface drop. Traffic pushes road surface even further down. Pothole is fully developed.

The Tribune
Democrat
3/9/1992

70

## Fresh Water

Because of the dramatic increases in word's population, many regions of our earth are experiencing shortages in the fresh water supply. HYDROLOGY, the study of location, uses, control, conservation and other topics dealing with fresh water, is an important field of study in geography. The water resources are not only in short supply in the desert nations, but are becoming scarce in many other parts of the world.

Oceans contain over 97% of the world's water, but that water is, obviously, not suitable for drinking. To convert the ocean's salt water to fresh water is a very expensive process and is not widely practiced worldwide.

The second largest sources of water are the glaciers and icebergs, which contain 2% of the earth's water. Recently, the number of icebergs breaking away from Antarctica have been increasing, possibly as a result of a rise in the earth's temperature. Whether this will be a continuing trend, is difficult to forecast, but the polar regions are sensitive indicators of change in the earth's climate. Scientists believe that the increase in the amount of carbon dioxide and other gases in the atmosphere in the past half century have been associated with rising temperatures. Some climatologists warn that this temperature increase, amounting to one or two degrees Fahrenheit, could lead to major climatic changes, including melting of the ice in the polar regions. This, in turn, could cause a rise in the ocean level around the world and accelerate major changes in weather patterns.

The remaining one percent of the world's water is found in lakes, rivers, streams, and under ground. Ground water supplies nearly **one third** of the total fresh water needs for North America.

Fresh water is unevenly distributed throughout the world. Over 1/3 of it is located in Canada and Russia alone. Other nations, especially those with high population densities, face constant challenge in their quest to produce enough safe drinking water for their citizens.

Worldwide demand for water is skyrocketing ! Industry uses approximately 2,000 gallons of water a day to produce goods and services for each person living in the industrial society. Although households account for less than 10% of all water used, this usage is increasing. In an American household, approximately 35 gallons of water is used for a bath, 10 for a shower and 5 to flush a toilet. A single slowly dripping faucet can waste 15 gallons of water each day, and it is estimated that nearly one fourth of the water piped through major eastern cities is lost to leakage. Overall, agriculture is the main user of fresh water.

Meeting the voracious demand for fresh water will require new and innovative techniques. There have been proposals, for example, to pipe fresh water from Alaska to the American south–west; to construct a cross–country pipeline to carry water from the Great Lakes, which contain 20% of the world's fresh water, to needed areas; and even to desalinate and use water from the Pacific and the Atlantic oceans. The latter is technologically possible but the cost of the operation would be approximately 30 cents per cubic yard of water, and that is some ten times more expensive than the cost of water today.

Water pollution has become a world-wide problem. Chemical pollution from industrial processes and pesticides are of particular concern. These pollutants, along with untreated sewage, fertilizers and other waste are washed into our waterways killing wildlife and fish, and contaminating both surface water and groundwater. Radioactive waste is even more dangerous and remains in the water for some 400 to 500 years !

In the underdeveloped world, where water is untreated, some diseases which are spread by contaminated water include cholera, schistosomiasis, bilharzia, and dysentery. Since the underdeveloped world has the highest rate of population growth, the availability and safety of drinking water will be a major concern for these regions in the 21st century.

HYDROLOGIC CYCLE
Water enters the atmosphere by evaporation from various water bodies and by transpiration from plants. As it cools it falls back to earth in the form of precipitation, and returns to the oceans in rivers and streams or through the subsoil as groundwater. Some is locked up in icebergs for a long period of time. This constant exchange of water from one source to another is called the HYDROLOGIC CYCLE. (see next page).

EVAPOTRANSPIRATION: The combined evaporation from the soil surface and the transpiration from plants that represents the transport of water from the earth back to the atmosphere.

The chart below shows the usage of ground water in the USA:

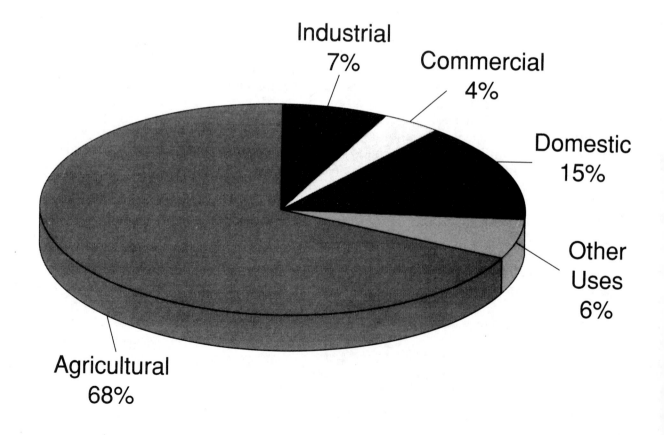

Industrial 7%
Commercial 4%
Domestic 15%
Other Uses 6%
Agricultural 68%

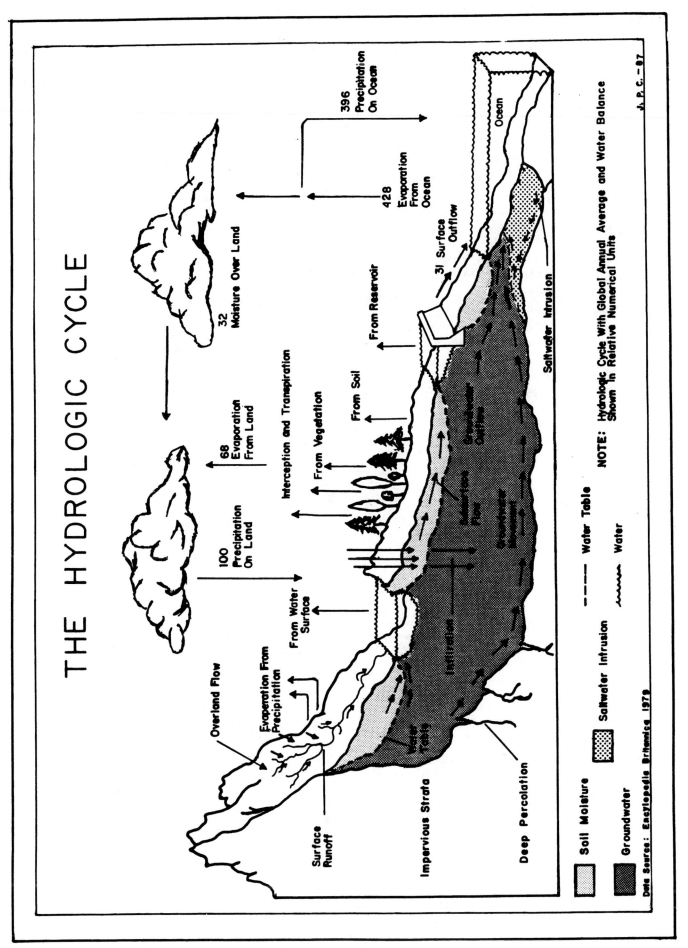

THE HYDROLOGIC CYCLE

396 Precipitation On Ocean

428 Evaporation From Ocean

32 Moisture Over Land

From Reservoir

31 Surface Outflow

Saltwater Intrusion

Ocean

Interception and Transpiration

From Soil

From Vegetation

68 Evaporation From Land

100 Precipitation On Land

From Water Surface

Overland Flow

Evaporation From Precipitation

Surface Runoff

Impervious Strata

Deep Percolation

Infiltration

NOTE: Hydrologic Cycle With Global Annual Average and Water Balance Shown In Relative Numerical Units

J. P. C. — 87

Soil Moisture

Saltwater Intrusion

Groundwater

Water Table

Water

Data Source: Encyclopedia Britannica 1979

73

## VIII. CULTURAL GEOGRAPHY

Although all fields of geography are inter-related, the emphasis may differ among the various sub-fields. Cultural Geography is concerned with human systems of technologies and the cultural practices which develop in particular regions of the earth over time. The cultural groups do not operate in isolation; there are transfers of ideas among the groups and continuous interaction of humans with their environment. Cultural geographers strive to understand the spatial dimensions and relationships of people with those features on the earth's surface which have been created, altered or modified by human action. Thus, such topics as the origin of the human species, spread and development of different languages and religious practices, the political organization of groups, cultivation of land, drastic changes in the landscape through urbanization, development in transportation, and technological achievements, are of interest to cultural geographers.

Four major components of cultural geographers include LANGUAGE; RELIGION; POLITICAL ORGANIZATION; and LEVEL OF TECHNOLOGY.

Culture should not be equated to the notion of race. The above mentioned components of culture, namely language, religion, political organization and level of technology are all learned and not inherited. Any person, living any place on earth, can learn English, German or Zulu; become a Muslim, Hindu or Lutheran; be a citizen under a particular political system; and study and learn advanced technologies. Race, on the other hand, is a biological trait which is inherited and can not be learned. With a continuing trend of interaction among different groups of people, the racial classifications are becoming blurred and should be less relevant.

LANGUAGE: there are approximately 5,000 languages spoken in the world today. The principal groups are shown in the chart below:

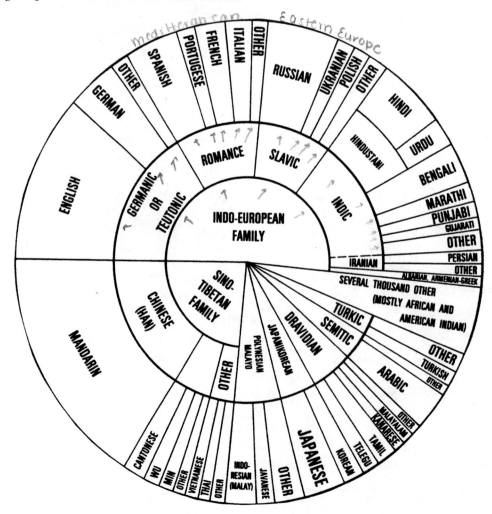

74

Of the Indo-European family of languages, English is the most widely used language in the world. Other European languages like French, Spanish and Portuguese are still used as official languages in countries which were once colonies of those European nations. Spanish is the official language in most of South and Central America, Portuguese is spoken in Brazil and in the African nations of Mozambique and Angola, and French is the official language in dozens of nations in Africa. In fact, most nations in Africa use a European language as their official language. This is a remaining legacy of European colonialism on the continent. The one exception to this rule is northern Africa which was inhabited by the Arab population. Thus, when the European colonialism ended here, ARABIC replaced French as the official language in the region.

MOST WIDELY SPOKEN LANGUAGES
Mandarin (China and other places)..............................900 million
English................................................................500 million
Hindi (mostly in India)...........................................450 million
Spanish...............................................................400 million
Russian...............................................................270 million
Arabic................................................................220 million
Bengali (Bangladesh and India)................................200 million
Portuguese..........................................................180 million
French................................................................125 million
Japanese.............................................................125 million

Many theories exist regarding the relationship among the world's languages. One recent theory suggests, for example, that all languages spoken by Native Americans can be grouped into three families, corresponding to three waves of migration from Asia to the New World thousands of years ago. This controversial view generated much debate among linguists, and is still not resolved. Another theory claimed that Sanskrit, a language of ancient Indian religious and literary texts, is closely tied to Greek and Latin. Still another argues that languages are total products of cultural evolution. Whatever theories are accepted, two things are certain regarding human languages: one is that cultures can not develop without a language and second, many languages are related and have common roots. Some examples are shown below:

| ENGLISH | GERMAN | SPANISH | RUSSIAN |
|---------|--------|---------|---------|
| sun | sonne | sol | solntze |
| salad | salat | Ensalada | salat |
| school | schule | escuela | shkola |
| cat | katze | el gato | koshka |
| water | wasser | del agua | vada |

Language can be a unifying force in a nation or a source of contention. There is a debate in the United States about making English the official language of the country. This debate was prompted by a large inflow of legal and illegal migrants into the United States. The largest group is coming from Mexico and speaking their native Spanish in this country. The Hispanics are now the largest minority group residing in the United States and their numbers are increasing due to their continuous migration across a poorly guarded US-Mexico border. The opponents of the one official language (English) proposal want to make Spanish a co-equal language in the United States. The debate is likely to continue as the numbers of Spanish speaking people increases and their political clout grows.

## RELIGION

Religion continues to play a major role in human cultures. Many conflicts throughout the world may be attributed to religious differences. These include hostilities in the Middle East, Northern Ireland, former Yugoslavia, north-west India and other places. The Jonestown, Guyana tragedy, the site where more than 900 people died in 1978 in the worst mass cult suicide and murder in modern history, shows the extent to which people will go for their beliefs. The Japanese kamikazes and the suicide bombers in the Middle East are other examples.

Although there are many organized religious systems in the world, most have a number of common features. All seek to establish and maintain norms regarding morality, marriage, funeral ceremonies, leadership, codes of behavior and rituals. All have forms of punishment for those who stray from the set rules. Most religions also dictate diets for their adherents (no pork consumption for Muslims or beef for Hindus, for example), have specific days for group worship, suggest dress code and head coverings, practice designed rituals and help the poor. Christians and Muslims, in particular, have pursued missionary work for converting people to their, using brute force at times to enforce their missionary zeal.

There are over 4,000 different religions in the world and at least 10 have 4 million adherents or more. The table below gives approximate number of members of the world's major religions:

| | |
|---|---|
| Christians | 2,000,000,000 |
|    Roman Catholics | 1,000,000.000 |
|    Protestants | 400,000,000 |
|    Orthodox | 220,000,000 |
|    Muslims | 1,200,000,000 |
| Hindus | 800,000,000 |
| Buddhists | 350,000,000 |
| Sikhs | 22,000,000 |
| Jews | 14,000,000 |
| Confucians | 6,000,000 |

## POLITICAL ORGANIZATION OF NATION STATES

Why do some nation-states practice parliamentary democracy while others are ruled by military dictators or monarchs? It is a question difficult to answer. The nation's political structure is <u>not</u> based on its geographic location, the language or religion practices of its citizens or the racial composition of the population. There seems to be a correlation between nations having a dictatorial regime with those which were formerly ruled by European colonial powers. There are, however, many exceptions to this axiom and, therefore, should not be considered as a causal relationship.

**Examples of Nation-States which are ruled by:**
PARLIAMENTARY PROCESS-
These include most of the European nations, Canada, United States of America, Australia, Mexico, and others.

ONE PARTY-
China, Cuba, North Korea, Vietnam, Syria, and others

DICTATORS- these are described as leaders who came to power without holding periodic democratic elections subject to their removal. They did not inherit their position nor are they supported by a broad base single party system.
Libya, Sudan, Ethiopia, Kazakhstan and others

MONARCHS-
Saudi Arabia, Kuwait, Jordan, Morocco, United Arab Emirates, Qatar, Bahrain, Oman, Nepal and others

There are substantial differences in the political power wielded by the world's monarchs. Queen Elizabeth of Great Britain, for example, is a titular head of Great Britain and does not possess the governing power of an elected executive.
On the other side of the spectrum, King Mohammed VI of Morocco is the undisputed leader of his country. Taking over after his father's death in 1999, the young King has initiated a number of reforms. Educated in France with a degree in international law and having a great interest in technology, Mohammed represents a new breed of monarchs who are bringing reforms and more democratization to their countries.
Another young monarch is King Abdullah of Jordan who also came to power after his father's death in 1999. Educated in Britain's prestigious Sandhurst military academy, the monarch is trying to bring some harmony to the various factions in Jordan, especially to the large number of Palestinian refugees.          Outside the Middle East, few places on earth are ruled by monarchs.

## LEVELS OF TECHNOLOGY

Level of technology is the major yardstick used to separate the world into developed and underdeveloped nations. While some countries develop sophisticated technology to send people to the moon, provide complex medical treatment for patients and have the latest, innovative machinery, other nations are unable to supply even the simplest of needs for their citizens.
The United States of America even awards the National Medal of Technology to deserving individuals. The honor, established by Congress in 1980, is administered by the U.S. Department of Commerce. The medal is awarded for technological innovation and the advancement of U.S. global competitiveness.

## CULTURE AND THE ENVIRONMENT

The relationship of culture and the environment continues to be an important element in the study of geography. Since all cultures exist in some environmental setting, to what degree does that environment mold the character of that culture and its inhabitants? Although geographers have abandoned the theory of "Environmental Determinism", human beings continue to live in and react to their environment. This "ecosystem" includes human activities and the physical processes within a single network, bridging the gap between cultural, physical and human geography. An ecosystem can be of any size, with the earth itself being an ecosystem. As the population of the world continues to grow, the delicate balance between the environment and people has been and continues to be disrupted. The resulting ecological deterioration may be difficult to repair.

There are many environmental issues which this and future generations will have to solve. Pollution, deforestation, population growth, depletion of fossil fuel, and the disappearance of various animal and plant species are just some of the problems facing humanity. Urban sprawl, as the one shown below of Sun City, Arizona, is another issue of concern in America and elsewhere.

# HUMAN SPECIES: A brief outline

* MULTI versus SINGLE ORIGIN OF THE HUMAN SPECIES
* East Africa as the original home of the human species
* CHARLES DARWIN: "The Origin of Species" - first published in London in 1859
* LEWIS AND RICHARD LEAKEY'S WORK IN EAST AFRICA
* Appearance of Homo Sapiens about 70,000 years ago in the tropical rainforest region

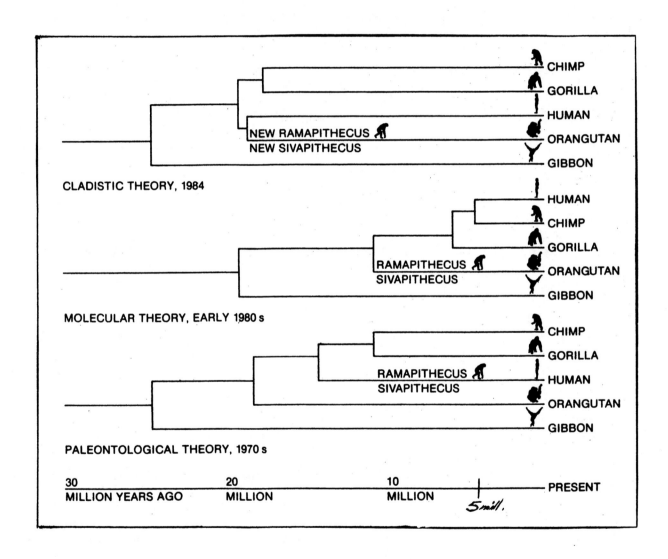

CLADISTIC THEORY, 1984

NEW RAMAPITHECUS
NEW SIVAPITHECUS

CHIMP
GORILLA
HUMAN
ORANGUTAN
GIBBON

MOLECULAR THEORY, EARLY 1980 s

RAMAPITHECUS
SIVAPITHECUS

HUMAN
CHIMP
GORILLA
ORANGUTAN
GIBBON

PALEONTOLOGICAL THEORY, 1970 s

RAMAPITHECUS
SIVAPITHECUS

CHIMP
GORILLA
HUMAN
ORANGUTAN
GIBBON

30          20          10          PRESENT
MILLION YEARS AGO   MILLION      MILLION      5 mill.

## IX. POPULATION GEOGRAPHY

The study of population geography incorporates the basics of geography with demography. Both population geography and demography are concerned with general population numbers; human fertility and mortality; migration; population distribution and other data dealing with human beings. Geographers however, are most interested in the spatial dimensions of these topics and in their areal trends through time(1). In other words, geographers ask questions like "where," "why there," and "what are the consequences of being there," when dealing with population issues.

"Getting a feel" for population numbers is an important first step in understanding the demographic patterns of our world. Knowing some key population figures will allow for logical estimations of population numbers of various places.

Table IX-1 Population of the world and selected areas (Population Reference Bureau-2009):
WORLD.................................. 6.81 billion (6,810,000,000) people
CHINA (1.33 billion); INDIA (1.17 billion) – these are two largest nations on earth
  These 2 nations hold 36.7% of the world's population
USA .................................. 307 million – third largest   (4.5% of world's pop.)
CALIFORNIA........................... 37 million – largest state in the USA
PENNSYLVANIA........................ 12.6 million – 6th largest state in the USA
JOHNSTOWN........................... 23,000

In order to understand and try to resolve the many population issues facing us, it is important to know the APPROXIMATE RANGE of numbers for places such as those given above. If we know that California is the largest State with nearly 40 million people and Pennsylvania is sixth with nearly 13 million, then New York - out third largest State - would fall somewhere between those two. In fact, New York's population is 19.5 million people.

There are 11 nations in the world which have over 100,000,000 people. Six of these are in Asia, two in North America - USA and Mexico, one in South America – Brazil, one in Africa – Nigeria, and the last one is Russia.

### Largest in Population

| | | |
|---|---|---|
| 1. | China | 1,333,010,000 |
| 2. | India | 1,169,050,000 |
| 3. | United States | 307,411,000 |
| 4. | Indonesia | 229,965,000 |
| 5. | Brazil | 191,864,000 |
| 6. | Pakistan | 167,455,000 |
| 7. | Bangladesh | 162,221,000 |
| 8. | Nigeria | 154,729,000 |
| 9. | Russia | 141,860,000 |
| 10. | Japan | 127,590,000 |
| 11. | Mexico | 107,550,697 |

### Largest Countries in Area (In Square miles)

| | | |
|---|---|---|
| 1. | Russia | 6,601,668 |
| 2. | Canada | 3,855,100 |
| 3. | United States | 3,717,813 |
| 4. | China | 3,705,407 - 3,721,904 |
| 5. | Brazil | 3,287,612 |
| 6. | Australia | 2,969,907 |
| 7. | India | 1,269,219 |
| 8. | Argentina | 1,073,500 |
| 9. | Kazakhstan | 1,052,100 |
| 10. | Sudan | 967,500 |

Only 5 nations are in the top 11 both in population and in area.


MOST POPULOUS NATIONS IN THE WORLD:

| Rank ⋈ | Country / Territory ⋈ | Population ⋈ | Date Last Updated ⋈ | % of World Population ⋈ | Source ⋈ |
|---|---|---|---|---|---|
| 1 ■ China [5] | | 1,338,156,900 | May 10, 2009 | 19.87% | Chinese Population clock Hong Kong Statistics Macau statistics Figure for Mainland China is 1,330,598,800 |
| 2 ▦ India | | 1,163,780,000 | May 28 2009 | 17.16% | Indian Population clock |
| 3 ▦ United States | | 306,507,000 | May 28 2009 | 4.52% | Official USA Population clock |
| 4 ■ Indonesia | | 230,227,687 | May 18, 2009 | 3.42% | Indonesian Population clock |
| 5 ◆ Brazil | | 191,332,756 | May 28 2009 | 2.81% | Official Brazilian Population clock |
| 6 ◗ Pakistan | | 166,460,500 | May 23, 2009 | 2.47% | Official Pakistani Population clock |
| 7 ■ Bangladesh | | 162,221,000 | | 2.41% | UN estimate |
| 8 ▐ ▌ Nigeria | | 154,729,000 | | 2.3% | UN estimate |
| 9 ■ Russia | | 141,825,000 | May 10, 2009 | 2.11% | Russian Population clock |
| 10 ● Japan | | 127,630,000 | February 1, 2009 | 1.9% | Official Japan Statistics Bureau estimate |
| 11 ▐•▌ Mexico | | 109,610,000 | | 1.63% | UN estimate |

George Schnell and Mark Monmonier coined the definition of population geography, sited on previous page, in their book The Study of Population (1). Although published in 1983, it is a must read item for anyone interested in this topic. The book touches on all the major issues in the study of population including birth rates, death rates, infant mortality rates, population distribution, migration patterns and more. All of these population issues are linked to the social, political, and economic situation of the world's nations and are of general concern and interest to population geographers.

## WORLD'S POPULATION GROWTH

The debate among the population experts continues regarding the escalating growth of the world's population. Some see it as the most pressing issue to resolve in order to raise the standard of living for all peoples of the world. They argue that a small decrease in the birth rates would automatically increase the per capita income of any given area. Others argue that the redistribution of resources should be the first step for the increase in the living standard of people in the developing areas.

One demographic fact is irrefutable. The human race has been growing at a rate unmatched by most other living beings. It took the human population thousands of years to reach its first billion. Since then, the population has been increasing at a very rapid rate. (see the table below):

| Population | Year Reached | Time span between billions |
|---|---|---|
| 1 billion | 1830 | thousands of years |
| 2 billion | 1930 | 100 years |
| 3 billion | 1960 | 30 years |
| 4 billion | 1975 | 15 years |
| 5 billion | 1986 | 11 years |
| 6 billion | 1999 | 13 years |
| 7 billion | 2012 or 2013 projected | 12-13 years |

World's population growth is due to NATURAL INCREASE (births minus deaths). In the various countries of the world migration also plays a role in the growth or decline of the total population. Migration is an important component in the study of population geography. Why, for example, do people migrate over long distances? Why is the United States the biggest population importing country in the world? Will men or women be more likely to migrate over short distances? These are some of the questions geographers deal with when examining the human migration process.

Human fertility is another important topic in the study of population. Why, for example, do women in the underdeveloped world have much higher birth rates than women in the developed nations? The total fertility rate, which is the number of children that a female will have in her reproductive years, is much higher among women in Iraq – 4.4 than for the females in the USA – 2.1

Even in the developed nations, fertility varies among women of different socio-economic status. Those women at the bottom of the economic ladder tend to have higher birth rates. There is also a significant difference in the birth rates among American women of different generations. It was much higher, for example, for women three generations ago than it is today.

## Life Expectancy and Median Age in the USA

The life expectancy of the American population continues to increase as new medical techniques are developed. As people live longer, the elderly population (those sixty-five years old and older) grows both numerically and as a percent of the total population. This group now comprises slightly over 13% of the total population, or over 40 million people. High percentage of this population is active and is demanding services to benefit their lifestyle. They are also politically involved and can influence legislature in their favor. The field of gerontology (a study of all aspects of the elderly) is a growing field within demography and population geography, offering opportunities for those with an interest in that topic.

The elderly continue to migrate to areas with warm climates. Florida has the highest proportion of elderly in its population, followed by Pennsylvania. Why is that the case for Pennsylvania ? What is the overall spatial distribution of the elderly population in the United States? in Johnstown? What are the implications? These are the kind of questions of interest to population geographers.

Table IX-2: Median age and life expectancy for the American population

| YEAR | MEDIAN AGE | ~~~~~~LIFE EXPECTANCY~~~~~~~~ | | | MALE/FEMALE DIFFERENCE | |
|------|------------|-------|------|--------|------------|---|
| | | TOTAL | MALE | FEMALE | | |
| 1900 | 22.9 | 47.3 | 46.3 | 48.3 | 2.0 YEARS | |
| 1910 | 24.1 | 50.0 | 48.4 | 51.8 | 3.4 | |
| 1920 | 25.3 | 54.1 | 53.6 | 54.6 | 1.0 | |
| 1930 | 26.5 | 59.7 | 58.1 | 61.6 | 3.5 | |
| 1940 | 29.0 | 62.9 | 60.8 | 65.2 | 4.4 | |
| 1950 | 30.2 | 68.2 | 65.6 | 71.1 | 5.5 | |
| 1960 | 29.2 | 69.7 | 66.6 | 73.1 | 6.5 | |
| 1970 | 28.1 | 70.8 | 67.1 | 74.6 | 7.3 | |
| 1980 | 30.2 | 73.3 | 69.4 | 77.4 | 8.0 | |
| 1990 | 32.8 | 75.0 | 70.8 | 79.1 | 8.3 | |
| 2000 | 35.3 | 76.9 | 74.3 | 79.7 | 5.4 | |
| 2009 | 35.5 | 78 | 75 | 80 | 5 | (estimated) |
| 2010 | | | | | | |

What are the social implications of the increasing life expectancy for the American population? Why has the median age been rising over the decades?

1.

2.

In 1990 American females, on an average, lived over eight years longer than the American males. By the year 2000, that difference was reduced to about five and a half years. Why do American females live longer than American males? Is this a desirable social condition? Will this trend continue in the future?

## Sex Ratio

Sex ratio is defined as the number of males, living in an area, for every 100 females. From the 2000 USA Census, the sex ratio in the United States was 96.3, meaning that for every 100 females there were only 96.3 males. That figure was estimated to be 97 in 2009.

## MORTALITY

Mortality rates vary greatly among various population groups. Geographers study and interpret such differences. <u>Crude death rate</u> (CDR) or just <u>death rate</u> is defined as the number of deaths occurring in a year for every 1,000 inhabitants residing in a given area. For example, in Mexico the CDR is 5 per 1000 while for the United States, it is 8 per 1000. Why is it higher in the USA ?  Because in a random sample of 1000 Americans, there will be more older people tan in a sample of 1000 Mexicans.

## INFANT MORTALITY RATE (IMR)

IMR is defined as the number of infants who die before reaching age one, out of every 1,000 <u>births</u>, for a given place, and in a given year.

The infant mortality rate in Mexico in 2009 was approximately 20, while in the USA it was slightly under 7. The reason for the lower IMR in the USA is due to better medical care in the country, among other variables. Infant mortality rate is used as one measure to determine if a nation is developed or underdeveloped. The lower the IMR  in a given nation, the higher are the chance that it is more developed. Some underdeveloped nations have a very high IMR. These include Afghanistan (155), Angola (125), Burundi (120), Somalia (111), and Mali (110), among others.

Although the USA has a low IMR, many nations, including Finland, Japan, Norway, Sweden, Iceland, Canada, and Switzerland have lower rates. One of the reasons for this is that these nations have a much more homogeneous population with a more equitable socio-economic status. In the USA, the minority populations are usually at the lower end of the socio-economic ladder and thus have a higher IMR.

## POPULATION GROWTH AND CHANGE IN THE USA

The U.S. Census Bureau will be collecting population data in 2010 and the results will give a good demographic portrait of the nation. In the last census, taken in 2000, Texas was one of the fastest growing states in the country. The "Lone Star" state added nearly 4 million people in the decade of the 1990's and took over 2nd place (from New York) with its population of 21 million. New York, with just over 18 million dropped to third while Florida stayed in fourth place (16 million people). Pennsylvania dropped to sixth with 12 million, and may drop even lower as the 2010 data become available.

## WORLD'S REGIONAL POPULATION DISTRIBUTION:  2009

| | |
|---|---|
| Africa: | 1 Billion |
| North America: | 450 million |
| Central and South America: | 540 million |
| Asia: | 4.1 Billion |
| Europe: | 740 million |

The Population Reference Bureau of Washington D.C projects the population to be:
WORLD...........................slightly over 8 billion in 2025
USA............... ...................approximately 360 million in 2025

## THOMAS MALTHUS and KARL MARX on POPULATION

The theories of Malthus, who wrote in the early 1800's, and Marx, who wrote in the mid-1800's, concerning population, were somewhat contradictory. Malthus, a British political economist and a preacher, is credited with being the first scholar to write in depth about population problems. He expressed his views in the work entitled ESSAY ON THE PRINCIPLE OF POPULATION. In spite of its faults and limitations, the essay marks the beginning of scientific demographic theory. Marx, writing half a century later, had the advantage of pointing out the faults of the theory and postulating his own views.

Malthus used an easily understood mathematical approach to state that world population increased at a much faster rate than its ability to produce the necessary resources to support that population. His famous assertion that the growth of population fits the geometric curve (1,2,4,8,16,...) while the food production fits the arithmetic curve(1,2,3,4,5,...) forms what Malthus called "the principle ultimate check to population". He pointed to two specific population checks which assured the continuation of the species. These he termed preventive and positive checks. The main preventive check dealt with moral restraints. This meant postponement of marriage thus lowering, in principle, the number of offsprings a couple would produce.  Abortion and other "vices" were also considered preventive checks by Malthus.

The positive checks, about which Malthus wrote, included wars, famines, and diseases, all of which rapidly increase the mortality rate of a population.  The positive and preventive checks, according to Malthus, worked independently of each other. For example, areas with high mortality would have virtually no preventive checks. On the other hand, areas with low mortality, would have virtually no positive checks.

To summarize, Malthus believed that the world's population could be controlled by delaying marriage, preventing promiscuity and adultery, and educating people to accept these ideas. He believed that the poor would be most affected by positive checks on population as described above.

Marx vehemently disagreed with the Malthusian population theory. He felt that every historic mode of production has its own specific laws of population, historically valid within its own limits. He argued that "population problem" should not be isolated from other social problems, and stated that as economic, political, and social changes occur, the high rate of population growth (high birth rate) would decline automatically with other improvements.

The term "OVER-POPULATION" was interpreted by Marx as a "relative surplus" of labor. Marx felt that it was essential for a capitalist society but that it would not happen in a socialist society. In the latter, according to Marx, where excessive profit and individual wealth does not exist, the problem of over-population never arises. Marx, therefore, totally discounted the population theory developed by Malthus on the basis that it had no relevance in the society which Marx was trying to develop. Malthusian theory, Marx stated, was harmful because it diverted attention from a truly scientific ways of increasing the well-being of the working population.

The debate of who was correct continues to this day. Supporters of Malthus point to the fact that an estimated 10 million people died of starvation in the 18th century, 25 million died in the 19th century, and an estimated 30 to 35 million will die of hunger in the 20th century. In addition, one fourth of the world's population is almost always hungry and one tenth is on the brink of death because of too little food. Also, Marx's writings give no explanation why today's modern capitalist societies have very low birth rates.

Opponents of Malthus counter that man's ability to produce great amount of food negates his mathematical model and argue that the reason why people are starving is because of unwillingness of the capitalist world to share its resources with the poor of the world. They also point to the fact that in every instant where a society turned to socialism, the birth rate declined along with other improvements for the working population of that society.

The debate continues in the demographic circles to the present day.

WINCH, DONALD. <u>MALTHUS</u>, OXFORD UNIVERSITY PRESS, NEW YORK, 1987.
*************************************************************************


## #9: HUMAN MIGRATION

Name: _____

International vs. Internal Migration
Forced vs. Voluntary Migration

## REASONS FOR MIGRATION:

1. Economic Opportunities

2.

3.

4.

5.

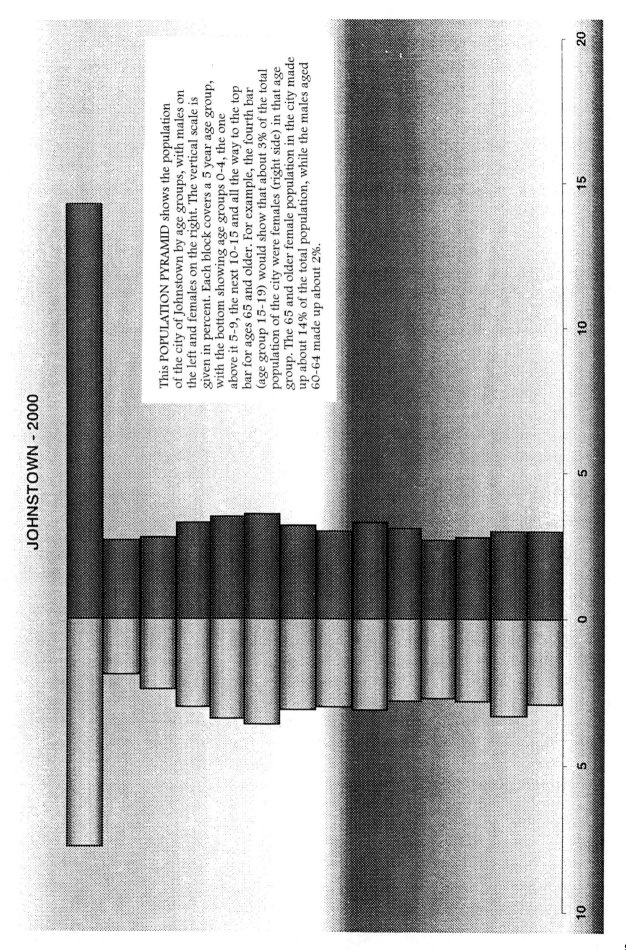

JOHNSTOWN - 2000

This POPULATION PYRAMID shows the population of the city of Johnstown by age groups, with males on the left and females on the right. The vertical scale is given in percent. Each block covers a 5 year age group, with the bottom showing age groups 0-4, the one above it 5-9, the next 10-15 and all the way to the top bar for ages 65 and older. For example, the fourth bar (age group 15-19) would show that about 3% of the total population of the city were females (right side) in that age group. The 65 and older female population in the city made up about 14% of the total population, while the males aged 60-64 made up about 2%.

Geography and the concept of "spatial diffusion".

Diffusion can be defined as the spread of ideas, cultures, diseases and people from one place to another over time. Geographers have been studying this concept for a long time and have written volumes of material on the subject. Some examples of spatial diffusion include:

- the migration and the resulting distribution of Mexicans from that country to the United States
- the spread of the religion of Islam from its origin to other parts of the world
- the spread of a particular fashion from New York, for example, to the rest of the world
- the spread of American "Rock and Roll" to other locations
- the travel of news and the adaptation of an innovative farming technique
- the speed of the spread of some deadly disease
- the spread of English (or another language) in the colonies of that nation

Numerous other examples may be found regarding this concept.

Spatial diffusion may be divided into <u>contagious diffusion</u> and <u>hierarchical diffusion</u>.

Contagious Diffusion –


Hierarchical Diffusion –


Give three additional examples of spatial diffusion
1.


2.


3.

## X. NORTH AMERICAN REALM

The North American realm is comprised of the UNITED STATES OF AMERICA (area: 3.6 million sq. miles), CANADA (area: 3.9 million sq. miles), MEXICO (area: 760,000 sq. miles), and GREENLAND (area: 840,000 sq. miles). The first three are independent nations while Greenland is a province of Denmark.

The demographic profiles of the three nations are shown below ~ 2009:

| country | population | cbr | cdr | natural increase | pop. in yr. 2025 | i.m.r. | l.e. | urban | per cap. g.n.p. |
|---|---|---|---|---|---|---|---|---|---|
| U.S.A. | 307 mill. | 14 | 8 | 0.6% | 357 m. | 7.0 | 78 | 79% | $47,000 |
| CANADA | 34 mill. | 11 | 7 | 0.4% | 38 m. | 5.0 | 81 | 81% | $36,200 |
| MEXICO | 110 mill. | 20 | 5 | 1.6% | 123 m. | 20.0 | 75 | 76% | $14,270 |

Source: 2009 World Population Date Sheet, Population Reference Bureau, Washington, D.C.

One striking difference between the American and Canadian populations on the one hand and Mexican population on the other is the age composition and structure. In Mexico, about a third of the total population is under the age of 15, and only 6% of the total is over the age of 65. In the USA, these figures are 20% and 13%, while in Canada they are 17% and 14%. Thus the young, dependent population in Mexico is nearly twice as large as it is in the USA and Canada. This is due to a much higher birth rate in Mexico. It takes a huge proportion of Mexico's resources to educate, house, feed and maintain this young, dependent population.

Another difference is in the workforce of the nations. For example, nearly 40% of Mexico's labor force is engaged in agriculture while the figures for USA and Canada are 3% and 5% respectively. The labor force in Mexico is less skilled than that in the USA or Canada and most of the illegal Mexicans coming into the USA are usually engaged in jobs not coveted by the great majority of the American workers.

The ethnic population composition of the nations is also quite different. Mexico has three main ethnic groups.  One is comprised of people of European descent (primarily Spanish) who make up approximately 10 % of the total and are the wealthiest of the groups. About one-third of the population is full-blooded Indian, living mostly in the southern part of the country. This is the poorest group of the Mexican population. They engage primarily in agriculture. The largest group is made up of the Mestizos, people of the mixed Spanish and Indian blood.

One-fourth of Mexico's population resides in and around Mexico City, the nation's mile high capital. Mexico City is one of the largest cities in the world and faces many of the problems associated with mega-cities. It has one of the highest pollution levels in the world, the traffic jams are the norm, the crime rate is soaring, unemployment is rampant, there is inadequate housing, and migration into the city continues unabated. The future prospects of alleviating these and other problems are not very promising.

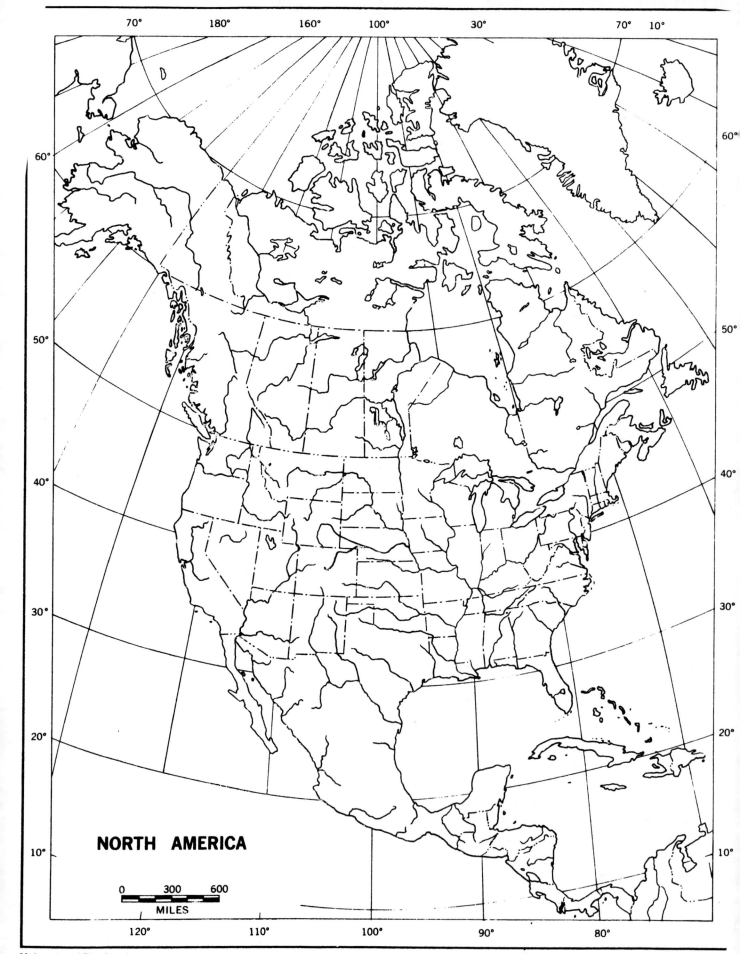

70°    180°    160°    100°    30°    70°  10°

60°

50°

40°

30°

20°

10°

**NORTH AMERICA**

0    300    600

MILES

120°    110°    100°    90°    80°

University of Pittsburgh

90

# MEXICO

Mexico, America's neighbor to the south, has an area of about three times the size of Texas (764,000 sq. miles). The nation's topography varies from a low desert plain in the north to a great central plateau, 1500 miles long and, in parts, 500 miles wide. Mexico City, the nation's capital, sits on this plateau at an elevation of 8,000 feet above sea level.

The Sierra Madre Occidental mountains run north-west to south-east near the west coast; the Sierra Madre Oriental mountains run near the Gulf of Mexico. The two mountain chains join south of Mexico City.

A lack of rainfall throughout the year contributes to Mexico's relatively dry climate. About half of the country's land is arid. The coastal lowlands are tropical. The south, depleted of much of its rainforest, is the home of the majority of the Indian population of Mexico.

Until conquered by H. Cortez and his Spanish army in 1520, present-day Mexico was the home of the highly advanced Mayan and Aztec civilizations. As a result of the conquest, the territory became a Spanish colony. It remained under the Spanish crown for almost 300 years until 1810, when independence was proclaimed.

The history of Mexico is inundated with uprisings, revolutions, and civil wars. It is also marked by interventions into its internal affairs by the United States (1914, 1916-1917), and the acquisition of land by the U.S. from Mexico (ex. nearly 340 million acres in 1848). The overthrow of the Diaz dictatorship in 1911 and the civil war that followed gave rise to many colorful national figures, such as "Pancho" Villa, who raided U.S. border areas and had skirmishes with the U.S. army, and Emiliano Zapata, a dedicated agrarian reform leader and revolutionary.

Modern Mexico may be said to date from 1921, when initial steps were taken toward carrying out the social programs set forth by the Constitution of 1917. The constitution allows the elected president to serve only one term for a period of six years. Corruption and graft are rampant in the country, contributing to its lack luster economy. Mexico's chief export crops include cotton, coffee, and sugar cane, along with such other commodities as silver, lead, gold, and petroleum.

Each year, over one million Mexicans enter the country's labor force but only some 250,000 new jobs are created. This leaves nearly 3/4 of a million people without full employment. Many of these people choose to go to the United States in search of a better life. Many enter the United States illegally along the 1,933 mile border between the USA and Mexico. Much of this border is poorly guarded, and in recent years, millions of Mexicans have entered the USA. This illegal migration and the rapid growth of Hispanic population in the USA have stimulated much debate, both in the legislature and among the general public. Should the border be better patrolled? Should all the illegals be shipped back to Mexico? Should a person employing the illegal migrants be heavily fined? Should the schools in the United States provide instruction in Spanish for the children of the illegal immigrants? Should these migrants be entitled to welfare payments? All these questions will continue to be debated until the Mexican economy is improved and the illegal migration stops or is drastically decreased. The free-trade agreement among the USA, Canada, and Mexico signed some years ago has not solved the immigration issue.

# THE STATES OF MEXICO

STATES-

1. BAJA CALIFORNIA NORTE
2. BAJA CALIFORNIA SUR
3. SONORA
4. CHIHUAHUA
5. SINALOA
6. DURANGO
7. COAHUILA
8. NUEVO LEON
9. ZACATECAS
10. SAN LUIS POTOSI
11. TAMAULIPAS
12. NAYARIT
13. AGUASCALIENTES
14. JALISCO
15. GUANAJUATO

16. QUERETARO
17. HIDALGO
18. COLIMA
19. MICHOACAN
20. MEXICO
21. MORELOS
22. TLAXCALA
23. PUEBLA
24. VERACRUZ
25. GUERRERO
26. OAXACA
27. CHIAPAS
28. TABASCO
29. CAMPECHE
30. YUCATAN
31. QUINTANA ROO

■ DISTRITO FEDERAL

—— NATIONAL BOUNDARY
—— STATE BOUNDARY

BELIZE

GUATEMALA

GOLFO DE CALIFORNIA

N

0    150    300
miles

J.P.C. 88

U.R.J. GEOGRAPHY DEPARTMENT

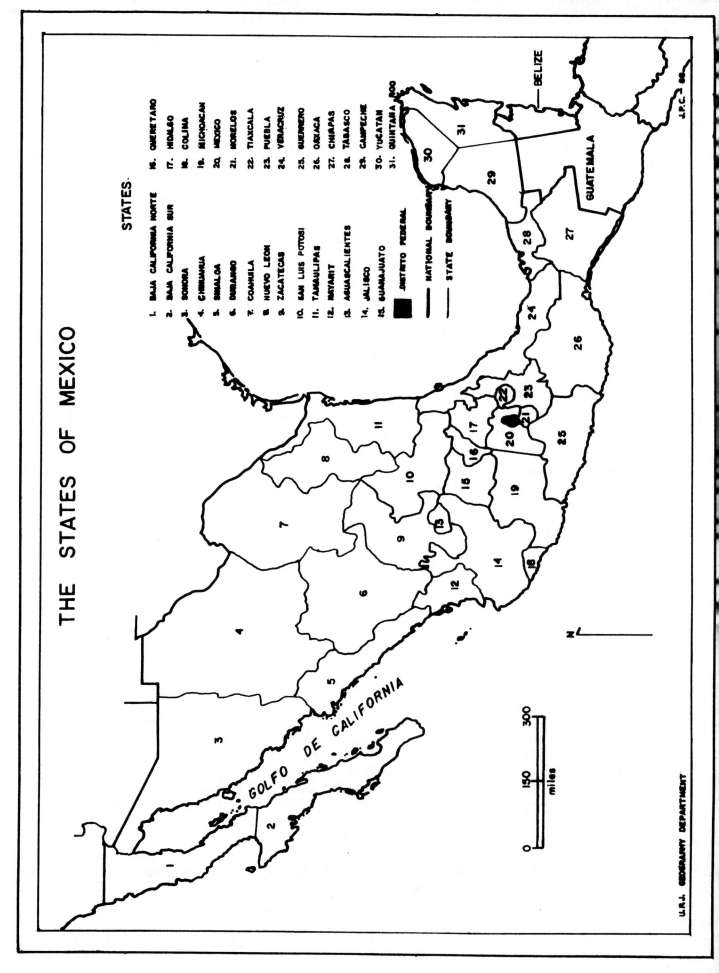

92

Many Americans have a certain image of Mexico and Mexicans, which does not, necessarily convey the true picture of the country or its people. (Picture below)

Approximately 13% of the total American population classify themselves as Hispanic. They now constitute the largest minority group in the United States, surpassing the African-Americans. A large percentage of Hispanics are immigrants from Mexico, with nearly 90% of these being Roman Catholic. The Hispanic population is unevenly distributed in the country.

The tables below show the States with the largest numbers and percentages of HISPANICS:

| States with the largest Hispanic Population | States with the largest % of Hispanic population |
|---|---|
| California – 11 million | New Mexico – 42 |
| Texas – 6.7 million | California – 32.5 |
| Florida – 2.7 million | Texas – 32 |
| Illinois – 1.5 million | Arizona – 25.5 |
| Arizona – 1.3 million | Colorado – 17 |

The States with the smallest percent of Hispanic population include Maine (0.7), West Virginia (0.7), Vermont (0.9), North Dakota (1.2) and South Dakota (1.4).

# CANADA

Canada has been a good friend and a major trading partner of the United States of America for a long time. Majority of the country uses English as the official language, while Quebec, a province east of the Hudson Bay, has a French speaking population. The people of Quebec have been pushing for independence from Canada since the 18th century, and that has caused some internal problems for the country.

A major event occurred in Canada with a creation of a new <u>Territory</u> on April 1, 1999. The Canadian government, after apologizing to the native population for a century of mistreatment, carved out the <u>NUNAVUT</u> ("OUR LAND") TERRITORY as a homeland for the INUIT people. Nunavut, formed from the Northwest Territories, became the largest political unit in Canada with the smallest population – just over 24,000 ! The region, rich in oil, gas and other minerals will share the royalties from the sale of these resources with the federal government.

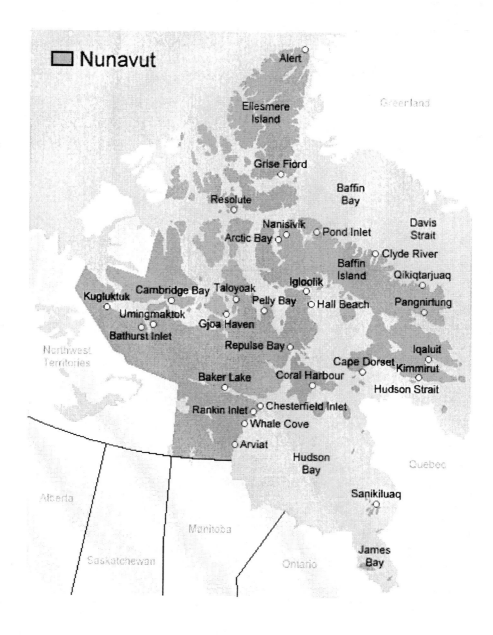

Canada's political units include TEN Provinces and THREE Territories. The major difference between the two is that a Province is a creation of the Constitutional act, while a Territory is created by federal law. This gives the federal government more direct control over the Territories. In addition, the Territories can not vote for any changes in the nation's constitution as the Provinces can. There are some exceptions for the newly created Nunavut Territory; a privilege granted to it by the federal government when the Territory was formed in 1999.

CANADA'S PROVINCES AND TERRITORIES

| Place | area (sq. mi.) | population (in thousands) |
|---|---|---|
| Canada | 3,851,788 | 31,000 |
| Alberta | 255,287 | 3,000 |
| British Columbia | 365,948 | 4,000 |
| Manitoba | 250,947 | 1,150 |
| New Brunswick | 28,355 | 760 |
| Newfoundland | 156,649 | 540 |
| Nova Scotia | 21,425 | 940 |
| Ontario | 412,581 | 11,000 |
| Prince Edward Island | 2,185 | 140 |
| Quebec | 594,880 | 7,400 |
| Saskatchewan | 251,866 | 1,020 |
| *Northwest Territories* | *503,951* | *42* |
| *Yukon Territory* | *186,661* | *31* |
| *Nunavut Territory* | *818,959* | *24* |

# The Provinces of Canada

## GREENLAND

The island was named by the Viking explorer Eric the Red who visited the area some one thousand years ago. He may have chosen to name the ice-covered island "Greenland" to attract settlers to the island. A more likely reason, however, was because Eric and his men visited only the western coast of the island in the summer, when it is free of ice and is covered with vegetation. The island, biggest in the world, covers 1.5% of the earth's land area. Over 80% of it is covered by permanent ice, as much as two miles deep in places. Only along the coast is there a thin strip of ice-free land, and the mountainous coastline is slashed by countless fjords.

Politically, the island is a province of Denmark which has granted Greenland "home rule" - the freedom to control its internal affairs. Denmark, however, provides the island with nearly 90% of its budget; $350 million dollars a year. The island is nearly 50 times bigger than Denmark in area, but has only about 53,000 inhabitants. This makes it one of the least densely populated areas on the face of the earth. Four out of five inhabitants are native Inuits, who are related by language and custom to the Eskimos of Alaska, Canada, and Siberia.

There is chronic unemployment on the island. The U.S. Air Force was closing Greenland's only international airport, a Canadian-owned lead and zinc mine was closing, and the off-shore oil exploration is not yielding any results. Alcoholism is rampant, and the suicide rate is the highest in the world. About 50 islanders kill themselves every year.

In 1989, the former Danish colony celebrated 10 years of semi-independence under a home-rule scheme. Greenland has its own parliament and two legislators from the island sit in the Danish parliament in Copenhagen. In November of that year, Danish and Canadian geologists reported finding gold on a 1.6 square mile patch of land on the east coast of the island. By all account the gold reserves are very large. Mining could begin in 3 to 5 years and yield $150 million dollars annually. This would solve much of the economic difficulty on the island.

Below: street in Nuuk, the capital city of Greenland

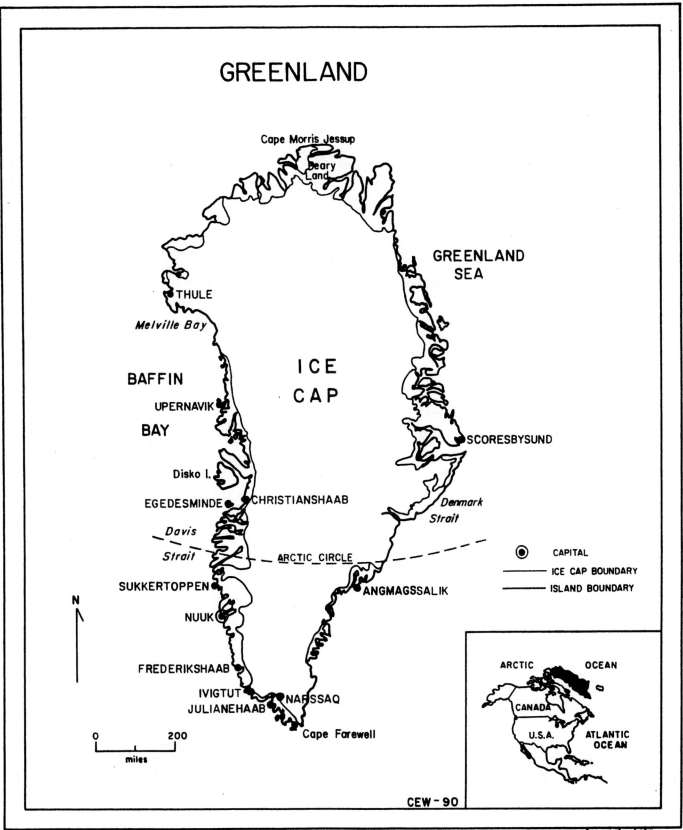

# GREENLAND

Cape Morris Jessup

Peary Land

GREENLAND
SEA

THULE

*Melville Bay*

BAFFIN

ICE
CAP

UPERNAVIK

BAY

SCORESBYSUND

Disko I.

EGEDESMINDE ● ● CHRISTIANSHAAB

*Davis*

*Denmark*
*Strait*

*Strait*

ARCTIC CIRCLE

◉ CAPITAL
—— ICE CAP BOUNDARY
—— ISLAND BOUNDARY

SUKKERTOPPEN

ANGMAGSSALIK

N

NUUK

FREDERIKSHAAB

IVIGTUT ● NARSSAQ
JULIANEHAAB

ARCTIC OCEAN

Cape Farewell

CANADA

ATLANTIC
OCEAN

U.S.A.

0        200

miles

CEW-90

97

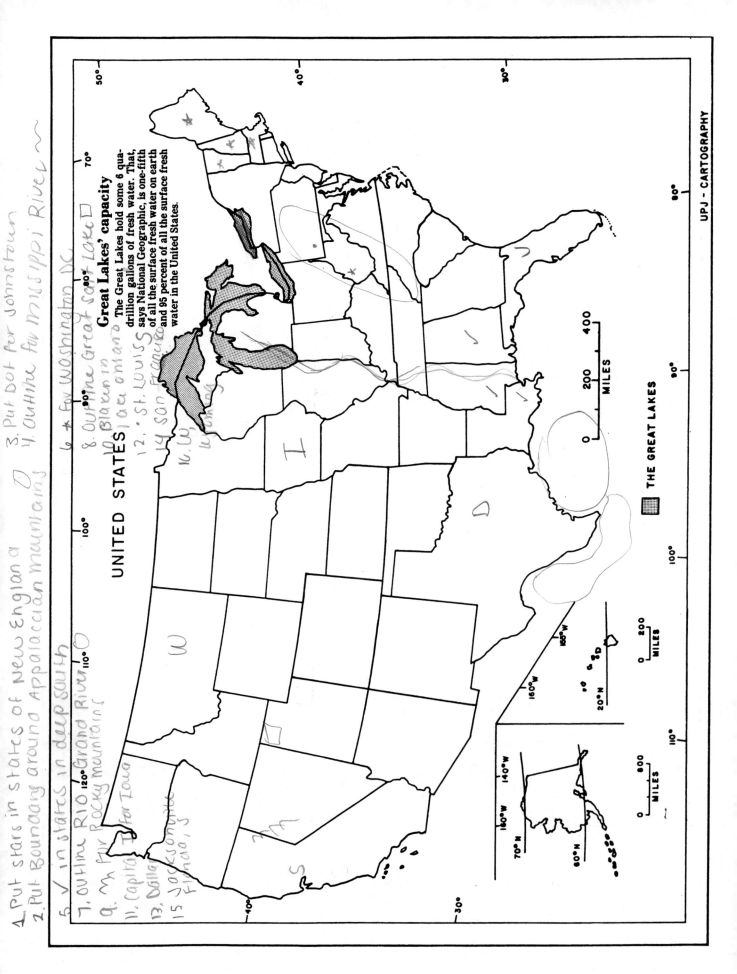

1. Put stars in states of New England ☆
2. Put boundary around Appalachian mountains
3. Put dot for Johnstown ⚫
4. Outline for Mississippi River

5. ✓ in states in deep south
6. ☆ for Washington DC
7. Outline RIO Grande River ◯
8. Outline Great ☆ Lake □
9. ⋀ for Rocky mountains
10. Blacken Lake ontario
11. Capital ☰ for Iowa
12. ⚫ St. Louis S
13. Dallas ⚫
14. San Francisco ⚫
15. Jacksonville ⚫
16. W, Wyoming
Florida S

## UNITED STATES

### Great Lakes' capacity

The Great Lakes hold some 6 quadrillion gallons of fresh water. That, says National Geographic, is one-fifth of all the surface fresh water on earth and 95 percent of all the surface fresh water in the United States.

MILES
0   200   400

□ THE GREAT LAKES

UPJ - CARTOGRAPHY

## THE UNITED STATES OF AMERICA

What images do the following cities convey to you?

1. WASHINGTON, D.C.

White House

2. DENVER

Airport

3. LAS VEGAS

Casino

4. NEW YORK

Statue of Liberty

5. JOHNSTOWN, PA

Inclined Plane

_____

St. Louis Arc (Gateway to West)

WELCOME to

# RUGBY

## NORTH DAKOTA

*The Geographical Center of North America*

-midae btw canada+mexico

Rugby, North Dakota
Geographical Center of North America

# THE UNITED STATES OF AMERICA

The United States of America (USA) is a large and a diverse nation. Its climate ranges from the tropical (Hawaii) to the ice cap (Alaska), with the bulk of the nation having the "C" and "D" type climates. Its topography is just as varied: from the Rockies in the west to the Great Plains in the mid west to the Appalachian Mountains and the coastal plains in the east. The economy of the nation is also complex and diversified.

The major emphasis in this unit will be on the population issues and urbanization in the United States of America.

## POPULATION

The USA is the third largest nation on earth with the population estimated to be 307 million people in 2010. Only China with 1.3 billion people and India with 1.2 billion people are bigger.

Since the results of the 2010 Census of population were not available for this edition, the data from 2000 census and census estimates are used here. There were some unexpected and interesting results emerging from the 2000 Population Census. The 13.2% increase in population from 1990 to 2000 was much higher than expected. One of the reasons for this increase was a better accounting of the Hispanic population, which increased by over 60% in that decade. The soaring Hispanic population was driven largely by waves of new immigrants from Mexico, both legal and illegal. As the migration continues and the birth rate of the immigrants is high, the Hispanics have recently surpassed African-Americans as the largest minority group in the USA. Some forty million people are classified as Hispanics, making up over 13% of America's total population.

The Hispanics are still concentrated in the Southwestern states (especially in California, Arizona, New Mexico and Texas), and in Florida and New York. They continue, however, to move to other parts of the country. North Carolina, Georgia, Iowa and Idaho, for example, have seen a large influx of immigrants from Mexico and South America. A decade ago, the Hispanic population was almost nonexistent in those states. The growing Hispanic population underscores the fact that for the first time since the early 1930's, one in every 10 Americans is foreign born.

California continues to be the largest state in the union with nearly 34 million people (2000). It gained over 4 million people between 1990 and 2000 contains more people than the whole nation of Canada! Nevada had the largest **percentage** increase, soaring by over 66%. On the other end of the spectrum, Wyoming continued as the smallest state with less than half a million people, while North Dakota had the smallest gain in population (3,400 people) and the smallest percent gain (0.5). (See the following table)

Surprisingly, not one state had a net loss in population between 1990 and 2000. In contrast, **WEST VIRGINIA, IOWA, WYOMING and NORTH DAKOTA** had net population losses between 1980 and 1990.

The migration flow within the country continues from the industrialized north-east and agricultural mid-west to the south and west. This pattern has not changed for decades and has been instrumental in realigning political representation in Congress. For example, based on the 2000 Census data, Pennsylvania and New York each lost two congressmen in the House of Representatives, while Florida, Georgia, Texas and Arizona each gained two. An additional four states gained one congressman while eight others lost one. The total membership (435) in the House of Representatives has not changed in over one hundred years. The projected pattern for the 2010 Census will follow that of the last Census.

# POPULATION OF THE UNITED STATES: 1990 - 2000

*(proportional)* *Judge by* ↓

| Area | April 1, 2000 | April 1, 1990 | Numeric Change | Percent Change |
|------|--------------:|--------------:|---------------:|---------------:|
| Alabama | 4,447,100 | 4,040,587 | 406,513 | 10.1 |
| Alaska | 626,932 | 550,043 | 76,889 | 14.0 |
| Arizona | 5,130,632 | 3,665,228 | 1,465,404 | 40.0 |
| Arkansas | 2,673,400 | 2,350,725 | 322,675 | 13.7 |
| California | 33,871,648 | 29,760,021 | 4,111,627 | 13.8 |
| Colorado | 4,301,261 | 3,294,394 | 1,006,867 | 30.6 |
| Connecticut | 3,405,565 | 3,287,116 | 118,449 | 3.6 |
| Delaware | 783,600 | 666,168 | 117,432 | 17.6 |
| District of Columbia | 572,059 | 606,900 | -34,841 | -5.7 |
| Florida | 15,982,378 | 12,937,926 | 3,044,452 | 23.5 |
| Georgia | 8,186,453 | 6,478,216 | 1,708,237 | 26.4 |
| Hawaii | 1,211,537 | 1,108,229 | 103,308 | 9.3 |
| Idaho | 1,293,953 | 1,006,749 | 287,204 | 28.5 |
| Illinois | 12,419,293 | 11,430,602 | 988,691 | 8.6 |
| Indiana | 6,080,485 | 5,544,159 | 536,326 | 9.7 |
| Iowa | 2,926,324 | 2,776,755 | 149,569 | 5.4 |
| Kansas | 2,688,418 | 2,477,574 | 210,844 | 8.5 |
| Kentucky | 4,041,769 | 3,685,296 | 356,473 | 9.7 |
| Louisiana | 4,468,976 | 4,219,973 | 249,003 | 5.9 |
| Maine | 1,274,923 | 1,227,928 | 46,995 | 3.8 |
| Maryland | 5,296,486 | 4,781,468 | 515,018 | 10.8 |
| Massachusetts | 6,349,097 | 6,016,425 | 332,672 | 5.5 |
| Michigan | 9,938,444 | 9,295,297 | 643,147 | 6.9 |
| Minnesota | 4,919,479 | 4,375,099 | 544,380 | 12.4 |
| Mississippi | 2,844,658 | 2,573,216 | 271,442 | 10.5 |
| Missouri | 5,595,211 | 5,117,073 | 478,138 | 9.3 |
| Montana | 902,195 | 799,065 | 103,130 | 12.9 |
| Nebraska | 1,711,263 | 1,578,385 | 132,878 | 8.4 |
| Nevada | 1,998,257 | 1,201,833 | 796,424 | 66.3 |
| New Hampshire | 1,235,786 | 1,109,252 | 126,534 | 11.4 |
| New Jersey | 8,414,350 | 7,730,188 | 684,162 | 8.9 |
| New Mexico | 1,819,046 | 1,515,069 | 303,977 | 20.1 |
| New York | 18,976,457 | 17,990,455 | 986,002 | 5.5 |
| North Carolina | 8,049,313 | 6,628,637 | 1,420,676 | 21.4 |
| North Dakota | 642,200 | 638,800 | 3,400 | 0.5 |
| Ohio | 11,353,140 | 10,847,115 | 506,025 | 4.7 |
| Oklahoma | 3,450,654 | 3,145,585 | 305,069 | 9.7 |
| Oregon | 3,421,399 | 2,842,321 | 579,078 | 20.4 |
| Pennsylvania | 12,281,054 | 11,881,643 | 399,411 | 3.4 |
| Rhode Island | 1,048,319 | 1,003,464 | 44,855 | 4.5 |
| South Carolina | 4,012,012 | 3,486,703 | 525,309 | 15.1 |
| South Dakota | 754,844 | 696,004 | 58,840 | 8.5 |
| Tennessee | 5,689,283 | 4,877,185 | 812,098 | 16.7 |
| Texas | 20,851,820 | 16,986,510 | 3,865,310 | 22.8 |
| Utah | 2,233,169 | 1,722,850 | 510,319 | 29.6 |
| Vermont | 608,827 | 562,758 | 46,069 | 8.2 |
| Virginia | 7,078,515 | 6,187,358 | 891,157 | 14.4 |
| Washington | 5,894,121 | 4,866,692 | 1,027,429 | 21.1 |
| West Virginia | 1,808,344 | 1,793,477 | 14,867 | 0.8 |
| Wisconsin | 5,363,675 | 4,891,769 | 471,906 | 9.6 |
| Wyoming | 493,782 | 453,588 | 40,194 | 8.9 |
| Total Resident Population | 281,421,906 | 248,709,873 | 32,712,033 | 13.2 % |

✱ 30 million

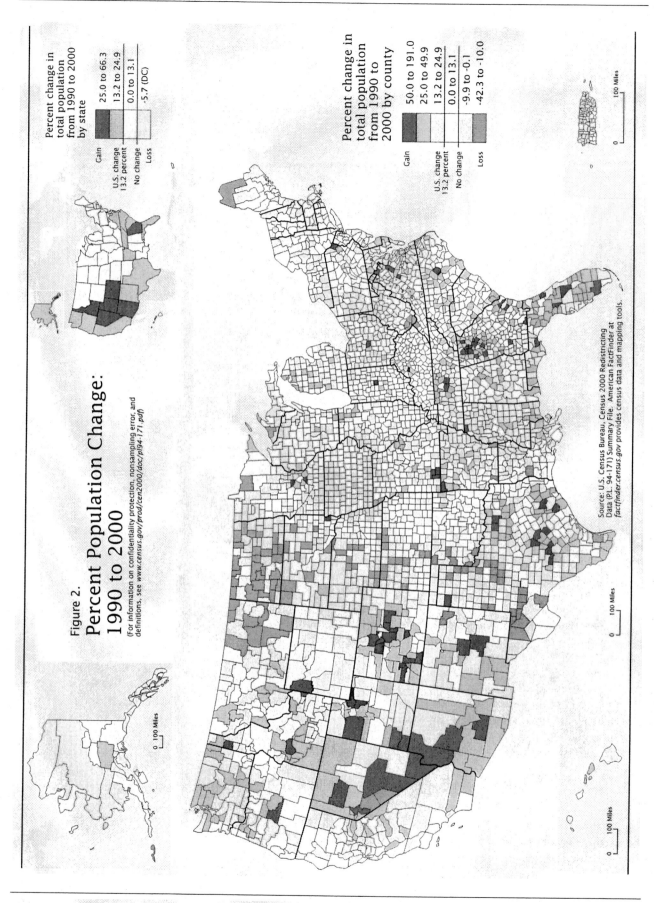

Figure 2.
## Percent Population Change: 1990 to 2000

(For information on confidentiality protection, nonsampling error, and definitions, see *www.census.gov/prod/cen2000/doc/pl94-171.pdf*)

Percent change in total population from 1990 to 2000 by state

Gain
- 25.0 to 66.3
- 13.2 to 24.9

U.S. change 13.2 percent
- 0.0 to 13.1

No change
Loss
- -5.7 (DC)

Percent change in total population from 1990 to 2000 by county

Gain
- 50.0 to 191.0
- 25.0 to 49.9
- 13.2 to 24.9

U.S. change 13.2 percent
- 0.0 to 13.1

No change
- -9.9 to -0.1

Loss
- -42.3 to -10.0

100 Miles

0    100 Miles

0    100 Miles

0    100 Miles

Source: U.S. Census Bureau, Census 2000 Redistricting Data (P.L. 94-171) Summary File. American FactFinder at *factfinder.census.gov* provides census data and mapping tools.

# Number of People, 2000

## Hispanic or Latino Origin
## All Races

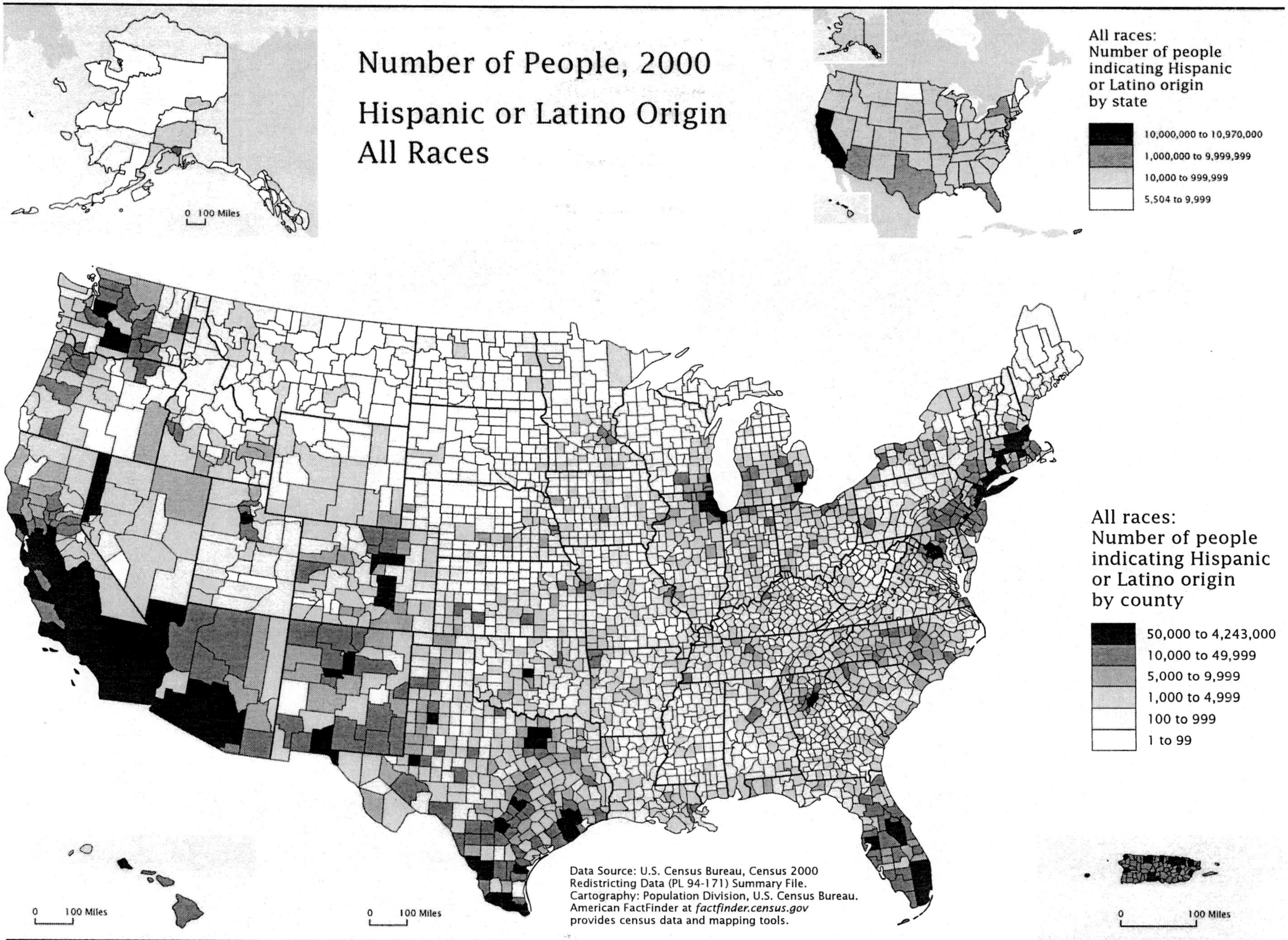

All races:
Number of people
indicating Hispanic
or Latino origin
by state

- 10,000,000 to 10,970,000
- 1,000,000 to 9,999,999
- 10,000 to 999,999
- 5,504 to 9,999

All races:
Number of people
indicating Hispanic
or Latino origin
by county

- 50,000 to 4,243,000
- 10,000 to 49,999
- 5,000 to 9,999
- 1,000 to 4,999
- 100 to 999
- 1 to 99

0 ___ 100 Miles

Data Source: U.S. Census Bureau, Census 2000
Redistricting Data (PL 94-171) Summary File.
Cartography: Population Division, U.S. Census Bureau.
American FactFinder at factfinder.census.gov
provides census data and mapping tools.

0 ___ 100 Miles

0 ___ 100 Miles

0 ___ 100 Miles

U.S. Census Bureau

Mapping Census 2000: The Geography of U.S. Diversity

# Percent of Black or African American Population Indicating One Race, 2000

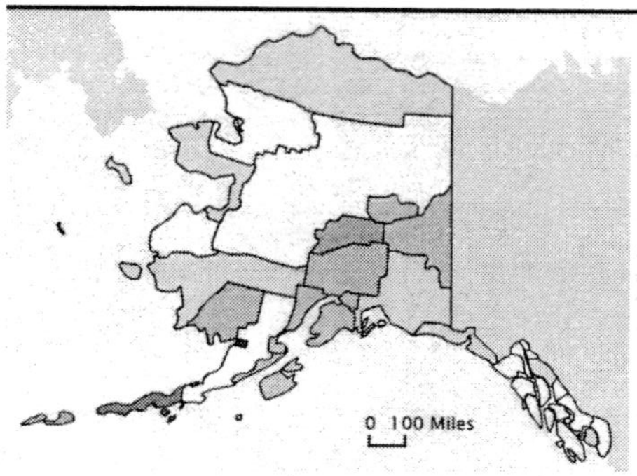

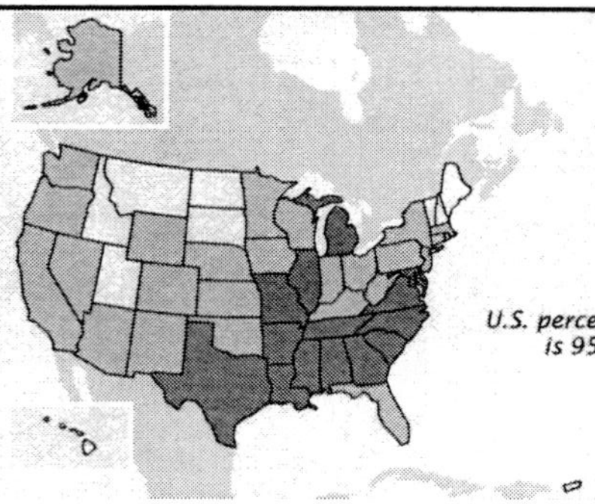

People indicating one race, Black, as a percent of those indicating one or more races including Black by state

*U.S. percent is 95.2*

- 95.2 to 99.2
- 75.0 to 95.1
- 60.6 to 74.9

This map is one of a series of six "Percent Indicating One Race" maps with comparable categories for counties. Breaks defining the highest categories differ among maps for groups with the highest U.S. percents.

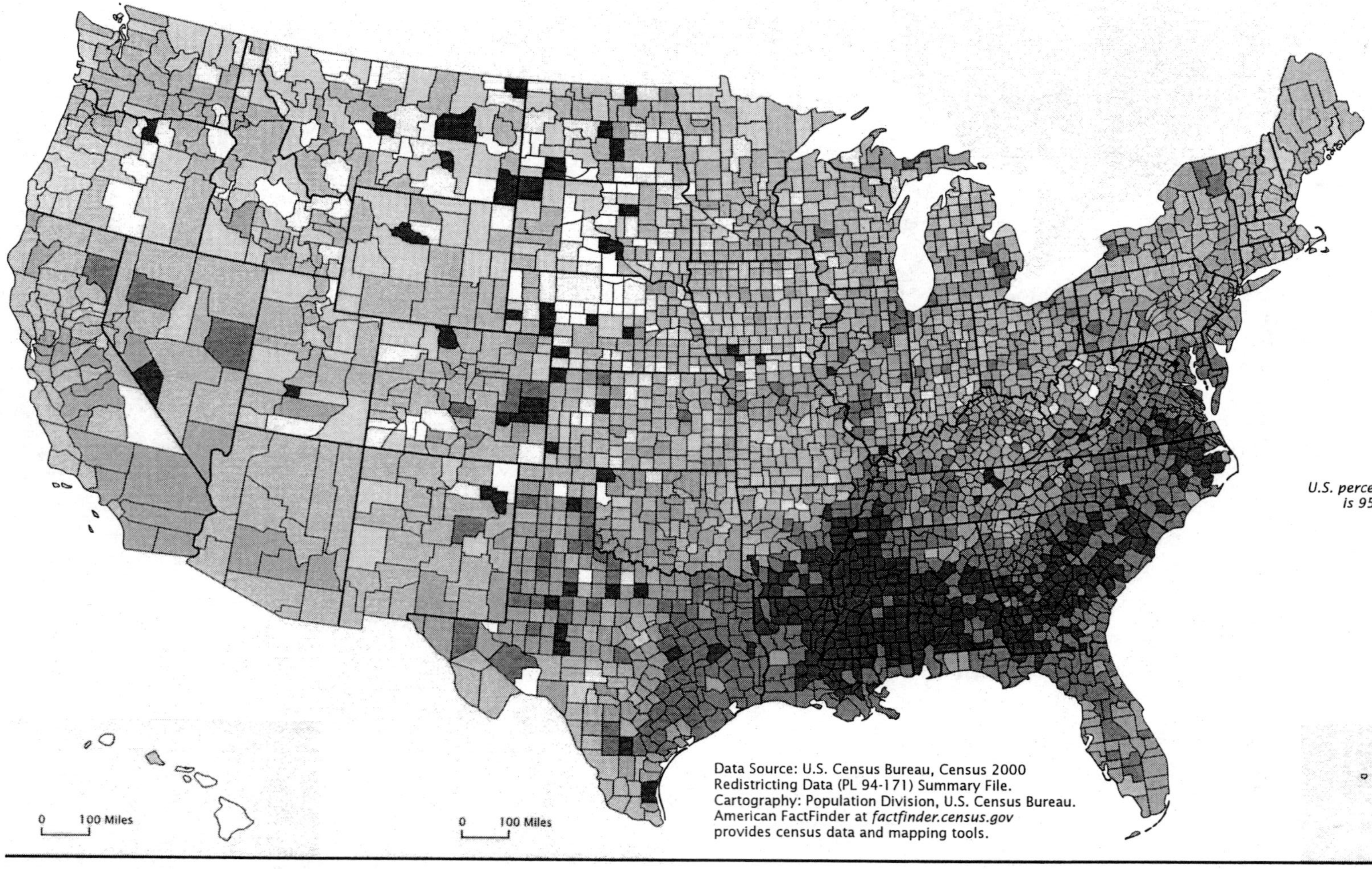

People indicating one race, Black or African American, as a percent of those indicating one or more races including Black or African American by county

*U.S. percent is 95.2*

- 99.0 to 100.0
- 95.2 to 98.9
- 86.1 to 95.1
- 60.1 to 86.0
- 45.6 to 60.0
- 20.0 to 45.5
- 0.0 to 19.9

No Black population in county

0 — 100 Miles

Data Source: U.S. Census Bureau, Census 2000 Redistricting Data (PL 94-171) Summary File. Cartography: Population Division, U.S. Census Bureau. American FactFinder at *factfinder.census.gov* provides census data and mapping tools.

0 — 100 Miles

0 — 100 Miles

Mapping Census 2000: The Geography of U.S. Diversity

U.S. Census Bureau

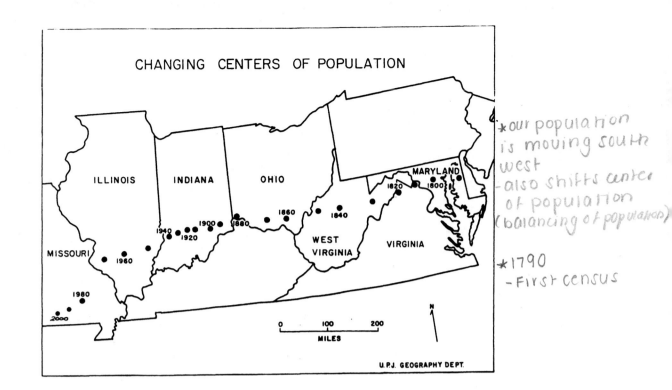

CHANGING CENTERS OF POPULATION

*our population is moving south west
-also shifts center of population (balancing of population)

*1790
-First census

U.P.J. GEOGRAPHY DEPT.

*don't need to worry about* ✓

## Past Centers of Population of the United States

Table A gives past centers of population of the United States from the first Census of Population in 1790 up through Census 2000. For ease of use in computer systems, the latitude and longitude positions are given in decimal degree equivalents rather than traditional degrees/minutes/seconds.

| Census year | North latitude | West longitude | Approximate location |
|---|---|---|---|
| Table A. **Mean Center of Population of the United States: 1790 through 2000** ||||
| United States: ||||
| 2000 | 37.69699 | 91.80957 | Phelps County, MO, 2.8 miles east of Edgar Springs |
| 1990 | 37.87222 | 91.21528 | Crawford County, MO, 9.7 miles southeast of Steelville. |
| 1980 | 38.13694 | 90.57389 | Jefferson County, MO, 1/4 mile west of DeSoto. |
| 1970 | 38.46306 | 89.70611 | St. Clair County, IL, 5 miles east-southeast of Mascoutah. |
| 1960 | 38.59944 | 89.20972 | Clinton County, IL, 6-1/2 miles northwest of Centralia. |
| 1950 | 38.80417 | 88.36889 | Clay County, IL, 3 miles northeast of Louisville. |
| Conterminous United States[1] ||||
| 1950 | 38.83917 | 88.15917 | Richland County, IL, 8 miles north-northwest of Olney. |
| 1940 | 38.94833 | 87.37639 | Sullivan County, IN, 2 miles southeast by east of Carlisle. |
| 1930 | 39.06250 | 87.13500 | Greene County, IN, 3 miles northeast of Linton. |
| 1920 | 39.17250 | 86.72083 | Owen County, IN, 8 miles south-southeast of Spencer. |
| 1910 | 39.17000 | 86.53889 | Monroe County, IN, in the city of Bloomington. |
| 1900 | 39.16000 | 85.81500 | Bartholomew County, IN, 6 miles southeast of Columbus. |
| 1890 | 39.19889 | 85.54806 | Decatur County, IN, 20 miles east of Columbus. |
| 1880 | 39.06889 | 84.66111 | Boone County, KY, 8 miles west by south of Cincinnati, OH. |
| 1870 | 39.20000 | 83.59500 | Highland County, OH, 48 miles east by north of Cincinnati. |
| 1860 | 39.00667 | 82.81333 | Pike County, OH, 20 miles south by east of Chillcothe. |
| 1850 | 38.98333 | 81.31667 | Wirt County, WV, 23 miles southeast of Parkersburg [2]. |
| 1840 | 39.03333 | 80.30000 | Upshur County, WV, 16 miles south of Clarksburg. Upshur County was formed from parts of Barbour, Lewis, and Randolph Counties in 1851[2]. |
| 1830 | 38.96500 | 79.28167 | Grant County, WV, 19 miles west-southwest of Morefiled. Grant County was formed from part of Hardy County in 1866 [2]. |
| 1820 | 39.09500 | 78.55000 | Hardy County, WV, 16 miles east of Moorefield [2]. |
| 1810 | 39.19167 | 77.62000 | Loudoun County, VA, 40 miles northwest by west of Washington, DC. |
| 1800 | 39.26833 | 76.94167 | Howard County, MD, 18 miles west of Baltimore. Howard County was formed from part of Anne Arundel County in 1851. |
| 1790 | 39.27500 | 76.18667 | Kent County, MD, 23 miles east of Baltimore. |
| [1] Conterminous United States excludes Alaska and Hawaii. ||||
| [2] West Virginia was set off from Virginia, December 31, 1862, and admitted as a State June 19, 1863. ||||

## XI. URBANIZATION AND GEOGRAPHY

Urban Geography is perhaps the largest sub-field within geography. Urban geographers study all aspects of cities in different regions of the world. They compare, contrast, classify, collect data and formulate theories about the urban environment. They deal with and examine issues like the spatial location of cities, poverty, crime, racial segregation, transportation, economic activities, demographics and other matters which defining the urban landscape.

Many theories have evolved centering on urban issues. There is the behavioral approach to urban geography, a Marxist interpretation, a social/cultural view and postmodern or antiscientific version. One of the more famous is the CENTRAL PLACE THEORY developed by a German geographer in the 1930's. The theory is concerned with the ideal spatial distribution of settlements over a landscape. A brief summary is outlined below:

- The theory was developed by Walter Christaller in the 1930's based on his observations in Bavaria, a southern region of Germany
- The theory attempts to explain the growth and development of urban systems and why certain places become larger while other remain small
- Size and spacing of settlements is explained by consumption – shopping behavior
- Goods and services are categorized on a continuum from "high order" to "low order"
- High-order goods tend to be expensive and not frequently use by consumers
- Just the opposite is true for low-order goods
- The range of a good is the maximum distance that a consumer will travel to obtain a particular product or service
- The threshold of a good is the minimum market size required to make the sale of a particular product or service profitable
- In practice, the urban patterns suggested by the Central Place Theory are often modified by:
  - Locationally-dependent functions (natural resource exploitation)
  - Transportation technology (transfer costs become distorted)
  - Political differentiation (tax and regulatory environments)
- Central Place Theory finds a great deal of use in retail geography. The concept of marketing area is frequently used by stores, restaurants, banks and other places of business.

The above is a modified summary based on material supplied by John Maher

Rank-Size Rule
Another theory which applies reasonably well to the American cities is the RANK-SIZE RULE. It states that there is a relationship between the size of a city and its position within the urban hierarchy. Thus, the city occupying the Nth rank by size should have 1/Nth the population of the largest city. For example, in a system where the largest city has a population of ten million, the fifth largest city should have a population of 2 million. (10,000,000/5=2,000,000)

The above and many other theories have been developed to better understand the urban phenomena which is associated with the development of the United States. The grown, decline, and the rebuilding of American cities is tied closely with the history of the country. The following pages deal with the evolution of the American city over time.

## URBANIZATION IN AMERICA

The number of Americans who are classified as urban is approaching 80% of the total population. This is a dramatic change from the figure in the 1880 Census, when only 28% of Americans were classified as urban. The chart below shows the American urban population in the various census years:

| | | |
|---|---|---|
| 2000 – 77 % | | |
| 1990 - 75 % | 1950 - 64.0% | 1910 - 45.6% |
| 1980 - 73.7% | 1940 - 56.5% | 1900 - 39.6% |
| 1970 - 73.6% | 1930 - 56.1% | 1890 - 35.1% |
| 1960 - 69.9% | 1920 - 51.2% | 1880 - 28.2% |

What is the pull factor that attracts so many Americans to the urban life style? A century ago, less than half of the population was urban; today nearly 250 million Americans are urbanites. The cities offer employment, diversity of population, cultural attractions, big time sporting events and the "bright lights" atmosphere which attracts many people. The cities also have a rich history which they developed since the founding of the country.

### Stages in the evolution and growth of the American cities
There are specific and recognizable stages which shaped the American cities over time.

STAGE I. <u>From the early European settlement to about 1800</u>:
*** Cities, especially along the east coast, emerged **prior** to the development of <u>commercial agriculture</u>. The later refers to cities which develop based on a particular crop which is exported from its ports to other parts of the world.
*** The first cities and towns functioned as <u>outposts</u> of western Europe and were replicas of those places
*** Development of New York, Philadelphia, Boston and other coastal American cities

STAGE II. <u>1800 TO 1860's</u>:
*** The nation's emphasis and orientation shifted from looking across the Atlantic toward Europe to exploring and settling the western interior of the country - <u>MANIFEST DESTINY</u>
(see next page for the discussion of Manifest Destiny)
*** Construction of canals and railroads influence the location and growth of new cities in the interior of the nation.
*** Military forts were built to protect the settlers from Native-Americans. Later these forts developed into cities and towns.
*** New York City became the nation's metropolis and the cultural and financial center
*** Chicago, St. Louis, and Cincinnati become important cities which served as gateways to further western expansion and as centers of commercial agriculture
*** North-eastern cities served the nation as bustling industrial centers

Under a quarter of the nation's population lived in cities by the end of this stage. The nation was primarily an agricultural state on the eve of the American Civil War (1861-1865). Cities such as Minneapolis, Phoenix, Wichita, Birmingham and Orlando did not exist until a few years after the Civil War.

## MANIFEST DESTINY

This was the term used to describe the expansionist drive of the United States in the westerly direction, beginning in the early 19th Century. It became a doctrine of the American government which meant western expansion, prearranged by Heaven, over an area not clearly defined. (1) It started from the East coast of the United States and moved west to reach a "natural boundary". That natural boundary continuously shifted: from the Appalachian Mountains to the Mississippi River to the Rocky Mountains to the deserts of the southwest to the Pacific Ocean, and beyond (Hawaii).

(1) Merk, Frederick. <u>Manifest Destiny and Mission in American History</u>,
    Alfred A. Knopf, New York, 1963, p. 24.

To some leaders, Manifest Destiny meant western expansion only to the Pacific Ocean. To others it meant a takeover of the North American continent. To a few, it was a doctrine to dominate the whole hemisphere. Most shared a belief in the cultural superiority of Anglo-Saxons and viewed the concept as a fulfillment of a divine mission.

The term was coined by John L. O'Sullivan, a New York City writer who felt that exploring and expanding into new territory was a natural growth and fate of humans. The purpose for the expansionism in North America, according to O'Sullivan, was to unify the people between the Atlantic and the Pacific oceans. He first used the term in a July 1845 publication where he was justifying the annexation of Texas.

This policy also signaled the beginning of the end for the Native-American culture as their lands were systematically annexed, their hunting grounds taken and distributed among the settlers and any resistance suppressed by the US Army. The combating warriors, like the Sioux group pictured below, disappeared as a fighting force by the end of the 19th century.

STAGE III. <u>1860's to World War I:</u>
*** After the Civil War, industrialization continued and the cities in the north-east attracted large waves of migrants both from overseas and from the rural interior of the U.S.A. From the late 1880's to the turn of the 20th century three distinct groups of people poured into the cities, competing for jobs, housing, education and social status. These groups included:
1. <u>the blacks from the rural south</u>
2. <u>the white American rural farm population</u>
3. <u>the Europeans from eastern and southern nations of Europe</u>

The Eastern Europeans included the Poles, Hungarians, Slovaks, Serbians, and Russians among others, while the Southern Europeans were people like the Italians and Greeks. This was a different wave of migrants than the British and other western Europeans who came to America earlier. The new immigrants did not speak the language, were primarily Roman Catholic or Eastern Orthodox and had different customs and views. They formed their ghettos in the cities and were treated as second class citizens.

The Irish, who came in large numbers in the 1840's and 1850's spoke English but were Roman Catholics and experienced their share of discrimination.
*** Other cities grew and developed during this period including New Orleans (the southern gateway), Minneapolis (the northern gateway), Denver, Los Angeles with Hollywood, and San Francisco.
*** Many southern cities, including Atlanta, were destroyed by the Union Army. Many would not be restored for some time after the Civil War

STAGE IV. <u>World War I to World War II:</u>
*** The Great Depression (following the stock market crash in October 1929) of the early 1930's was very instrumental in reducing migration to the cities. Some two million young men took to the road to find employment, as jobless rates in the cities skyrocketed. In Cleveland, for example, the unemployment rate stood at 50%, while it was 60% and 80% in Akron and Toledo, respectively.
*** Between 1930 and 1933, 9,000 banks closed, with depositors losing $2.5 billion. People could not pay off their mortgages, and many were forced to leave their homes in the cities.
*** Urban decay, on a large scale, started during this stage.
*** Many government programs were instituted by President F.D. Roosevelt to help the urban unemployed, but the Depression basically lasted until the US entered World War II.

STAGE V. <u>Post World War II:</u>
*** The returning veterans were coming to the cities in search of jobs, housing, and a better way of life.
*** The industry turned quickly from the war based products to consumer goods. Autos, televisions, washers, refrigerators and other items were produced requiring workers, and the cities flourished.
*** The suburbs emerged in the 1950's, becoming a uniquely American phenomenon.
*** SMSA's (Standard Metropolitan Statistical Areas), later replaced by MSA's, (Metropolitan Statistical Areas) became part of the American urban scene, combining the city's jobs with suburban living.
*** Megalopolises, such as <u>BOSWASH</u>, <u>CHIPITTS</u>, and <u>SANSAN</u> came into being as the urban population swelled. (see following page)

Note the lights identifying the various MEGALOPOLISES in the United States.

San Fran to
San Diego

* BOSWASH  *SANSAN  *CHIPITTS  *OTHERS ?

-Boston to
Washington, DC

Chicago
to
Pittsburgh

The present state of American cities leaves much to be desired. Escalating crime rates, the drug epidemic, confrontational race relations, poor quality of education, pollution, deteriorating housing conditions and antiquated public transportation systems, all contribute to the declining quality of life for people living in the cities. The flight of the white middle class to the suburbs continues, leaving the cities with less revenues to operate its social services and dividing the population into the richer, predominantly white suburbs and the poorer, mostly black inner cities. As can be seen from the chart below, the proportion of the non-white population continues to grow in the cities while remaining relatively steady in the suburbs.

*all live in segregated styles of living*

**Population, by race, in selected Metropolitan Statistical Areas:    1950 - 2000**

| area | percent of nonwhite population | | | | | |
| | 1950 | 1960 | 1970 | 1980 | 1990 | 2000 |
|---|---|---|---|---|---|---|
| NEW YORK MSA | 9 | 12 | 18 | 33 | 39 | 42 |
| CITY | 10 | 15 | 23 | 36 | 60 | 55 |
| SUBURBS | 4 | 5 | 6 | 7 | 10 | 20 |
| | | | | | | |
| CHICAGO MSA | 11 | 15 | 19 | 27 | 34 | 34 |
| CITY | 14 | 24 | 34 | 50 | 63 | 58 |
| SUBURBS | 3 | 3 | 4 | 9 | 14 | 21 |
| | | | | | | |
| DETROIT MSA | 12 | 15 | 18 | 22 | 25 | 29 |
| CITY | 16 | 29 | 45 | 66 | 80 | 88 |
| SUBURBS | 5 | 4 | 4 | 6 | 9 | 12 |
| | | | | | | |
| BOSTON MSA | 2 | 3 | 4 | 9 | 13 | 17 |
| CITY | 5 | 10 | 18 | 30 | 42 | 46 |
| SUBURBS | 1 | 1 | 2 | 3 | 5 | 11 |
| | | | | | | |
| PITTSBURGH MSA | 6 | 7 | 7 | 8 | 9 | 10 |
| CITY | 12 | 17 | 21 | 25 | 29 | 33 |
| SUBURBS | 3 | 3 | 4 | 5 | 7 | 7 |
| | | | | | | |
| ST. LOUIS MSA | 12 | 14 | 16 | 18 | 19 | 23 |
| CITY | 18 | 29 | 41 | 47 | 50 | 56 |
| SUBURBS | 7 | 6 | 8 | 11 | 14 | 16 |
| | | | | | | |
| WASHINGTON D.C. MSA | 23 | 24 | 26 | 32 | 38 | 40 |
| CITY | 35 | 55 | 72 | 73 | 74 | 69 |
| SUBURBS | 9 | 7 | 9 | 21 | 26 | 36 |

*city + all surrounding areas*

*→ non white population → b/c whites moving to suburbs*

Source: U.S. Census Bureau

What do the above figures tell us about residential place selection of the American population? What conclusions might one draw from these examples?

111

METROPOLITAN STATISTICAL AREAS
MICROPOLITAN STATISTICAL AREAS
COMBINED STATISTICAL AREAS

In an effort of defining the urban population living in the cities and their extended suburbs, the US Census and other related federal agencies continue to revise and update the concept of "urban" dwellers. The United States Office of Management and Budget(OMB) has adopted the following definitions in conjunction with the data from the Census Bureau:

The **Metropolitan Statistical Area** (MeSA) is a geographically designated area consisting of a large population nucleus together with adjacent communities and areas having a high degree of economic and social integration with that nucleus. It has at least one urbanized area of 50,000 or more people and consists of one or more contiguous counties.

The purpose of the MeSA classification is to allow all federal agencies to use a nationally consistent set of definitions of metropolitan areas suitable for the collecting, tabulating, and publishing of federal statistics. The MeSA designation is also used for non-statistical purposes by some federal agencies, including the allocation of funding to specific areas. At the state and at the local government levels, as well as in the private sector, this classification is used for planning and marketing purposes.

Since the early 1970's, there has been increased pressure to broaden the concept of metropolitan status to include smaller areas. The reason for the suggested inclusion is the fact that the federal money is allocated based on the population numbers in the metropolitan areas.

The **Micropolitan Statistical Area** (MiSA) is a geographically designated area consisting of at least one urban cluster of between 10,000 and 50,000 people with the adjacent territory having a high degree of social and economic integration with the core area. It may consist of one or core contiguous counties. JOHNSTOWN, including the whole of Cambria county, is an example of MiSA.

Both of the above areas are defined in terms of entire counties, except in the six New England states where they are defined in terms of cities and towns (townships). In addition to the county where the main city is located, an MSA may also include additional counties having strong economic and social ties to the stated county.

If a metropolitan area contains more than one million inhabitants, and meets a number of other requirements, it is called a **Consolidated Metropolitan Statistical Area** (CMSA). Several large MSA's are combined to form the **Primary Metropolitan Statistical Areas** (PMSA's). These concepts were developed by the Census Bureau in the mid-1980's to better define the growing number of large metropolitan regions which began to spring up as a result of growing suburbanization in the country. (These designations may be modified or replaced in the 2010 Census).

**Combined Statistical Areas(CSA)** are defined as adjacent Metropolitan and Micropolitan Statistical areas if specifies criteria are met as set up by the OMB. In 2006, 126 such areas existed in the USA.
See the following table for the largest CSA in the United States.

# COMBINED STATISTICAL AREAS IN THE UNITED STATES: 2000 TO 2009

| RANK | CSA | 2009 POPULATION | 2000 POPULATION | % CHANGE |
|------|-----|-----------------|-----------------|----------|
| 1 | New York | 22.2 million | 21.4 million | 4.1 |
| 2 | Los Angeles | 17.8 million | 16.4 million | 8.8 |
| 3 | Chicago | 9.8 million | 9.3 million | 5.3 |
| 4 | Washington/Baltimore | 8.4 million | 7.6 million | 11.5 |
| 5 | Boston | 7.6 million | 7.3 million | 4.3 |
| 6 | San Hose/San Francisco | 7.4 million | 7.1 million | 4.7 |
| 7 | Dallas/Fort Worth | 6.8 million | 5.5 million | 22.0 |
| 8 | Philadelphia | 6.5 million | 6.2 million | 5.3 |
| 9 | Houston | 6.0 million | 4.8 million | 24.0 |
| 10 | Atlanta | 5.8 million | 4.6 million | 28.0 |
| 11 | Detroit | 5.3 million | 5.3 million | -0.6 |
| 12 | Seattle/Tacoma | 4.2 million | 3.7 million | 12.2 |

Source: U.S. Census of Population - projections

## City vs MSA

It is important to differentiate between the city and the MSA. For example, the city of Johnstown has a population of approximately 24,000 people. Johnstown MiSA, on the other hand, has a population of over 150,000 and is made of all people residing in Cambria County. Philadelphia is a city of a million and a half inhabitants, while its CSA (made up of counties in Pennsylvania, New Jersey, Delaware and Maryland) has a population of over six million people.

The following maps show the MSA's of Pennsylvania and the USA.

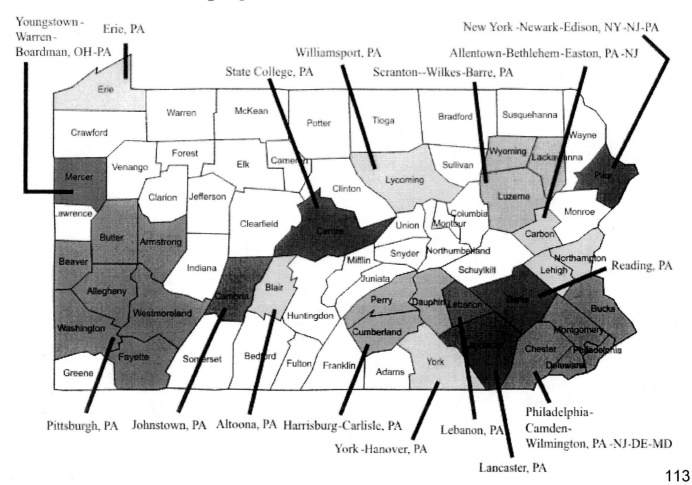

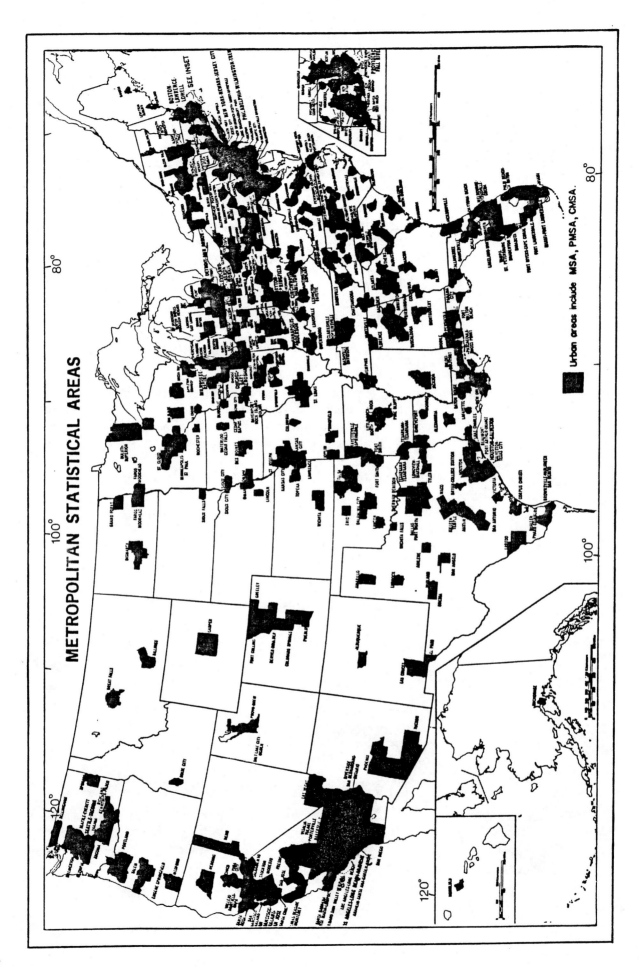

# METROPOLITAN STATISTICAL AREAS

Urban areas include MSA, PMSA, CMSA.

TEN MOST POPULOUS <u>CITIES</u> IN THE UNITED STATES – 1990 and 2000 (Census Figures)
(from the 2000 U.S. Population Census – <u>population in 1,000</u>)

| <u>city</u> | <u>1990</u> | <u>2000</u> | <u>rank</u> | <u>% change (1990-2000)</u> | <u>% of</u><br>African-Americans |
|---|---|---|---|---|---|
| 1. NEW YORK | 7,323 | 8,008 | 1 | 9.4 | 26.6 |
| 2. LOS ANGELES | 3,485 | 3,695 | 2 | 6.0 | 11.2 |
| 3. CHICAGO | 2,784 | 2,896 | 3 | 4.0 | 36.8 |
| 4. HOUSTON | 1,631 | 1,954 | 4 | 19.8 | 25.2 |
| 5. PHILADELPHIA | 1,586 | 1,518 | 5 | -4.3 | 43.2 |
| 6. SAN DIEGO | 1,111 | 1,223 | 7 | 10.2 | 7.9 |
| 7. DETROIT | 1,028 | 951 | 10 | -7.5 | 81.6 |
| 8. DALLAS | 1,007 | 1,189 | 8 | 18.0 | 25.9 |
| 9. PHOENIX | 983 | 1,321 | 6 | 34.3 | 5.1 |
| 10. SAN ANTONIO | 936 | 1,145 | 9 | 22.3 | 6.8 |

Eight of the largest cities in 2000 gained population in the 1990's; only Philadelphia and Detroit declined in size. New York City remained the largest city, passing the 8 million mark for the first time. Phoenix was the fastest growing city, increasing its population by over one third. Six of the ten top cities were located in the warm climates and nine of the ten contained over one million inhabitants. The same top ten cities remained from 1990, although some changed their rankings.

The data from the 2010 Census was not available for this edition of the book. The table below shows the US Census population estimates for the largest cities in the USA for the year 2008.

→ get sense of largest cities

Population Estimates for the 20 Most Populous American Cities – 2008

| | |
|---|---|
| New York | 8,364,000 |
| Los Angeles | 3,834,000 |
| Chicago | 2,853,000 |
| Houston | 2,242,000 |
| Phoenix | 1,568,000 |
| Philadelphia | 1,549,000 |
| San Antonio | 1,351,000 |
| Dallas | 1,280,000 |
| San Diego | 1,279,000 |
| San Jose | 948,000 |
| Detroit | 912,000 |
| San Francisco | 809,000 |
| Jacksonville | 808,000 |
| Indianapolis | 798,000 |
| Austin | 758,000 |
| Columbus | 755,000 |
| Fort Worth | 703,000 |
| Charlotte | 687,000 |
| Memphis | 670,000 |
| Baltimore | 637,000 |

## Cities: the Good and the Bad

It is interesting to note that only six of the above twenty cities do not have a NFL (National Football League) franchise. Three of these cities are in Texas, two are in California and the sixth is Columbus, Ohio. Ohio has two NFL teams in cities smaller than Columbus, Texas has franchises in Dallas and Houston, while California has teams in three of its cities. What are some of the reasons why San Antonio and Los Angeles (cities with over a million and nearly four million inhabitants respectively) do not have NFL teams?

Of the 32 teams in the NFL (see the following map), only six are located in the western half of the country, with three being in California. The other two states with three NFL franchises are Florida and New York. Will Texas be the next State to have three of its cities with a NFL franchises? Will it be Ohio? Since the NFL teams bring economic benefits to the city, in addition to prestige, civic pride and fan following, many cities have fought hard to bring a team to their localities. Geographers have examined the spatial dimensions of this phenomenon as part of the overall understanding of the American urban landscape.

NFL team for Columbus, Ohio ?

# Teams

**Teams by Conference**

**American Football Conference**

**East**
Buffalo Bills
Miami Dolphins
New England Patriots
New York Jets

**North**
Baltimore Ravens
Cincinnati Bengals
Cleveland Browns
Pittsburgh Steelers

**South**
Houston Texans
Indianapolis Colts
Jacksonville Jaguars
Tennessee Titans

**West**
Denver Broncos
Kansas City Chiefs
Oakland Raiders
San Diego Chargers

**National Football Conference**

**East**
Dallas Cowboys
New York Giants
Philadelphia Eagles
Washington Redskins

**North**
Chicago Bears
Detroit Lions
Green Bay Packers
Minnesota Vikings

**South**
Atlanta Falcons
Carolina Panthers
New Orleans Saints
Tampa Bay Buccaneers

**West**
Arizona Cardinals
St. Louis Rams
San Francisco 49ers
Seattle Seahawks

| Money Magazine's Top 10 list of the best places to live in the East: | | |
|---|---|---|
| **Large (1,000,000+)** | **Medium (250,000-999,999)** | **Small (100,000-249,999)** |
| 1. Washington, D.C. | 1. Trenton, N.J. | 1. Manchester, N.H. |
| 2. Boston | 2. Dutchess County, N.Y. | 2. Portland, Maine |
| 3. New York | 3. Wilmington, Del. | 3. Nashua, N.H. |
| 4. Nassau, N.Y. | 4. New Haven, Conn. | **4. Johnstown, Pa.** |
| 5. Monmouth, N.J. | 5. Harrisburg, Pa. | 5. State College, Pa. |
| 6. Baltimore | 6. Albany, N.Y. | 6. Waterbury, Conn. |
| 7. Pittsburgh | 7. Stamford, Conn. | 7. Hagerstown, Md. |
| 8. Middlesex, N.J. | 8. Bridgeport, Conn. | 8. Danbury, Conn. |
| 9. Philadelphia | 9. Worcester, Mass. | 9. Fitchburg, Mass. |
| 10. Rochester, N.Y. | 10. Scranton, Pa. | 10. Portsmouth, N.H. |

Johnstown, number four in the small-city category.

# Best in the state

## Johnstown garners high marks from Money

**By JEFF McCREADY**
TRIBUNE-DEMOCRAT BUSINESS WRITER

A low crime rate, better-than-average appreciation in the price of homes and above-average air quality helped the two-county Johnstown area become the best place to live in Pennsylvania, Money magazine says in its annual survey released Wednesday.

The survey ranks the nation's 300 metropolitan statistical areas by region and size. The Johnstown area had the highest ranking of any Pennsylvania city in the three population divisions in the eastern U.S.

That was good news to community leaders because the Cambria-Somerset county area has, at 8 percent, the highest unemployment rate of the state's 14 largest areas.

"It's something to beat our chest about," Robert Layo, president of the Greater Johnstown/Cambria County Chamber of Commerce, said from his office Wednesday.

Johnstown ranked fourth of the 21 small-city areas in the East – the three higher ones were in New Hampshire and Maine. That ranking takes in areas with a population of 100,000 to 249,999. State College was 5th and Altoona, 12th.

Johnstown also had the best ranking of any Pennsylvania city in two other size categories for the East.

Pittsburgh ranked seventh of the large cities with populations of 100,000 or more and Harrisburg was fifth of the medium-sized cities, or those with populations of 250,000 to 999,999. Washington ranked first of the large cities; Trenton, N.J., was No. 1 of the medium-sized cities; and Manchester, N.H., topped the smaller cities.

"This is something we can use in our advertising," Layo said of Johnstown's ranking.

Low crime, clean air and clean water – areas in which Johnstown did well – are three of the main things that people are concerned with, Money found in interviews with 500 households across the nation.

This area's low crime was a factor that helped the good rating, said Daniel Essner, a Money reporter who worked on the five-month survey.

Sources on city rankings: Places Rated Almanac;

# Why do we call New York City "The Big Apple"?

In the early years of the nineteenth century, refugees from war-torn Europe began arriving in New York in great numbers. Many were remnants of the crumbling French aristocracy, forced to seek refuge abroad from the dread "Monsieur Guillotine." Arriving here without funds or friends, many of these were forced to survive, as one contemporary put it, "by their wits or worse."

One of these, arriving in late 1803 or early 1804, was Mlle. Evelyn Claudine de Saint-Évremond. Daughter of a noted courtier, wit, and littérateur, and herself a favorite of Marie Antoinette, Evelyn was by all accounts remarkably attractive: beautiful, vivacious, and well-educated, and she was soon a society favorite. For reasons never disclosed, however, a planned marriage the following year to John Hamilton, son of the late Alexander Hamilton, was called off at the last minute. Soon after, with support from several highly placed admirers, she established a salon -- in fact, it appears to have been an elegantly furnished bordello -- in a substantial house that still stands at 142 Bond Street, then one of the city's most exclusive residential districts.

Evelyn's establishment quickly won, and for several decades maintained, a formidable reputation as the most entertaining and discreet of the city's many "temples of love," a place not only for lovemaking, but also for elegant dinners, high-stakes gambling, and witty conversation. The girls, many of them fresh arrivals from Paris or London, were noted for their beauty and bearing. More than a few of them, apparently, were actually able to secure wealthy husbands from among the establishment's clientele.

When New Yorkers insisted on anglicizing her name to "Eve," Evelyn apparently found the biblical reference highly amusing, and for her part would refer to the temptresses in her employ as "my irresistable apples." The young men-about-town soon got into the habit of referring to their amorous adventures as "having a taste of Eve's Apples." This knowing phrase established the speaker as one of the "in" crowd, and at the same time made it clear he had no need to visit one of the coarser establishments that crowded nearby Mercer Street, for instance. The enigmatic reference in Philip Hone's famous diary to "Ida, sweet as apple cider" (October 4, 1838) has been described as an oblique reference to a visit to what had by then become a notorious but cherished civic institution.

The rest, as they say, is etymological history.

The sexual connotation of the word "apple" was well known in New York and throughout the country until around World War I. The *Gentleman's Directory of New York City*, a privately published (1870) guide to the town's "houses of assignation," confidently asserted that "in freshness, sweetness, beauty, and firmness to the touch, New York's apples are superior to any in the New World or indeed the Old." Meanwhile, various "apple" catch-phrases -- "the Apple Tree," "the Real Apple," etc. -- were used as synonyms for New York City itself, which boasted (if that is the term) more houses of ill repute *per capita* than any other major U.S. municipality.

William Jennings Bryan, though hardly the first to denounce New York as a sink of iniquity, appears to have been the first to use the "apple" epithet in public discourse, branding the city, in a widely reprinted 1892 campaign speech, as "the foulest Rotten Apple on the Tree of decadent Federalism." The *double-entendre* – i.e., as a reference to both political and sexual corruption -- would have been well understood by voters of the time.

Crime in the American Cities

There is no doubt that people look at the city's crime rates as they make their decision to relocate. It is also a fact that the United States has one of the highest crime rates in the world.

Geographers have done a significant amount of research on crime in America. Keith Harries, George Rengert, Leon Pettiway, and Steve Herbert are some of the researchers who have made scholarly contributions to the field. The Geography of Crime and Justice, written by Keith Harris in 1974, paved the way for other geographers to do significant research on the subject. In 1999, Harris wrote another book called Mapping Crime: Principle and Practice. In that book, Harris correlated the evolution of crime mapping to the history of cartography. He continued by showing the practicality of map making and the usage of GIS for faster and more efficient ways to show various components of criminal activity.

There is little argument that the United States has a major issue of crime in its cities. Some years ago, an article in Argosy magazine stated that the "chances of a person born in Atlanta and being murdered in his lifetime was 1 in 28." Future projections indicated that if the crime rate continued at the present rate, the chances would increase to 1 in 11 !!!!! As America celebrated its Bicentennial Year – 1976, there were more homicides in that year than the combined number of U.S. battle deaths recorded during the Revolution, the War of 1812, and the wars with Mexico and Spain. The homicide situation is not much different today. In 2008, the following cities had the dubious distinction of having the highest murder rates in the country:

Cities with the highest number of homicides per 100,000 people

| City | Number of homicides per 100,000 inhabitants |
| --- | --- |
| New Orleans | 67 |
| St. Louis | 47 |
| Baltimore | 37 |
| Detroit | 34 |
| Washington, DC | 32 |
| Oakland | 29 |
| Kansas City | 26 |
| Cleveland | 24 |
| Newark | 24 |
| Philadelphia | 23 |
| Pittsburgh | 23 |
| Cincinnati | 22 |
| Memphis | 21 |
| Atlanta | 20 |

Source: FBI web page

As a result of these and other crimes, the prison population in the United States numbered well over one and a half million persons. Nearly one quarter of a million were inmates incarcerated in the federal run facilities.

In 2009, the number of inmates in U.S. state prisons dropped for the first time in nearly forty years. The Pew Research Center cited the economy as a contributing factor in the reduction of prisoners. It costs about $80 a day to house a prisoner versus $4 a day to fund a probation program. Many states have chosen an extended probation option for non violent offenders without jeopardizing the safety of the general population. California led the nation in prisoner reduction followed by Michigan and New York. Pennsylvania led all states in the absolute increase of its prison population.

Name: _____

**If you were given an opportunity to live in any city in the United States, what would be your first choice ?**

City: _____

What would be the three specific reasons for this choice?

1.


2.


3.

What would be your 2ⁿᵈ and 3ʳᵈ choices?

_____

_____


Which three cities in the United States would you list as the worst to live in

1.

2.

3.

Why ?

- assume chosen as
  mayor
  $1 million of betterment
        of city

# JOHNSTOWN MSA

Johnstown MSA (Metropolitan Statistical Area) is made up of all the people residing in *CAMBRIA* and *SOMERSET* Counties. The population in the area has been declining dramatically over the past number of decades.

| County | Year | total population | Year | total population | population change 1990 to 2000 |
|--------|------|------------------|------|------------------|-------------------------------|
| CAMBRIA | 2000.......152,598 | | 1990........163,029 | | - 10,431 |
| SOMERSET | 2000..........80,023 | | 1990.........78,218 | | + 1,805 |

Cambria County's population loss of over 10,000 people (between 1990 and 2000), which was 6.4% of its total population can be attributed to the declining coal and steel industries, as people leave the area in search of employment.
Cambria's percentage population loss was the highest of the Commonwealth's 67 counties.

For the whole of Johnstown's <u>MSA</u> (Cambria and Somerset numbers combined) the figures were: 232,621 people in 2000 and 241,247 people in 1990. This was a loss of 8,626 people (3.5 %) for the MSA in the decade of the 1990's

The city of Johnstown, the largest municipality in the Cambria/Somerset region, fared even worse. It declined from 28,125 residents in 1990 to 23,906 in 2000. The loss of 4,219 people represented a 15 % decline. The losses for the city in the decade of the 1980's were even higher; a staggering 21 % !!!

Of the twenty municipalities comprising the Greater Johnstown Region, nineteen lost people between 1990 and 2000. The trend is likely to continue if the economy does not improve.

Municipalities of the Greater Johnstown Area with the largest population losses between 1990 and 2000:
Scalp Level...........................26.5%
Franklin................................21.8%
City of Johnstown...................15.0%
West Taylor..........................13.4%
East Conemaugh....................12.2%
East Taylor...........................11.3%
Conamaugh Township.............10.6%
Stoneycreek..........................10.1%

All the municipalities of Greater Johnstown region, along with all other townships and boroughs of Cambria County are shown on the following map. The County is made up of 30 townships, 33 boroughs and the City of Johnstown. Is it time for political consolidation for some of these municipalities ?

# Cambria County

## Minor Civil Divisions

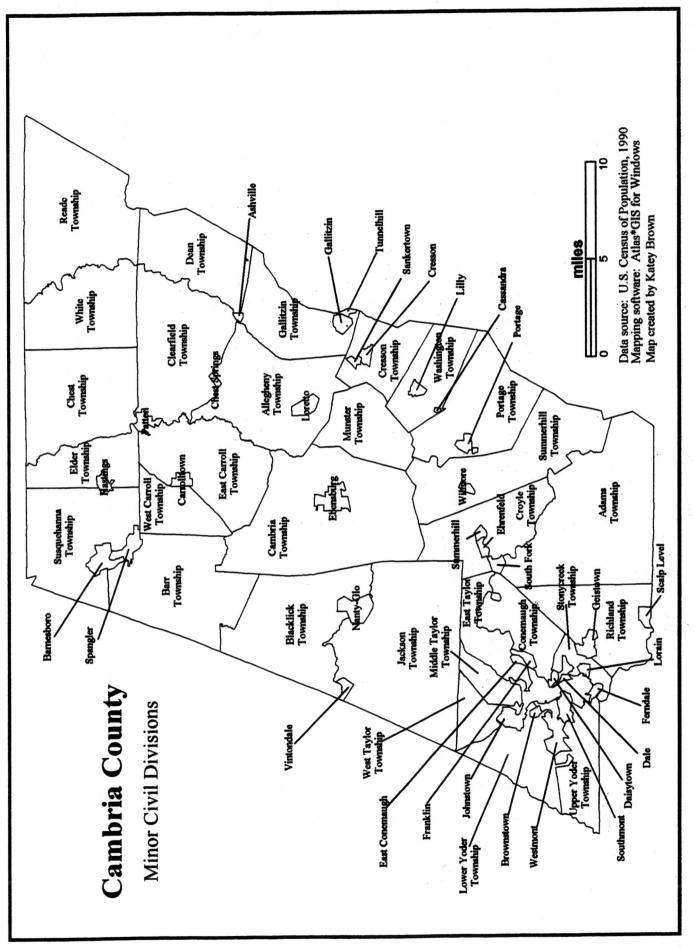

Data source: U.S. Census of Population, 1990
Mapping software: Atlas*GIS for Windows
Map created by Katey Brown

miles

0    5    10

## XII ~ EUROPE

The European realm may be defined as a part of the earth surface which is bounded by the Atlantic Ocean to the west (Iceland is included in this realm), Mediterranean Sea to the south (Turkey is excluded), and the Arctic Ocean to the north. It is more difficult to draw the eastern boundary of Europe, especially since the break-up of the Soviet Union into a number of independent states which occurred in 1991. The former Soviet Republics of Estonia, Latvia, Lithuania, Moldova, Belarus and the Ukraine, all independent nations today, are part of the European realm. Russia, although a European country, is excluded from this section and will be examined as a single unit in the following chapter of the book. The old notion that Europe and Asia are separated by the Ural Mountains should be discarded. The eastern boundary for Europe, therefore, may be considered to be the border with Russia.

Europe covers approximately 2.2 million square miles (excluding Russia) making it about 60% the size of the United States. Its population of approximately 750 million people (excluding Russia) is about two and a half times larger than the USA. The "big six" European nations in population include: Germany (with some 82 million people), Italy, United Kingdom, and France with about 60 million people each, and the Ukraine and Spain with nearly 50 million each. Poland follows with nearly 40 million people. These seven nations account for about half of Europe's total population.

There are a number of "microstates" in Europe with a very small number of inhabitants. These include ANDORRA; SAN MARINO; MONACO; VATICAN CITY; and LIECHTENSTEIN (bordering Austria and Switzerland). Malta, although a small island nation located south of Sicily in the Mediterranean Sea, has a population of nearly half a million people ~ substantially larger than the five microstates. Malta, along with Andorra, Monaco, San Marino and Liechtenstein are members of the United Nations.

Over 40 languages are spoken by large groups of people in Europe. Three major groupings include: 1. GERMANIC languages of northern Europe, 2. ROMANCE languages of southern Europe, and 3. SLAVIC languages of Eastern Europe. Other languages, spoken by a smaller number of people include Celtic (in Ireland), Finno-Ugric (in Finland, Estonia and Hungary), and Greek. A subset of Germanic languages also includes Scandinavian languages, spoken in SWEDEN, NORWAY, DENMARK and ICELAND.

Based on major religions, Europe may be divided into PROTESTANT north, CATHOLIC south, and CHRISTIAN ORTHODOX east. Judaism and Islam are also practiced, but on a much smaller scale. The number of Islamic faithful is on the increase in Europe as immigrants from north Africa, Turkey and other less developed nations continue to come to Europe. Many settle in urban centers and constitute the lower economic class in these countries. They tend to maintain their culture and religion, without rapidly integrating into the European societies.

Most of the nations of Europe are members of the EUROPEAN UNION, a powerful economic block, and many are members of NATO (North Atlantic Treaty Organization) which is a political/military organization bound together for military alliance. These are discussed later in the book.

IBERIA is a term given to the area comprised of Spain and Portugal, while BENELUX is a term defining the nations of Belgium, Netherlands and Luxemburg.

# Nation-States of Europe

*on Exam

Compiled by: Aaron Mulhollen
Data: Esri
September 2006

# THE NATIONS OF EUROPE

| NAME | CAPITAL | AREA (sq. mi.) | 2009 POPULATION |
|---|---|---|---|
| ALBANIA | TIRANA | 11,100 | 3.2 mill. |
| AUSTRIA | VIENNA | 32,374 | 8.4 mill. |
| *BELARUS | MINSK | 80,200 | 9.7 mill. |
| BELGIUM | BRUSSELS | 11,779 | 10.8 mill. |
| BULGARIA | SOFIA | 42,829 | 7.6 mill. |
| CZECH REPUBLIC | PRAGUE | 30,590 | 10.5 mill. |
| DENMARK | COPENHAGEN | 17,028 | 5.5 mill. |
| *ESTONIA | TALLINN | 17,410 | 1.3 mill. |
| FINLAND | HELSINKI | 130,119 ^ | 5.3 mill. |
| FRANCE | PARIS | 211,000 (2)^ | 62.6 mill. |
| GERMANY | BERLIN | 136,461 (5)^ | 82.0 mill. |
| GREECE | ATHENS | 50,547 | 11.3 mill. |
| HUNGARY | BUDAPEST | 35,919 | 10.0 mill. |
| ICELAND | REYKJAVIK | 39,702 | .3 mill. |
| IRELAND | DUBLIN | 26,600 | 4.5 mill. |
| ITALY | ROME | 116,303 ^ | 60.3 mill. |
| *LATVIA | RIGA | 24,900 | 2.3 mill. |
| *LITHUANIA | VILNIUS | 25,210 | 3.3 mill. |
| LUXEMBOURG | LUXEMBOURG | 999 | .5 mill. |
| MALTA | VALLETTA | 122 | .4 mill. |
| *MOLDOVA | CHISINAU | 14,170 | 4.1 mill. |
| NETHERLANDS | AMSTERDAM | 14,192 | 16.5 mill. |
| NORWAY | OSLO | 125,181 ^ | 4.8 mill. |
| POLAND | WARSAW | 120,359 ^ | 38.1 mill. |
| PORTUGAL | LISBON | 35,340 | 10.6 mill. |
| ROMANIA | BUCHAREST | 91,699 | 22.5 mill. |
| SLOVAKIA | BRATISLAVA | 18,790 | 5.4 mill. |
| SPAIN | MADRID | 194,883 (3)^ | 41.9 mill. |
| SWEDEN | STOCKHOLM | 173,665 (4)^ | 9.3 mill. |
| SWITZERLAND | BERN | 15,941 | 7.8 mill. |
| *UKRAINE | KIEV | 233,100 (1)^ | 46.0 mill. |
| UNITED KINGDOM | LONDON | 94,209 | 61.8 mill. |

(United Kingdom is comprised of Great Britain and Northern Ireland)

* these new nations were the former Republics of the Soviet Union (USSR) and became independent as the Soviet Union broke apart in 1991.

Nine nations of Europe (^) have an area of over 100,000 square miles, with the Ukraine and France being the largest with over 200,000 square miles each. By way of comparison, CALIFORNIA has an area of approximately 160,000 square miles; PENNSYLVANIA - 45,000 square miles; and NEW JERSEY - 8,000 square miles.

See the following maps of the MICROSTATES OF EUROPE.

# Microstates of Europe

### Andorra
**Size:** 450 sq. km.   **Population:** 54,428.
**Admitted to UN:** 7/28/93.

### Liechtenstein
**Size:** 160 sq. km.   **Population:** 28,642.
**Admitted to UN:** 9/18/90.

### Monaco
**Size:** 1.9 sq. km.   **Population:** 29,965.
**Admitted to UN:** 5/28/93.

### San Marino
**Size:** 60 sq. km.   **Population:** 23,404.
**Admitted to UN:** 3/2/92.

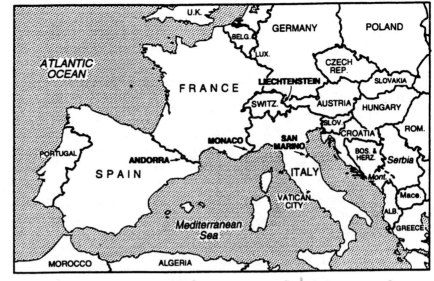

## Liechtenstein

## Monaco — coastline on mediterranean

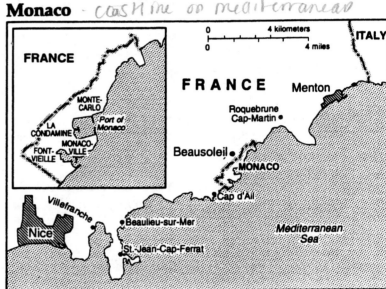

## San Marino — surround by Italy

## Andorra → Pyrenese Islands

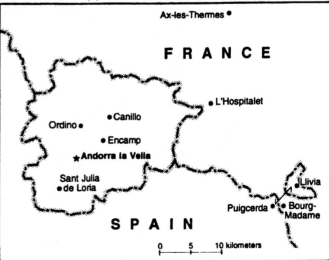

# THE VATICAN CITY → middle of Rome
where pope sit

The Vatican City occupies an area of slightly over 100 acres and is located approximately in the middle of Rome. It contains St. Peter's Basilica, the Apostolic Palace, the Vatican museum, a number of administrative and office buildings, several apartments, and a few other buildings. A number of additional structures, as well as the Pope's summer residence, are located near-by, and all are part of the sovereign state of the Vatican City. This independent status was a result of a 1929 treaty signed with Italy.

Some 1000 people live inside the compound, and the State of the Vatican City has its own post office, bank, railway station, and publishing house. The State issues its own stamps, coins and passports. An influential Vatican radio station broadcasts religious programs, while its press publishes daily and weekly papers in Italian, English, Spanish, Portuguese, German and French. Approximately 4,000 people work for the Vatican.

## The Holy See *

The Holy See is the "central government" of the Roman Catholic Church. The term "Holy See" refers to the composite authority, jurisdiction, and sovereignty vested in and exercised by the Pope and his advisers primarily in the spiritual direction and guidance of the Roman Catholic Church throughout the world. It is an institution which, under the international law, has a legal personality that allows it to enter into treaties as the juridical equal of a state and to send and receive diplomatic representatives. The Holy See has formal diplomatic relations with about 120 nations, including the United States.

Although not a full member of the United Nations, it has a permanent observer status in the organization and of the UN's many specialized and related agencies.

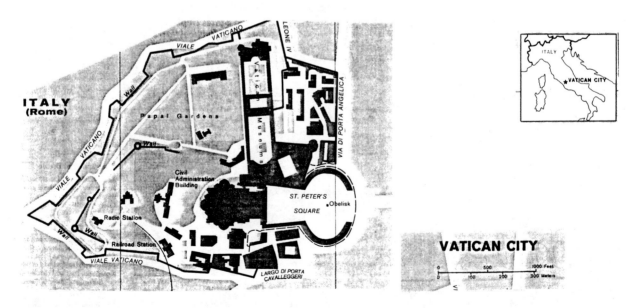

* THE HOLY SEE, Background Notes, U.S. Department of State, Bureau of Public Affairs, 1989.

128

## The Helsinki Agreement

On August 1, 1975, at a Conference on Security and Cooperation in Europe, 35 nations signed the Helsinki Agreement. The nations pledged to cooperate in economic and peacekeeping activities, the promotion of human rights and in a number of other areas. The major part of the agreement was the endorsement of post-World War II European boundaries initiated by the Soviet Union and its allies. The United States, represented by President G. Ford, pushed for the human rights segment of the document.

Besides the USA, SOVIET UNION, and CANADA, the following European nations signed the document: AUSTRIA, BELGIUM, BULGARIA, CYPRUS, CZECHOSLOVAKIA, DENMARK, EAST GERMANY, FINLAND, FRANCE, GREAT BRITAIN, GREECE, HUNGARY, ICELAND, IRELAND, ITALY, LIECHTENSTEIN, LUXEMBOURG, MALTA, MONACO, NETHERLANDS, NORWAY, POLAND, PORTUGAL, RUMANIA, SAN MARINO, SPAIN, SWEDEN, SWITZERLAND, THE VATICAN, WEST GERMANY, and YUGOSLAVIA. TURKEY, a non-European nation, also took part in the Conference and signed the agreement.

## The Changing Europe

As important as the Helsinki Agreement was in establishing national boundaries, it has been overshadowed by the geopolitical events which occurred in the 1990's. Six new European nations emerged from the old Soviet Union, Czechoslovakia split into the Czech and Slovak Republics and Yugoslavia no longer exists as a nation. With the demise of the Soviet Union in 1991, the nations of Eastern Europe (which were dominated by the Soviet Union) began to chart their own political and economic course. The economic and military alliances, forged in the past among the socialist countries (led by the former Soviet Union) to counteract those of the capitalist countries (led by the United States) have changed drastically. The North Atlantic Treaty Organization (NATO), for example, has expanded its membership while its counterpart organization the WARSAW PACT (led by the former Soviet Union) has been dismantled! West and East Germanys were united in October of 1990, and the European Union has expanded its membership to take in some of the former Communist nations.

## The European Union (EU)

The European Union is an organization whose goal is to provide an institutional framework for a united Europe. The EU evolved out of a smaller organization which started after World War II to help the war torn European nations to get back on their feet economically. The original name of the organization was the EUROPEAN COAL AND STEEL COMMUNITY (shortened to EUROPEAN COMMUNITY in 1993) and the charter members included The Federal Republic of Germany (West Germany), France, Italy, Belgium, the Netherlands and Luxemburg. The charter was established in 1952, and since that time additional nations have joined the organization.

The function of the organization expanded from a strictly economic approach to include other concerns. One of the major ones was to prevent another catastrophic war and lessen the tensions throughout the world. There are several governing bodies operating within the EU. Some of these include: The European Commission, which proposes legislation and policies and is responsible for administration; the Council, which places legislation into action throughout the EU territory; The European Parliament, which is used as a public forum for members to debate issue; The Court of Justice which, interprets the laws; The Court of Auditors, which monitors financial activities of the Union; The Economic and Social Committee, which represents employees and employers and must be consulted before any major decisions can be adopted; and finally The Committee of the Regions, which deals with decisions affecting regional interests.

The European Union, in cooperation with the United States, spearheaded many important issues impacting the whole world. Some of these were plans for a peaceful use of nuclear energy as an alternative to fossil fuels; economic help to underdeveloped nations; taking an active part in negotiating disputes among various nations; and drafting an agreement on customs cooperation. EU has huge investments in the Unites States, helping to provide approximately three million jobs for American workers.

The EURO, a common currency for the nations of the EU, should provide more economic stability for the organization, which now has diplomatic relations with over 130 nations. There is no doubt that the EUROPEAN UNION, along with the UNITED STATES and JAPAN, is a major economic player in the world.

When RUMANIA and BULGARIA joined the UE on January 1, 2007, the membership of the organization stood at 27 nations. A number of nations have their applications pending including ALBANIA and TURKEY. The latter is a Muslim nation while the former has a large Muslim minority among its population. Some experts suggest that the EU is reluctant to have these two nations join the Union because of the cultural differences with the rest of the European member states. That is the conjecture which the leaders of the European Union deny.

In addition to the above two nations, other nations also have expressed interest in joining the organization. These include the former Republics which made up the nation of YUGOSLAVIA. Yugoslavia no longer exists as a nation – see the following pages on the the short history and the demise of that nation.

European Union (EU) Member Nations – 2010          27 members

Joined in 2007

- Bulgaria
- Romania

| EU15 Member States: | | Member States as of May 1, 2004: EU25: |
|---|---|---|
| • Austria<br>• Belgium<br>• Denmark<br>• Finland<br>• France<br>• Germany<br>• Greece<br>• Ireland | • Italy<br>• Luxembourg<br>• The Netherlands<br>• Portugal<br>• Spain<br>• Sweden<br>• United Kingdom | • Cyprus<br>• Czech Republic<br>• Estonia<br>• Hungary<br>• Latvia<br>• Lithuania<br>• Malta<br>• Poland<br>• Slovakia<br>• Slovenia |

# FORMER YUGOSLAVIA

On June 3, 2006, Montenegro declared its independence and became the last republic to leave what was once the nation of Yugoslavia. The name "YUGOSLAVIA" was wiped from the map of Europe! Since 1992, six new nations emerged from what was once the Socialist Republic of Yugoslavia. They include: <u>CROATIA, SLOVENIA, MACEDONIA, SERBIA, MONTENEGRO, and BOSNIA-HERZEGOVINA.</u>

<u>The new nation of Montenegro</u>

## Background

Yugoslavia, which means "land of the southern Slavs", was established as a nation after World War I. It contained, within its borders, a number of diverse ethnic peoples who managed, in the past, to coexist under one flag. After World War II, the government was taken over by a socialist regime, led by Marshal Tito. Although nominally a socialist state, Yugoslavia was not closely allied with the former Soviet Union, and followed a policy of non-alignment in the international arena.

With the break-up of the Soviet Union in 1991, the collapse of the socialist regime in Yugoslavia in 1992, the rising nationalism among various ethnic groups in the country, and the inability of the federal army to keep the nation united, Yugoslavia dissolved into number of separate nations (see following map). <u>CROATIA, SLOVENIA, and MACEDONIA</u>, all former Republics within Yugoslavia, became independent nations. <u>BOSNIA-HERZEGOVINA</u>, a region in Yugoslavia with the Muslim majority, also declared independence. The conflict in the latter area, however, continued for some time as the Orthodox Serbians, living in the region, fought against the establishment of an Islamic state. "Ethnic cleansing" entered the vocabulary to describe killings of one ethnic group by another. With the independence of the above four nations, Yugoslavia lost population and was reduced in area. A short lived union of Serbia and Montenegro comprising Yugoslavia dissolved in 2006.

## Serbia and Kosovo

From the breakup of Yugoslavia into six independent nations, Serbia emerged as the largest and most powerful. The hostilities and fighting, however, continue in Serbia. The country's two provinces, VOJVODINA (V on the map below) in the north and *KOSOVO* (K on the map below) in the south, are home to a large number of non-Serbian minorities. The former has a substantial Hungarian minority, while Kosovo is populated by a very large ethnic Albanian population. The Albanians make up over 80% of the population in Kosovo, and want independence for that area from Serbia.

In February of 2008, the Albanians in Kosovo declared their independence and were recognized by 62 member states of the United Nations, including the United States. Russia and China, along with 130 member states of the UN, do not recognize Albania's independence, thus blocking Kosovo's membership in the UN. The UN troops patrol the area but the tensions remain high.

The map below shows the SIX nations which emerged from former Yugoslavia (underlined) and the Serbian province of KOSOVO (K on the map)

## PHYSICAL GEOGRAPHY OF EUROPE

Europe, as previously defined, has a number of unique physical characteristics. First, much of Europe is located close to large water bodies. This fact makes the climate of Europe temperate, given its high latitudinal position. Its winters are warmer and its summers cooler than in other regions located at similar latitudes. The proximity of the seas also enabled the early Europeans to develop navigational skills and invent various instruments for sea voyages to other parts of the world. With the help of these tools, the western Europeans traveled to various regions, parts of which they conquered and colonized.

The warm "GULF STREAM" also plays a role in a temperate climate of Europe. The Gulf Stream and the North Atlantic Drift flow north along the western shores of Europe bringing its warm waters as far north as the city of <u>Murmansk</u>. This Russian city-port, located north of the Arctic Circle, stays ice free most of the year.

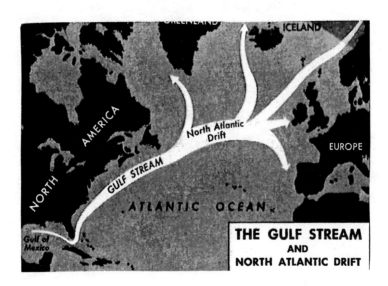

THE GULF STREAM
AND
NORTH ATLANTIC DRIFT

<u>ASSIGNMENT</u>                    Name: _____

To see the warming influence of the large water bodies on the climate of Europe, compare the European cities listed below with North American cities at the same LATITUDINAL location.

<u>European Cities</u>                    <u>North American Cities</u>
PARIS                              North Dakota, minnesota
BERLIN                            Southern Canada
LONDON
VIENNA

## The "CHUNNEL": An Engineering Marvel

The "Chunnel" is the name given to a tunnel, cut under the English Channel, connecting southern England with northern France. Long a dream of many Europeans, the project was finished in May of 1994. The 31 – mile tunnel was cut under water at 50 to 180 feet below the sea-bed. The travel time from one end of the tunnel to another is approximately half an hour. A traveler may now go from London to Paris without taking a boat across the English Channel.

View of Folkestone Terminal

<u>MAJOR PHYSICAL FEATURES OF EUROPE</u> (see following map):

Europe may be divided into FOUR major physical features and a number of minor ones. These are discussed below

1.  **Northern Mountains** - these mountains are made up of metamorphic rock, containing some rich metallic ores. Sweden, for example, is an exporter of iron ore, which is some of the purest in the world. The mountains cover much of Scandinavia, northern Great Britain and Ireland, and represent an older geomorphologic formation.
2.  **European Plain** – this region is made up of sedimentary rock with rich agricultural lands. It also contains some fossil fuels, with large petroleum deposits in Romania. The region is the most densely populated area of Europe and extends from the Paris Basin and London in the west through the Benelux (Belgium, Netherlands and Luxembourg) nations, northern Germany, Denmark, and into Poland.
3.  **Scattered Uplands** – these include IBERIA (comprised of Spain and Portugal); CENTRAL PLATEAU OF FRANCE; and the BAVARIAN PLATEAU of southern Germany, among others.
4.  **Alpine Mountains System** - in addition to the <u>ALPS</u>, the system also includes the <u>PYRENEES</u> which form a natural barrier between Spain and France, the <u>APENNINES</u> of Italy, Yugoslavia's <u>DINARIC RANGES</u>, and the <u>CARPATHIAN Mountains</u> of western Ukraine and central Romania. In Romania, these mountains are called the <u>TRANSYLVANIAN ALPS</u>, after a province of the same name.

Historically, the Transylvania region of present day Romania has been tied to the story of Dracula. Immortalized in a novel by Bram Stoker, an obscure British writer, in the early 20th century, the story of Dracula has been depicted on the movie screens, in plays, and even in scholarly works. The story is based on a historical figure, Vlad Dracul who lived in this area in the mid 1400's and terrorized both friend and foe. Known as Vlad the Impaler, he was finally assassinated in 1477. Today, the Romanian government is capitalizing on the legend to bring much needed tourist money from the eager, and rich, American and European "Dracula" enthusiasts.

VLAD THE IMPALER

## MINOR PHYSICAL REGIONS OF EUROPE

The are a number of minor physical regions of Europe which do not fit into the four major divisions. Some of these include:

- the Po River Valley of northern Italy; a rich agricultural region of the country
- the semi-arid island of Sicily, located in the Mediterranean Sea, south-west of Italy
- the Hungarian plain, a rich agricultural land
- the flat, cold region of most of Finland
- the Black Sea coastal plain
- the cold, wind-swept island of Iceland

## THE EUROPEAN RIVER SYSTEMS:

The RHINE River (824 miles long) flows through a highly industrialized RUHR area in western Germany and empties into the North Sea, where a free port of Rotterdam (Netherlands) is located.

The ODER (564 miles), ELBE (724 miles) and VISTULA (679 miles) are the other major rivers of Europe flowing in the northerly direction.

The DANUBE River (1771 miles) flows in the easterly direction and is the longest, most important and the most famous river in Europe. It is utilized for transportation, irrigation, hydro-electrical power, and for fishing. Some of the cities located on its shores include REGENSBURG (Germany), and the capital cities of VIENNA (Austria), BUDAPEST (Hungary), and BELGRADE (Serbia).

The MAJOR SOIL GROUPS IN EUROPE include:

* The **podzolic** (acidic) soils in the NORTH. These are poor soils, not well suited for agriculture.
* The richer **podzolic** soils of CENTRAL Europe. These soils are covered by coniferous and deciduous forests.
* The **steppe grasslands** soils in EASTERN Europe, along with some rich CHERNOZEM (Russian word meaning BLACK EARTH) soils. The latter are the most fertile soils in Europe especially found in the Ukraine. These soils are comprised of organic material with humus, giving it the blackish coloration.
* The **terra rosa** soils of SOUTHERN Europe. These soils, usually associated with the Mediterranean climate, are conducive for the growth of olives, grapes (especially for wine products), and a variety of citrus fruits.

Example of terra rosa soil

*know rivers for test*

# PHYSICAL GEOGRAPHY OF EUROPE

1. Atlantic Ocean
2. Northern mountains
3. English channel
4. North Sea
5. Baltic Sea
6. Rhine River
7. Oder River
8. Elbe River
9. Vistula River
10. Pyrenees mths
11. Alps
12. Danube River
13. Carpathian mtns
14. Appennine mtns.
15.
16. Gibralter
17. Mediterranean sea
18. Adriatic Sea
19. Black Sea
20. Aegean sea

0 ——— 400
miles

——— RIVER

—·—·— NATIONAL BOUNDARY

SOURCE: UPJ Geography Dept.

CEW-90

137

The St. Basil's Cathedral, standing in the Red Square of the city of Moscow, may be the most recognizable structure in Russia.

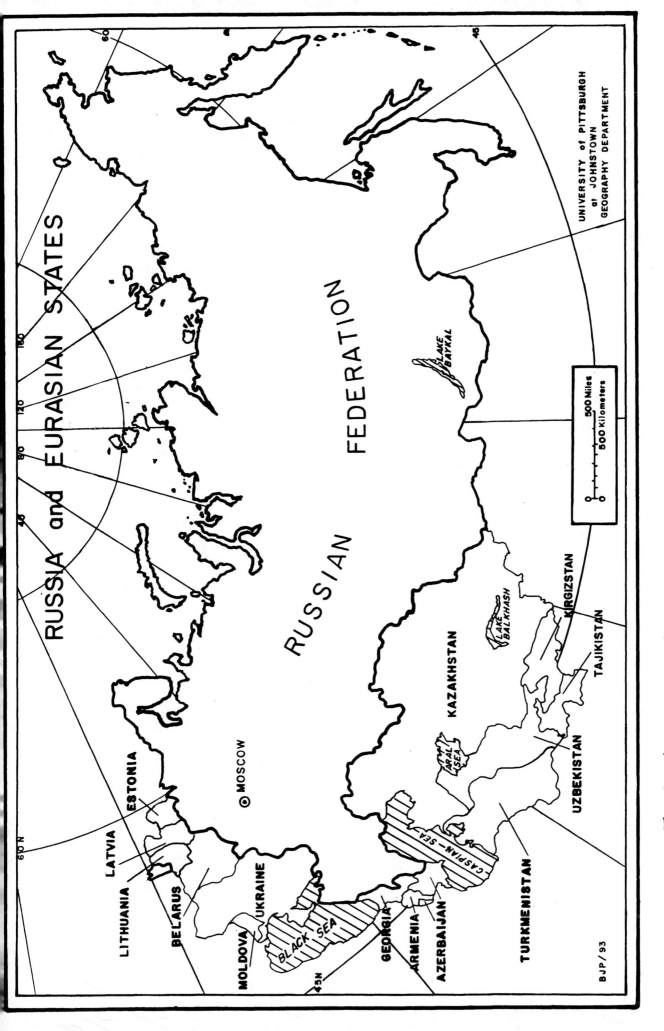

# RUSSIA and EURASIAN STATES

UNIVERSITY of PITTSBURGH at JOHNSTOWN GEOGRAPHY DEPARTMENT

RUSSIAN FEDERATION

LAKE BAYKAL

MOSCOW

LAKE BALKHASH

KAZAKHSTAN

ARAL SEA

CASPIAN SEA

BLACK SEA

LITHUANIA
LATVIA
ESTONIA
BELARUS
UKRAINE
MOLDOVA
GEORGIA
ARMENIA
AZERBAIJAN
TURKMENISTAN
UZBEKISTAN
TAJIKISTAN
KIRGIZSTAN

500 Miles
500 Kilometers

BJP/93

The Eurasian States are the 14 States shown with the Russian Federation (Russia). Together, they formed the Union of Soviet Socialist Republics (USSR) until that nation broke up in 1991.

139

## XIII – THE RUSSIAN FEDERATION (*Russia*)

The Russian Federation emerged out of the former UNION OF SOVIET SOCIALIST REPUBLICS (USSR). The latter dissolved in 1991, when its FIFTEEN Republics became independent nations (see map on previous page) and all joined the United Nations. The Russian Federation replaced USSR on the Security Council. The fourteen former Soviet Republics (excluding Russia) are referred to as THE EURASIAN STATES.

In late 1991, Russia, Ukraine and Byelorussia (today BELARUS) formed a COMMONWEALTH which was open to all of the other former Republics of the Soviet Union. Eleven Republics joined the organization forming THE COMMONWEALTH OF INDEPENDENT STATES. The Commonwealth was created primarily for economic cooperation for its members and to coordinate mutual military defenses. Today, the CIS is a very flaccid organization and its future is not very promising as the member states continue to pursue their own internal and international agendas.

The Soviet Union, prior to its break-up, was the largest nation in the world, covering 1/6 of the earth's land area. It measured approximately 6,000 miles east to west and 3,000 miles north to south. The country spanned 11 time zones and shared a common land boundary with 12 other nations. RUSSIA, the successor to the Soviet Union, is still the largest nation in the world. It is also one of the northernmost nations on earth. Its capital and largest city, MOSCOW, is located at the same latitude as Edmonton, Canada. Its second largest city, St. Petersburg (formerly Leningrad), is located at the same latitude as Anchorage, Alaska !

The USSR was formed after a successful overthrow of the Russian monarchy during the Communist Revolution of 1917. The formation of this new state, later to be comprised of 15 Republics, was formalized in 1922. The Soviet Union was preceded by the Russian Empire, which was ruled by autocratic czars of the Romanoff dynasty since 1613. For nearly 700 years before the Romanoffs took power, Russia was ruled by the Rurik dynasty. The country's spectacular growth occurred during the reign of a number of famous sovereigns including IVAN THE TERRIBLE (1533-1584), PETER THE GREAT (1682-1725), CATHERINE THE GREAT (1762-1796), and others. Vladimir Lenin, the first head of state of the USSR, solidified the nation by the time of his death in 1924. Joseph Stalin, who came to power after Lenin, expanded the country's domain as a result of Russia's victory over the nazis in World War II. The Soviet Union not only regained the lands which it lost after W.W. I, but extended its influence into Eastern Europe and later, into Asia and Africa.

The Soviet Union, the world's first Socialist state, was the second most powerful nation on earth after the United States. The two countries had the world divided into two camps: capitalist and socialist, and competed for influence among the world's nations. The possibility of nuclear confrontation was always present and almost occurred in October of 1962 during the "Cuban Missile Crisis".

The "Cold War" between the two nations began to diminish when President MIKHAIL GORBACHEV came to power in the Soviet Union in 1985. He allowed for much more freedom of expression, religion, economic restructuring and political reforms both at home and in nations controlled by the Soviet Union. It was during his Presidency that West Germany and East Germany were united into one Germany !

Total Population in nations which emerged from the former Soviet Union:
(2009 figures in millions)

| | |
|---|---|
| RUSSIAN FEDERATION (Russia) | 142.0 |
| UKRAINE | 46.0 |
| UZBEKISTAN | 27.6 |
| KAZAKHSTAN | 15.9 |
| BELARUS | 9.7 |
| AZERBAIJAN | 8.8 |
| TAJIKISTAN | 7.1 |
| KYRGYZSTAN | 5.3 |
| TURKMENISTAN | 5.1 |
| GEORGIA | 4.6 |
| MOLDOVA | 4.1 |
| LITHUANIA | 3.3 |
| ARMENIA | 3.1 |
| LATVIA | 2.3 |
| ESTONIA | 1.3 |

(Source: Population Reference Bureau, Washington, D.C.)

Percent of Russians in the total population living in the former Soviet Republics
(Source: CIA Fact Book – 2009)

| Eurasian Nations | Percent of Russians (in the total population) |
|---|---|
| UKRAINE | 17.3 |
| UZBEKISTAN | 5.5 |
| KAZAKHSTAN | 30.0 |
| BELARUS | 11.4 |
| AZERBAIJAN | 1.8 |
| TAJIKISTAN | 1.1 |
| TURKMENISRAN | 4.0 |
| KYRGYZSTAN | 12.5 |
| GEORGIA | 1.5 |
| MOLDOVA | 5.8 |
| LITHUANIA | 6.3 |
| ARMENIA | 0.5 |
| LATVIA | 29.6 |
| ESTONIA | 25.6 |

   Three nations have over a quarter of its population made up of ethnic Russians. Ukraine has over 17% of its population being ethnic Russians. These 8 million Russians, residing primarily in the eastern part of the Ukraine, have close linguistic, religious, historical and social links with the Ukrainian population. The Russians have encountered very little hostility in the Ukraine and there has not been a major exodus of Russians from the country.

   The nearly 5 million Russians living in Kazakhstan are located primarily in the northern half of the country, near the border with Russia.

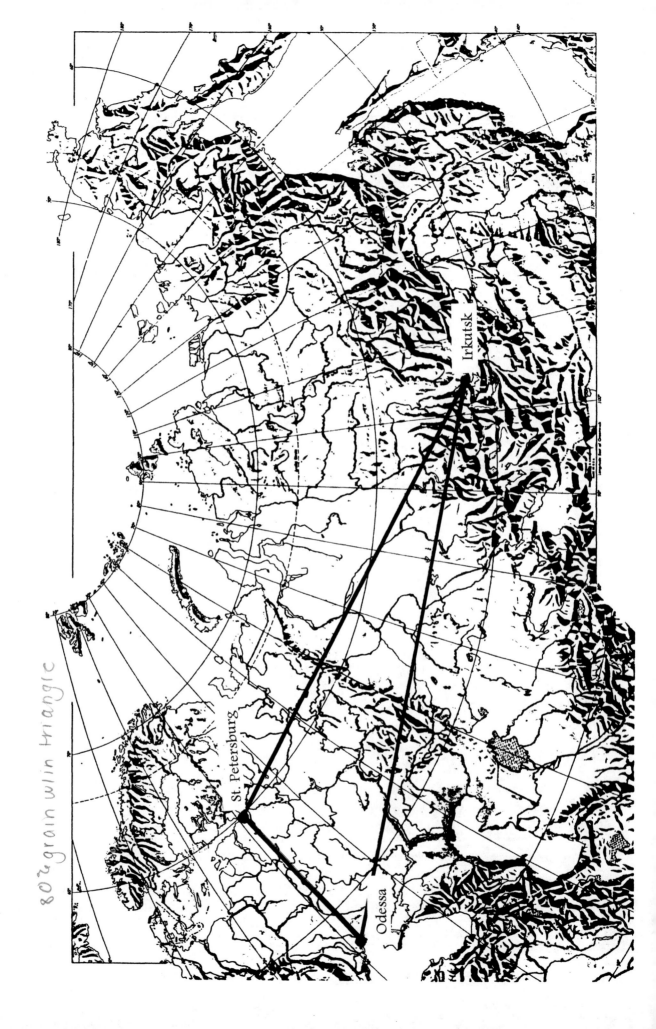

80% grain win triangle

Irkutsk

St. Petersburg

Odessa

## PHYSICAL GEOGRAPHY OF RUSSIA AND THE EURASIAN STATES
note: the Eurasian States are the former 14 Republics of the Soviet Union.

Russia has a continental climate, with very cold winters and hot summers. Temperatures of ~90 degrees F., the lowest outside of Antarctica, have been recorded in places like Verkhoyansk, a city east of the Verkhoyansk Mountains in Siberia. The severity of the climate is due, in part, to the geographical location of the country; the lack of east-west mountain ranges in the northern region of the nation; and to the absence of warm water bodies. Comparing the location of Russia to that of USA, it should be noted that while the USA is cut in half by 40 degrees north latitude, Russia is cut in half by 60 degrees north latitude ! That places Russia some twenty degrees further north than the United States, and accounts for a more severe winter climate in the country.

In elevation, Russia is relatively low in the north and west, with high mountains located in the south and in eastern Siberia. The Ural Mountains, running north to south, average between 4,000 and 6,000 feet in elevation. Most of the cities in the region are located in the southern third of the Ural Mountains.

## EIGHT MAJOR PHYSICAL REGIONS OF RUSSIA AND EURASIAN STATES:

1. **The Russian Plain** - this is a region extending from the western borders of the former Soviet Union to the Ural mountains in the east. Barents Sea, with the city of Murmansk, forms its northern boundary, while the Black Sea and the Crimean peninsula are to its south. The region is the "heart and soul" of the country and is the most important single section of the area. It contains the bulk of the cities, majority of the population, and the major industries. Much of the nation's grain is grown in the southern part of this region (Ukraine) where the fertile chernozem (black earth) soil is found. In fact, the great majority of agriculture is limited to an area called the fertile triangle (see the map on previous page), contained roughly within the boundaries drawn from the cities of Odessa to St. Petersburg (former Leningrad) to Irkutsk (near lake Baikal).

The great river Volga flows through this region and empties into the Caspian Sea. Many of the large cities, including Nizhniy Novgorod(formerly Gorkiy), Kazan, Samara, Saratov, and Volgograd (formerly Stalingrad) are located on the shores of the river. Near its mouth, at the city of Astrakhan, the river is a home for the sturgeon fish which is a source of caviar. This delicacy serves as an important export commodity for the Russian economy.
The Dnieper, flowing into the Black Sea and the Don flowing into the Sea of Azov are the other major rivers which flow in the southerly direction in the region.

Moscow, the capital city of the Russian Federation, is the central hub of this region which also contains the six former Soviet Republics of Estonia, Latvia, Lithuania, Ukraine, Belarus, and Moldova.

2. **The Caucasus Mountains** - this mountainous region is located between the Black and the Caspian seas and contains the republics of Armenia, Georgia, and Azerbaijan. Mt. Elbrus is the tallest peak (18,481') in this region. Part of the eastern shore of the Black Sea, around the city of Sukhumi, is the home of the Abkhazian people who have one of the highest longevity rates in the world.

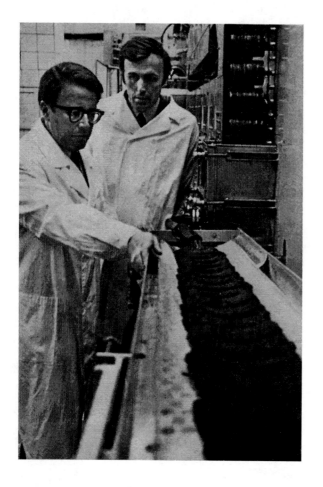

The sturgeon fish (above), found in the

Caspian Sea near the mouth of the

Volga River,  is the source of caviar produced

in Russia (left). The price of an ounce of caviar is

between $150 and $300 depending on its grade.

3.  <u>Southern Mountains</u> - these are the rugged mountains which form a boundary between Tajikistan and Kyrgyzstan with China. The Tien Shen, Altay and Pamir ranges have peeks that rise to over 24,000 feet in elevation, and have been a challenge to international mountain climbers.

(source of map, below: Geography Department, University of Bern)

<u>Tien Shan, Altai and Pamir Mountains</u>

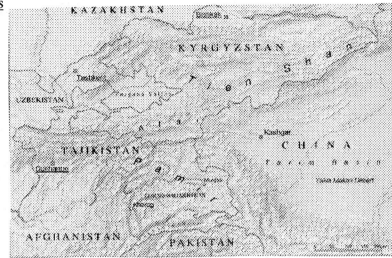

4.  <u>Ural Mountains</u> - averaging between 4000 and 6000 feet in elevation, these mountains contain many of the natural resources of Russia. They extend from the coast of the Arctic Ocean in the north to the steppes along the northern border of Kazakhstan in the south – a distance of over 1,550 miles. Formed about 250 million years ago during the Permian geological period, the area has been turned into an important industrial region of Russia. The cities, such as Perm, Ufa, Orenburg, Ekaterinburg, Chelyabinsk and others, which emerged in the southern part of the Ural Mountains, owe their existence to the abundance of natural resources found in the area. This region has large deposits of iron ore, coal, oil, natural gas, gold, silver, platinum, chromite, nickel, and many other minerals. Topaz, a precious stone, along with diamonds and other coveted stones are also mined and exported from the Urals.

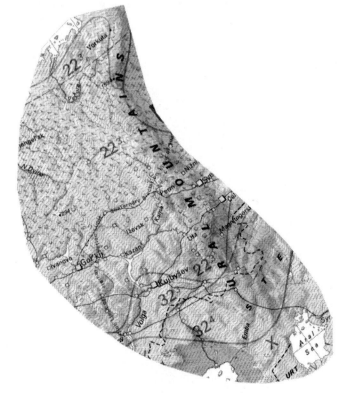

5. <u>Central Asian Desert</u> - this is the area containing the five "Dry Lands" Republics, populated by Asian ethnic peoples. The Aral Sea and Lake Balkash are located in this region, which is also the center of cotton growing and production. The Islamic culture is strong here and many of the people are Muslims. The largest Republic in the area is Kazakhstan, which contains the largest percentage of Russians of any of the former Soviet Republics (see following page).

## THE REPUBLIC OF KAZAKHSTAN

Of all the former Soviet Republics, Kazakhstan ranks second to the Russian Federation in land area. Its territory of 1,049,155 square miles makes it the ninth largest nation in the world.

Kazakhstan is located east of the Caspian Sea and borders Russia to the north and north-west, China on the east, and Turkmenistan, Uzbekistan and Kyrgyzstan to the south. The nation extends from the lower reaches of the Volga River to the Altay Mountains on the Chinese border. It shares the Aral Sea with Uzbekistan, while Lake Balkhash lies within its borders. The area is mostly arid with only 10 % being arable land. Cotton and grain are the major crops grown in the Republic.

The population of the area is approximately 17 million people, with nearly one-third being under 15 years of age. The average annual rate of population growth is under one percent, a decrease since the nation became independent in 1991. Six main ethnic groups live in the country. They include Kazakhs who make up 42 % of the total population, Russians with 37 % of the total, Ukrainians with 5 %, Germans with 4.5 %, and Uzbeks and Tatars with 2 % each. The remaining population is made up of other, smaller ethnic groups. The people are almost evenly divided between Moslems and Orthodox Christians.

The population resides primarily in the northern, eastern and south-eastern parts of the country. The density is 16 people per square mile and nearly two-thirds of the population is urban. The major urban centers include Astana, the capital, Almaty, Oksemen and Pavlodar.

Ethnic Composition of Population in Kazakhstan - 2005

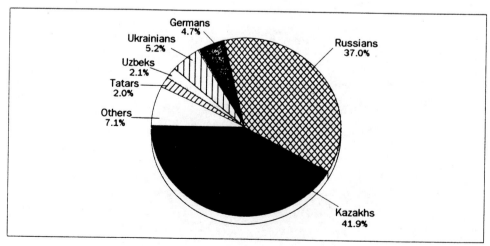

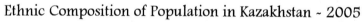

# SIBERIA

Siberia is the term used to identify all the land in Russia <u>east</u> of the Ural Mountains. It is a sparsely populated area except for the southern part of its three regions (see #6,7 and 8 below) where the Trans-Siberian and the newer Baikal Amur Mainline (BAM) railroads pass. The former, a 5,753 mile long railroad connects St. Petersburg with the city of Vladivostok and passes through hundreds of large and small town. It was completed in 1916, passes through seven time zones and takes eight days to complete the journey. The BAM railroad was completed in 1991 and runs north of the Trans-Siberian RR. It links Central Siberia with the Pacific Ocean and is 1,928 miles long.

Three long rivers are located in Siberia, all flowing in the northerly direction and emptying into the Arctic Ocean. They are, from west to east, the <u>Ob</u> (along with its tributary, the Irtysh River, it is the longest in Eurasia – 3,360 miles), <u>Yenisei</u> (465 miles long) and <u>Lena</u> (2,779 miles long). Vladimir I. Ulyanov (the first leader of the USSR, 1917-1924) took his alias – *LENIN* (1902) possibly because he was exiled to this region by the czarist regime for his anti-government activities.

Regional divisions of Siberia

6. <u>West Siberian Lowlands</u> – much of this flat region between the Ural Mountains and the Yenisei River is covered by <u>Taiga</u> – an evergreen, needle-leaf forest. (see next page).

7. <u>Central Siberian Plateau</u> – located between Yenisei and Lena Rivers, this area is rich in oil and natural gas. The Russians have recently built a pipe line from here to western Europe and are selling natural gas to that region.

   Lake Baikal, the deepest lake in the world at 3,939 feet, is located in the southern part of this region. The northern part of the Central Siberian Plateau has a <u>Tundra</u> (ET) and an <u>Ice Cap</u> (EF) type climates.

   One of the tributaries to the Yenisei River, the Lower Stony Tunguska River was the site of a huge explosion on June 30, 1908. Known as the famous "TUNGUSKA EVENT" the explosion is attributed to a large meteoroid or comet which detonated at an altitude of 3 to 6 miles above the earth's surface. The energy of the blast is estimated to be 1,000 times more powerful that the atomic bomb dropped on Hiroshima in 1945.

8. <u>Eastern Siberian Mountains</u> – this region takes in all the area east of the Lena River, including the <u>Kamchatka</u> peninsula, the <u>Sakhalin</u> island, and the sea of <u>Okhotsk</u>. It also contains the only usable, large Russian port city on the Pacific ocean – Vladivostok. The large Amur river in this area serves as part of a boundary between Russia and China.

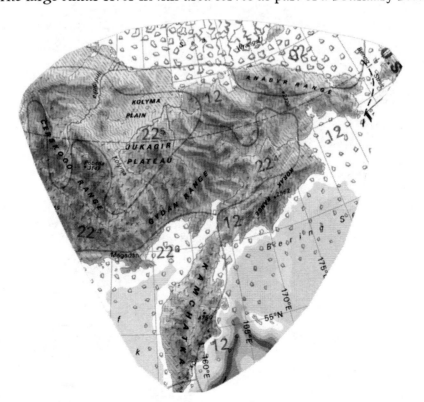

# NIZHNY NOVGOROD

Menin Square in Nizhny Novgorod

## The city of Baku

Name: _____

Take a city in RUSSIA or in one of the EURASIAN STATES and write a page long report. Do not take MOSCOW, VLADIVOSTOK or MURMANSK. See the next TWO pages for examples.

Your city: _____

Total population: _____

Location: _____

One major feature which makes this city unique:

Murmansk, Russia

Murmansk is located in the north-western part of Russia, on the Kola peninsula. The city is situated some 100 miles east of Finland and Norway, and serves as an important port for the Russian Federation. Although situated at approximately 69 degrees north latitude (about 100 miles north of the Arctic Circle), the port is ice free all year, due to the influence of the Gulf Stream. The sea water never freezes, and the open sea (Barents) is only 25 miles away.

The city was founded in 1915, and was connected by railroad to the Russian capital city of Petrograd in the following year. The city grew in population and importance between the two World Wars, serving the Soviet Union as one of its few major ports. During World War II (1941-1945), the United States and Great Britain sent war supplies to the Russians through the Port in Murmansk. Russia, the USA, Great Britain and France were the major united powers in the war against Nazi Germany.

The Polar Research Institute, two institutions of higher learning, and the Planning Institute of Fishing and Geography are located in the city. The port has many fishing boats docked in its harbor, and the fishermen provide the country with about 10% of the nation's total catch. The fish processing factory in the city is one of the largest in Russia. Timber industry is also important in the area, and much of the wood products are exported via the port.

Huge ship repair yards were located in the city and serviced much of the Russian fleet. There was also a naval installation in the area and an armament storage area. A recent accident in the munitions storage depot caused many fatalities. Since the collapse of the Soviet Union in 1991, the city has fallen on hard economic times. The ship repair facilities have been moved to other parts of Russia and the bustling naval base has been drastically downsized. The city's population has declined to under 370,000 and unemployment is high.

One positive economic aspect for the area is the mining of apatite concentrates, used as a base for phosphate fertilizers. This valuable commodity constitutes a large portion of the export revenue for the region. This mineral began to be exported from the Kola Peninsula in 1929 and is shipped to many parts of Russia and to some foreign nations.

Sources:

Kaiser, Robert G., Russia, Simon and Shuster, New York, 1994.

Murmansk, www.visitRussia.com, 2006.

Shoemaker, Wesley M., Russia, Stryker-Post Publication, 2009

## Vladivostok, Russia

Vladivostok is a city located in the Far Eastern Russia on a peninsula that separates the Amur River and Ussuri Bay on the Sea of Japan. It was founded in 1860 by Russian soldiers who were sent here by Russian authorities to establish military outposts which would strengthen Russia's presence in the eastern part of Siberia.

Vladivostok became an important outpost serving as the nation's sea port. It had a deep natural harbor and provided a link between western Russia and the Orient. It became a naval base and in 1872 the main Russian naval command for the Pacific was transferred here. This helped the city to grow in numbers and in importance.

By 1880, the city's population was thirteen thousand comprised of a variety of ethnic and national groups. Half of the residents were foreigners from America, Sweden, Germany, China and other places. This array of cultures made Vladivostok an international melting pot.

Work on the construction of the Ussuri railroad began in 1890. This railroad became part of the famous Trans-Siberian Railroad. After Russia's loss of Port Arthur in the Russo-Japanese War of 1905, Vladivostok became the principal post on Russia's east coast. The city was fortified, gun embankments were constructed, and bunkers with interconnecting tunnels dug.

The city remained the home of the Pacific fleet during the Soviet period. Between the late 1950's and the collapse of the Soviet Union in 1991, Vladivostok was closed to foreign shipping because of the city's military importance. After the Soviet period, its major role as a commercial port resurfaced. It now serves as a link between Russia and the nations of the far east, like China and Japan.

As the city continues to grow, many diverse industries emerge. Not only are there large ship-building and repair yards and railway workshops, Vladivostok also contains a variety of light industries, food processing, canning factories and a number of other businesses. It has also become a premier cultural and educational center of Russia's Far East. The city contains the Far Eastern Scientific Center, the Far Eastern State University, and a variety of institutes specializing in medicine, art education, commerce and law. The city has charisma and continues to grow and expand its economic and industrial base. It is amply deserving of its title as the "Pearl of Russia's Far East".

http://members.spree.com/travel/Vladivostok/history, 2005

The Russian Chronicles, Vladivostok, 2007

Vladivostok-Russia's port on the Pacific, 2009

## Internal Structure of the Russian Federation

The Russian Constitution, adopted shortly after the collapse of the Soviet Union in 1991, identified 89 administrative divisions in the country (see the map below). The most important are the 21 internal Republics which are the homes to the non-Russian people. Approximately 20% of Russia's total population is comprised of people who are ethnically not Russian.

One of these Republics is Chechnya, located in the south-western part of the Russian Federation. The Republic has over one million inhabitants with 95% being ethnic Chechens and majority practicing Islam. These people have been a thorn in Russia's side for centuries and continue to push for independence of their Republic. They have used terroristic methods like suicide bombings, assassinations of officials friendly to Russia, and general intimidation of population who disagree with their methods. A recent example of their tactics (April 2010) was to sent two female terrorists who blew themselves up in a Moscow subway killing over 40 civilian commuters, many of them students on the way to classes.

MAP OF ADMINISTRATIVE REGIONS OF RUSSIA

| | | | | | | | | |
|---|---|---|---|---|---|---|---|---|
| 1. Karelia | 11. Kaliningrad | 21. Smolensk | 31. Voronezh | 41. Saratov | 51. Stavropol | 61. Altay Krai | 71. Tuva | 80. Yakutia-Sokha |
| 2. Komi | 12. Bryansk | 22. Tver | 32. Kursk | 42. Ulyanovsk | 52. Rostov-Don | 62. Gorno Altay | 72. Khakassia | 81. Primor'ye (Maritime) |
| 3. Arkhangelsk | 13. Vladimir | 23. Tula | 33. Lipetsk | 43. Adygeya | 53. Bashkiria | 63. Kemerovo | 73. Krasnoyarsk | 82. Khabarovsk |
| 4. Nenets | 14. Ivanovo | 24. Yaroslavl | 34. Tambov | 44. Dagestan | 54. Udmurtia | 64. Novosibirsk | 74. Taymir (Dolgan-Nenets) | 83. Jewish-region |
| 5. Vologda | 15. Kaluga | 25. Mari-El | 35. Kalmykia | 45. Kabardin-Balkaria | 55. Kurgan | 65. Omsk | 75. Evenki | 84. Amur |
| 6. Murmansk | 16. Kostroma | 26. Mordovia | 36. Tatarstan | 46. Karachay-Cherkess | 56. Orenburg | 66. Tomsk | 76. Irkutsk | 85. Kamchatka |
| 7. Saint Petersburg | 17. Moscow-city | 27. Chuvashia | 37. Astrakhan | 47. North Ossetia | 57. Perm | 67. Tyumen | 77. Ust' Orda Buryat | 86. Koryak |
| 8. Leningrad | 18. Moscow-oblast | 28. Kirov | 38. Volgograd | 48. Chechnia | 58. Komi-Permyak | 68. Khanty Mansi | 78. Chita | 87. Magadan |
| 9. Novgorod | 19. Orel | 29. Nizhni Novgorod | 39. Penza | 49. Ingushetia | 59. Sverdlovsk | 69. Yamal Nenets | 79. Aguin Buryat | 88. Chukotka |
| 10. Pskov | 20. Ryazan | 30. Belgorod | 40. Samara | 50. Krasnodar | 60. Chelyabinsk | 70. Buryatia | | 89. Sakhalin |

## REPUBLICS IN THE RUSSIAN FEDERATION

1. Adygeya,
2. Altai (Gorno-Altay),
3. Bashkortostan,
4. Buryatia,
5. Chechnya,
6. Chuvashia,
7. Daghestan,
8. Ingushetia,
9. Kabardino-Balkaria,
10. Kalmykia,
11. Karachai-Cherkessia,
12. Karelia,
13. Khakassia,
14. Komi,
15. Mari El,
16. Mordovia (Mordvinia),
17. North Ossetia,
18. Tatarstan,
19. Tuva,
20. Udmurtia,
21. Yakutia

# XIV – ASIA: JAPAN and CHINA

## JAPAN

Lying off the east coast of Russia and the Koreas, Japan forms a 2,000 mile archipelago of nearly 3,000 islands, the four main ones being HOKKAIDO, HONSHU, SHIKOKU, and KYUSHU. Its area of 147,470 square miles is nearly as large as California. Nearly 130 million people are squeezed on this land; over four times the number living in California.

Although self sufficient in rice, Japan has few other natural resources and must import raw material needed for its industry. In spite of the lack of natural resources, Japan is a manufacturing and industrial giant whose products are sold throughout the world. Opened to outside trade and western technology only in the mid-19th century, after self imposed isolation, Japan became a world power by 1900.

The period in Japanese history from 1895 to the end of World War II in 1945 may be characterized as an era of expansionism and empire building wrapped in Japanese nationalism. During that time, "Asia for the Japanese" became their slogan, with Western imperialism, especially the policies of Great Britain and France, serving as an example for Japan's future colonial ambitions.

At the beginning of the twentieth century, Japan took steps on its road to empire building. The Anglo-Japanese Alliance with Great Britain, signed in 1902, not only allowed the Japanese a free hand in Asia, but also fostered an aggressive action against Russia over territorial differences in Korea. Early in 1905, the Japanese attacked and destroyed the Russian fleet at Port Arthur, a Russian naval base leased from China. In the summer of 1905, the rest of the Russian fleet was destroyed by the Japanese in Tsushima Straits, located between Japan and Korea. As a result, the two nations signed a peace treaty - Treaty of Portsmouth - mediated by President Theodore Roosevelt of the United States. The Japanese victory clearly placed the country on equal footing with other military-industrial powers of the world, gained them prestige, and erased the myth of the inferiority of the non-European nations.

During World War I (1914-1918), the Japanese declared war on Germany, but never sent its armed forces to Europe. They attacked and captured German possessions in China, and the German held islands in the Pacific. The control of these islands, including the Marianas, Marshalls, and Carolinas gave Japan a dominant hold on one fourth of the North Pacific region, between Hawaii and the Philippines.

Emerging as a victorious nation after World War I, Japan became a dominant economic and military power in Asia. Emperor Hirohito came to power in 1926 and the nation prospered as a result of open trade. The Great Depression of 1929 seriously affected Japan, precisely because of its dependency on world trade for its economic livelihood. The economic and political crisis which followed gave added power to the Japanese military. The rise of the military led, in turn, to the belief in the Divine Mission, where Japan would unite the world by controlling it.

The mission began with Japan's occupation of Manchuria, a part of China three times the size of the Japanese home islands. In 1932, the area was renamed Manchukuo and became part of the Japanese empire. In the summer of 1937, the Japanese invaded the rest of China, and its course was set on a path of conquest, which led directly to its involvement in World War II.

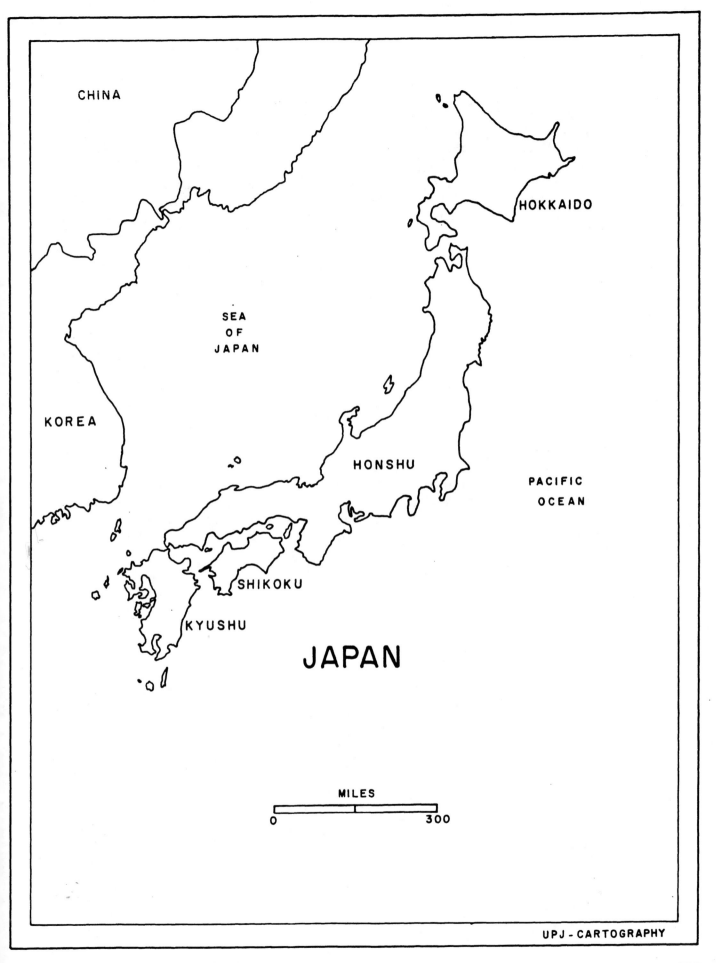

CHINA

HOKKAIDO

SEA
OF
JAPAN

KOREA

HONSHU

PACIFIC
OCEAN

SHIKOKU

KYUSHU

JAPAN

MILES

0          300

JAPAN AND WORLD WAR TWO

In 1936, Japan allied itself with Nazi Germany and Fascist Italy in the Anti-Comintern Pact. This pact gave Japan a free hand in China and in the rest of Asia. As a result of Japan's aggressive acts, the United States, in 1940, stopped the sale of strategic material to Japan. By 1941, diplomacy reached a breaking point between Tokyo and Washington, and the military leaders of Japan, who now dominated the government, decided on war against the United States. On Sunday morning of December 7, 1941, Japanese aircraft led a surprise attack against naval and air installations at Pearl Harbor on the island of Oahu in the Hawaiian Islands. The United States declared war on Japan the next day, and the whole world was now engulfed in a global conflict.

In mid-1942, the Japanese Empire held 25% of the world's population and all European colonial possessions were lost in Asia to the Japanese. They held most of China, Malaya, Singapore, Sumatra, Philippines, and most other regions of Asia.

Although making rapid and impressive gains, it soon became obvious that Japan underestimated its opponents, and lacked the man-power and resources to maintain its new conquered territories. Japan suffered its first major military defeat at the hands of the U.S. navy in the battle of the Coral Sea near the northeast coast of Australia. Other defeats followed at Midway, the Philippines, and on two islands south of Japan - Iwo Jima and Okinawa.

The war in Europe ended in May of 1945 with the unconditional surrender of nazi Germany to the Allies. The war with Japan, however, continued until the decision by President Truman (F.D. Roosevelt died in April of 1945 after being elected president for the fourth time, and Truman was his vice-president) to drop atomic bombs on Japan. On August 6, 1945 at 8:15 A.M. (Japanese time) the first atomic bomb exploded over the city of Hiroshima. 100,000 people died instantaneously, and another 100,000 were wounded. Three days later, on August 9 at 11 A.M., a second bomb was dropped on Nagasaki. On August 14, 1945 Japan surrendered unconditionally. The nuclear age was just beginning !

*AMERICAN PRESS*: Note the racist view of the Japanese during World War II:

156

### Japan and the Atomic Bomb

At 8:15 in the morning of August 6, 1945, an American Boeing B-29 bomber named ENOLA GAY dropped an atomic bomb on the city of Hiroshima. The bomb, nicknamed Little Boy, exploded at an altitude of 2000 feet above a building, which serves as a memorial today. The building is called the "A-Bomb Dome" and stands, as a ruin, on the shores of a river.

The bomb generated an enormous amount of energy in the form of air pressure and heat. It also emitted radiation which killed many people well after the initial impact of the bomb. Many people who witnessed the explosion thought they saw another sun in the sky. Scientists estimated that the fire-ball measured 250 feet in diameter with the heat in the center reaching the temperature of 1,800,000 degrees Fahrenheit. The heat on the ground at the center of the explosion was estimated at 10,000 degrees Fahrenheit.

As a result of the explosion, 100,000 people died instantly, another 100,000 were wounded, nearly 7,000 buildings were destroyed, 70% of all fire fighting equipment was damaged, 80% of all fire fighting personal was killed, 3 of 45 hospitals in the city remained operational, 90% of the physicians perished, and all communications in the city were destroyed.

The explosion set fires three miles away from the blast, and the people were unable to extinguish the blaze. The pressure exerted by the blast varied from 5 to 8 tons per square yard and many people were literally crushed to death. Scientists calculated that it would have taken a building with fifty-inch concrete walls to protect a person from radiation sickness.

The flash from the explosion cast permanent shadows on sidewalks and buildings. One was a shadow of a man and his cart etched on a bridge; another was a shadow of a painter on a ladder, dipping his brush in the paint can.

On August 9, 1945, just three days after the Hiroshima bombing, the United States dropped a second atomic bomb on the city of Nagasaki. Although the amount of energy generated by this bomb was significantly greater that the Hiroshima bomb, the damage on Nagasaki was less severe. This was due to the fact that Nagasaki is more mountainous than Hiroshima, and the mountains blocked the penetration of the blast into the surrounding area. It is estimated that a total of 70,000 people perished in Nagasaki as a result of the blast and the aftereffects.

On the morning of August 15, 1945, nine days after the bombing of Hiroshima, the Japanese emperor Hirohito addressed the Japanese people on the radio. He announced that Japan surrendered unconditionally to the Allies and World War II came to an end. An estimated fifty million people perished in the conflict !!!

Book: Hiroshima by John Hersey

Part of the city of Hiroshima after the atomic bomb was dropped on August 6, 1945.

China

　　With over 1.2 billion people, China is the most populous country in the world. Not only is it a population giant, but it is also a country with a long history of ancient civilizations. In relative isolation, China was ruled by **dynasties**, families that governed for long period of times, until the last dynasty (Manchu) fell in 1911. At this time, China was increasingly affected by the outside world. First, the European colonial powers asserted strong control over China leading to several rebellions and wars for independence. But China was also internally divided, resulting in a civil war that was not resolved until 1949 when the **Communists** took control over China, and they have ruled the country with a strong hand since then.

Map source: The World Factbook (CIA)

The city wall around Xian, which was the ancient capital of many of the Chinese dynasties.

FOCUS ON TAIWAN

The losing side of the civil war in China, the **Nationalists,** fled the Chinese mainland for the island of Taiwan. Taiwan became a *de facto* independent nation, but not in the eyes of China, which still claim it as their territory (Chinese maps show Taiwan simply as one among many regional provinces of China!). Taiwan went on to become economically successful – it was part of the Asian economic miracle and was often referred to as a **Newly Industrialized Country** (NIC) in the 1970s and 1980s (today, Taiwan has been industrialized for so long that the NIC term might not be appropriate anymore). Taiwan became a U.S. ally in the region, albeit not a democracy. When Taiwan had their first open elections in 1997, Chinese military maneuvers along the Taiwanese coast were viewed as a message to the island's political leaders that they should not pursue official sovereignty for Taiwan. Today, there is an ongoing domestic debate in Taiwan whether the future of the island lies in a declaration of political independence or if reunification with China should be the long-term goal.

To understand the physical geography of China, it might be instructive to make a comparison between China and the United States. First, the two countries are almost identical in size – circa 3.5-3.6 million sq. mi. They are also similar in shape and located approximately on the same latitudes in the northern hemisphere. Both have important and populous east coasts. These geographical factors mean that the U.S. and Chinese climates exhibit some similarities. Northeastern China has a D climate with cold winters not dissimilar to New England. The capital, **Beijing,** is located in this part of China. Further south, such as in the important cities of **Shanghai** and **Hong Kong** (see Focus on Hong Kong box), summers are hot and humid while winters are mild. This C climate resembles the American South. Due to these climatic differences, wheat is the staple crop in the north, while rice dominates in well watered central and southern China. The western interior of China is either high elevation such as the Plateau of Tibet and/or very dry, such as the Gobi and Taklamakan deserts. Not surprisingly, this area of the country is sparsely populated; instead, most of the population lives in the plains, river valleys and along the coast in the eastern half of the country. Western China is also characterized by its population of various ethnic minorities in a country that is relatively homogenous (93% is **Han Chinese,** a term derived from the Han dynasty that united China 2000 years ago). The instance where the comparison with the U.S. falters is that China does not have a west coast; in fact, the western edge of China is located in central Asia as far away from an ocean as one can get!

With China frequently in the news as a country that is economically successful and produces consumer items for almost the entire world, sometimes people are under the impression that China is an affluent country. Not so. Compare, for example, China's **GDP/capita** (the value of all goods and services produced in a country annually) in the figure with U.S. and some of the other countries in East Asia. And without an adjustment for the low cost of living (which is done in the figure), China's GDP/capita is only $3,500, according to the 2009 data. What is true, however, is that China has developed extremely rapidly the last

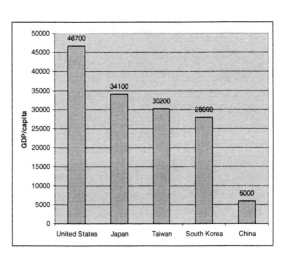

few decades – the economic growth rate has averaged an outstanding 8 percent annually – and it is far more prosperous and modern than it used to be.

The starting point of the current changes in China was the 1976 death of Chairman **Mao**, the leader of the communist revolution. Since then, China has gradually embraced capitalism while remaining a Communist state politically. These reforms have affected many different sectors of Chinese economy and society. In agriculture, many of the **communes** (farming enterprises that was operated collectively) of the Mao era were broken up in favor of smaller units run by individual farmers, which has improved productivity and food production. To best utilize the scarce resources available, it was also imperative for China to slow down its high level of population growth, which resulted in the infamous **one child policy** where each family is only allowed one offspring. The government has both penalized and rewarded individuals to assure compliance. The policy was widely unpopular, especially in rural areas, where many children make an important contribution to the family farm and as a "retirement plan." Nevertheless, the one child policy has largely achieved its goal of drastically reducing the population growth, which probably also had positive effects on the Chinese economy. Even if the policy is still in place, it is not enforced as strictly today and especially rural people and ethnic minorities are exempt. The **fertility rate** (the average number of children born per woman in her lifetime) in China is now at 1.6 which indicates that later in the 21$^{st}$ century, China's population will stabilize and even decline. Another effect of the one child policy is the changing gender ratio of the Chinese population. Today there are almost 120 males to every 100 females born in China (naturally there are slightly more males than females born, but the gender gap is extreme in China). With a preference for male children (a cultural attitude that is fairly common in traditional societies, and maybe even in the United States), a family facing a one child limit might use modern medical technology to determine the gender of a baby and selectively abort females.

The use of automobiles has expanded rapidly in China. Roads that used to be full of bikes are now taken over by car traffic and the bike lanes are increasingly squeezed out (although bikes are still very common in the Chinese landscape as the overwhelming majority cannot afford automobiles yet). Both pictures are from Beijing.

China today is a **hybrid economy** that exhibits traits of both a market-based economy as well as communism. This means that companies and industries are owned and operated in several different ways. Some are collectively owned, for example when a village or a municipality runs an enterprise. Today, there are also industries owned by private Chinese individuals, something unheard of not too long ago. Many large industries are still state properties, many of which are said to be inefficient money losers. The government in China is still willing to subsidize such enterprises because closing them down immediately would drive up unemployment, increase poverty, cause depopulation in many rural areas, and possibly lead to political instability in the country. (This approach can be compared with Russia's transition where a policy of rapid privatization of state property indeed led to many of these negative consequences.) Finally, an increasing number of foreign corporations are allowed, and even encouraged, to operate in China. A company like Japanese Sony is using the productive and inexpensive Chinese work force for the labor-intensive assembly of consumer electronics, which is subsequently exported globally. Others, such as Germany's Volkswagen, build automobiles for the expanding domestic Chinese market.

Not only have these economic developments created a booming Chinese economy, but the geographic implications thereof are dramatic and profound. The economy of the northeast of China is traditionally based on heavy manufacturing and natural resources. This old industrial region is now a "rustbelt" (another similarity with the U.S.!), while the central and southern coastal areas are expanding rapidly. Foreign investment has been concentrated in so called **Special Economic Zones** along the coast. To entice foreign companies, the Chinese government is offering special incentives – free land, lower taxes, less regulations, no import/export duties, etc – in these locations. This is a common strategy among many less developed countries that want to compete for foreign investment in the global economy (the Maquiladoras in northern Mexico is another prominent example).

A visitor to rapidly growing urban China will be impressed by the high level of building activity where skyscrapers appear almost daily. China is currently in the middle of a dramatic modernization process, but this transformation is not complete – the old and the new coexist side by side. It is as if the third world is meeting the gleaming, prosperous future of China. However, this is an uneven geographical process. The interior is less affected by rapid expansion and particularly rural areas are increasingly lagging behind. This has created high levels of **internal migration** in China, from rural to urban locations and from the interior to the coast. In China, people are officially classified as rural or urban residents and are not allowed to relocate without government permission (much like the one child policy, this is an

Traditional architecture and skyscrapers in a commercial area of rapidly changing Shanghai.

expression of the authoritarian character of the Chinese political system, which would be an unacceptable intrusion on the individual in any western country). But with the reality of high levels of job creation in coastal cities, there is nevertheless a substantial illegal stream of migrants in China. Rapid urbanization is a problem in many less developed countries as rural migrants often end up in very poor housing conditions in squatter settlements and slums that lack basic amenities. China has controlled this problem a little bit better as economic growth has enabled more housing construction, the official control over migration, and government policies to direct growth to areas beyond the largest cities in the country.

Despite these efforts, the transition towards a market economy is inevitably creating **spatial and individual inequalities.** In a market economy, investments and jobs are emerging in regions where profits are the greatest – currently in Shanghai and other coastal areas – while in a communist economy, the government, and not the market, is responsible for allocating resources, which usually means that jobs are going to be more equally dispersed between regions. While a growing gap between rich and poor may be antithetical to communist egalitarian ideology, the government is not inclined to regulate these market forces that create new wealth in China. However, the tension between strict political control and growing individualism in the economic sphere may be problematic as increasingly affluent Chinese are likely to demand more political freedom in the future. In 1989, a budding democracy movement, particularly among university students, led to demonstrations on **Tiananmen Square** in the center of Beijing, calling for greater political freedoms. Government forces eventually responded violently, crushed the demonstration, and since then no such overt demand for greater democracy has been made in China.

Tiananmen Square is a vast, treeless plaza surrounded by government buildings and The Forbidden City – the residence of past dynastic emperors that is now a major tourist attraction.

FOCUS ON HONG KONG

A recent territorial expansion of the People's Republic of China came in 1997 when the city of Hong Kong was returned to China by the British (in a parallel move, the smaller neighboring city of Macau was returned by Portugal in 1999). Hong Kong was one of the last vestiges of the British colonial empire of the 19th century. Britain had obtained a 99-year lease of Hong Kong, which developed as a capitalist enclave on the south Chinese coast. By 1997, when the lease expired, the city had become a very affluent center for finance, service industry, and manufacturing, and is by far the most prosperous part of China (Hong Kong's GDP/capita if measured separately is almost six times greater than the rest of China's). As most Hong Kong residents are of Chinese ethnicity, they were generally happy to cut the colonial tie, but at the same time felt uneasy about rejoining China. Today's Hong Kong retains more political autonomy vis-à-vis the central government than other parts of China, but its future status within communist China remains uncertain.

As an example of the Chinese government's policy to develop the interior as well as the coast, we can consider the **Three Gorges Dam** – the largest dam project in the world. The dam is located on the **Yangtze River** (a.k.a. Chang Jiang), which connects coastal Shanghai with densely populated agricultural and industrial areas in central China. The dam has multiple purposes:

- Electricity generation (The dam is projected to provide electricity for a large part of central China and is expected to be a regional economic growth engine.)
- Flood control (The Yangtze, much like its neighboring river to the north, the Huang He, a.k.a. the Yellow River, is prone to flooding which has caused major destruction throughout history.)
- Navigation (In the absence of major highways to the interior, the Yangtze is very important as a transportation route. The dam will increase navigability further upstream.)

Small city along the Yangtze River. Note the decaying structures in the front of the picture (now under water) and the newer buildings in the background (the city was moved uphill!).

However, critics have said that there are so many problems associated with the dam that it shouldn't be built. Here are some of their arguments:

- Displacement (The reservoir behind the dam will raise the water level and put many existing cities and rural communities under water. Over 1 million people were displaced and have relocated.)
- Loss of habitat (The dam will change the ecosystem of the river both upstream and downstream and many endangered species will not survive.)
- Loss of cultural heritage (Ancient temples, burial grounds and other types of historical structures are very common along the river and will be submerged. The scenic value of the Three Gorges area, which attracts large number of tourists, will severely diminish.)
- Safety (The river contains a large amount of silt that will accumulate in the reservoir. The rising water level has resulted in landslides. Earthquakes have occurred in the region and some flooding problems will remain as many tributaries are located below the dam. Critics contend that the dam's positive benefits could have been achieved with a series of less disruptive smaller dams, but the government pursued the large project as a matter of national pride – to show off to the world that they could do it.)

The Three Gorges Dam is almost finished and large areas have been flooded already, although the dam will not be fully completed until 2011. The dam is to many people a symbol of the environmental toll that the current economic development in China is demanding. Indeed, environmental problems are rampant in today's China. The abysmal air quality in virtually all densely populated areas due to unrestricted use of coal is perhaps the most obvious problem. Poor water quality and loss of farmland due to soil erosion are also major concerns. These environmental problems are only beginning to be addressed, but as the Chinese grow more affluent, they will likely demand a better living environment in the future.

The manual unloading of coal from barge to trucks on the Yangtze River. Individual homes are often directly heated by coal; a practice that contributes to the poor air quality.

The photo below shows the "Dome of the Rock" mosque in Jerusalem. It is located on the Temple Mount of the city and is one of the holy places for the worshipers of Islam. It was completed in 691 – 692 A.D. making it the oldest existing Islamic building in the world. Inside the mosque is a rock which, according to the Islamic tradition, is the spot from where Muhammad (the founder of the Islamic religion) ascended to Heaven accompanied by angel Gabriel.

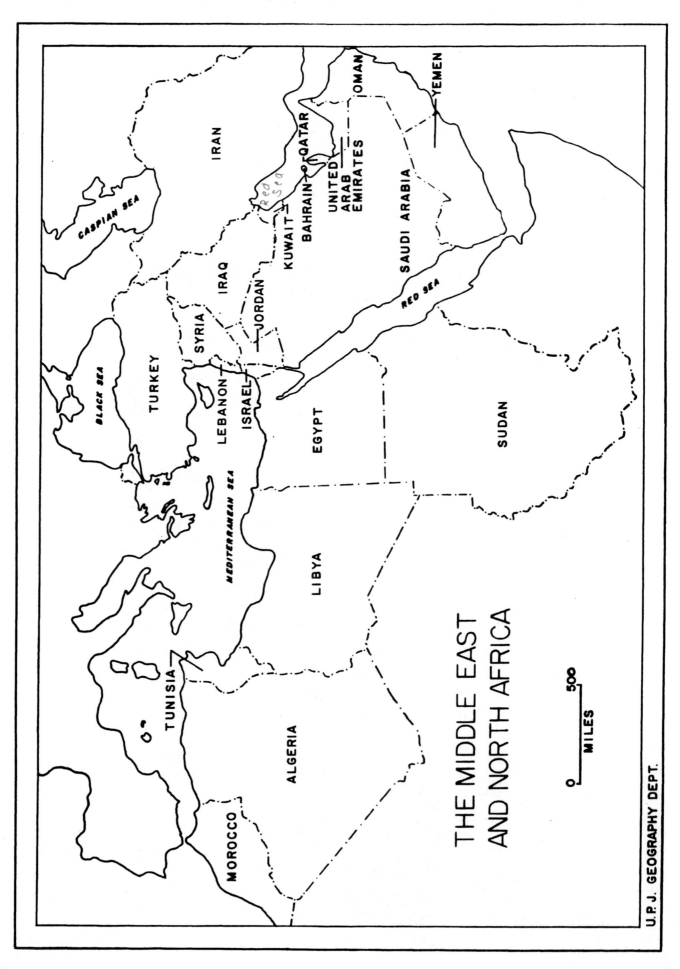

THE MIDDLE EAST
AND NORTH AFRICA

IRAN

CASPIAN SEA

OMAN

YEMEN

QATAR

BAHRAIN

UNITED
ARAB
EMIRATES

SAUDI ARABIA

Red Sea

KUWAIT

IRAQ

JORDAN

SYRIA

RED SEA

BLACK SEA

TURKEY

LEBANON

ISRAEL

EGYPT

SUDAN

MEDITERRANEAN SEA

LIBYA

TUNISIA

ALGERIA

MOROCCO

500

0

MILES

U.P.J. GEOGRAPHY DEPT.

168

## XV – THE MIDDLE EAST and NORTH AFRICA

The majority of people who reside in the Middle East and North Africa are Arabs who practice Islam. There are some exceptions; the population of Iran (former Persia) and the people of Turkey are not Arabs although Islam is the main religion in both nations. Israel is populated by Jews (along with a Palestinian minority) and Judaism is the religion of the state of Israel. Many of the Jews living in Israel are immigrants from Europe or their descendants. Some 75 % of Israel's total population of 7 and 1/4 million people is Jewish, the remaining 25% are mostly Palestinian Arabs. About 37% of the world's Jewish population resides in Israel. The continuous conflict in that nation reinforces the world's image of the Middle East as a place of terrorism and bloodshed. The invasion of Iraq by the United States in 2003 and the daily media portrayals of death and destruction in the nations of the Middle East keeps that image alive.

The attack on the Twin Towers in New York City on September 11, 2001, reinforced the view that the Middle East was the center of terrorism and that the goal of the leadership of these terrorist groups was the destruction of the United State and its allies. Most of the attackers of the Twin Towers were Arab Muslims from Saudi Arabia and all were willing to give up their lives for their cause.

Demonstration, like the one in Iran (below) is viewed by many people as a daily event in all of the Middle East.

Virtually all the nations in the Middle East are ruled by dictators or monarchs (Israel and Turkey are notable exceptions). Monarchs rule in Saudi Arabia, Morocco, Jordan, UAE, Oman, and Bahrain. The region is the last remaining part of the world where this type is government is found.

Islam is the dominant religion in the Middle East and is practiced by over one billion people world-wide. The word means "submission" in Arabic; that is submission to the will of Allah, an Arabic word for God. The religion was founded by Mohammed who was born in Mecca, Arabia in 570 A.D. Koran is the holy book of the Islamic faith.

The three holiest cities in Islam are <u>MECCA</u> – where Mohammed was born (see below)

THE ASSOCIATED PRESS

**Thousands of Muslims gather around the Kaaba during evening prayer in Mecca, Saudi Arabia.**

<u>MEDINA</u> where Mohammed established the first Islamic society and where he was buried, and <u>JERUSALEM</u>, site of the Dome of the Rock, believed to be where Mohammed Ascended to heaven. (see the Dome in the photo below)

The Mosque is an Islamic place of worship, used for daily prayers as well as Friday religious services. There are many sub-groups who practice Islam. The largest is the SUNNI which emphasizes the Sunna – a supplement to the Koran, based on the teachings and example of Mohammed. The second is the SHIITE which emphasizes the authority of Imams- the Moslem religious leaders.

## Images of the Middle East

The faithful pray near the KAABA (the black building in photo below) located in Mecca, Saudi Arabia and the most sacred site in Islam. Mecca, the holist Moslem city, is the birthplace of Prophet Mohammed. The Kaaba has a mosque built around it and all Moslems face the Kaaba when they pray, no matter where they are. Every person of Moslem faith is required, if capable, to perform the pilgrimage to Kaaba, along with others duties specified in the Koran (Qur'an), the Islamic holy book.

## THE MIDDLE EAST and OIL

Much of this region has abundant reserves of oil under its mostly desert landscape. Although not all nations in the Middle East have oil, those that do reap enormous economic benefits. The oil from the Middle East is exported primarily to the industrial nations. The United States leads the world, importing over <u>12 million barrels per day</u> ! This accounts for nearly 60 % of the total oil consumed (21 million barrels per day) in the USA. At $85 per barrel (April 2010) the total daily U.S. expenditure for imported oil is over 1 billion dollars ($1,020,000,000) each day !!!

China is a distant second in daily oil consumption – about 7 million barrels per day, followed by Japan at five and a half million.

Not all of the oil imported to the USA, for example, comes from the Middle East. In fact, of the top 4 exporters of oil to the USA, only SAUDI ARABIA is in the region. The other three are CANADA, MEXICO, and VENEZUELA.

A barrel of oil contains 42 gallons and is shown in the photograph on the next page.

Other major importers include France, Italy, Spain and the smaller European nations. They are more dependent of the Middle Eastern oil because of their proximity to that area. Great Britain has been self sufficient since 1980 when oil was discovered in the North Sea.

**The top exporting nations (with approximate number of barrels per day) include:**
<u>Saudi Arabia</u> – 9 million barrels per day
<u>Russia</u> – 7 million barrels per day
<u>Norway</u> – 3 million barrels per day

Other major exporting countries include Venezuela, Iran, Mexico, Nigeria, UAE, Kuwait, and Algeria.

At the current market price ($85 per barrel) Saudi Arabia makes $765 million per day; Russia makes $595 million per day and Norway – $255 million per day.

The price of a barrel of oil fluctuates based on a number of world events. These may include wars, changes in governments, internal conflicts, economic situations, new discoveries of oil and a number of other variables.

<u>The chart below shows the price fluctuations from 1947 – 2008</u>

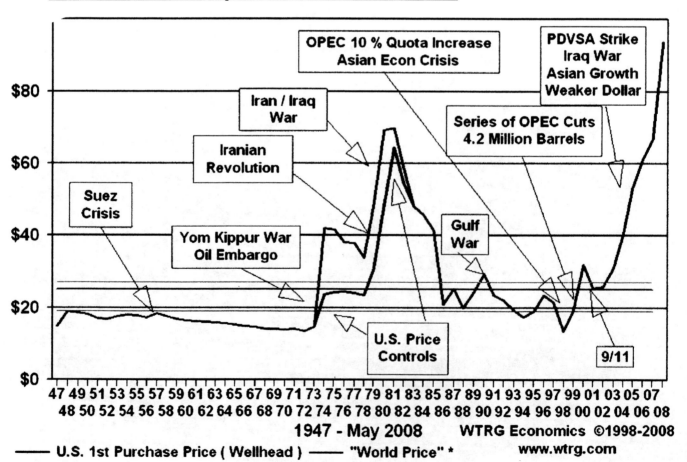

Barrels of oil are shown above. One barrel* contains 42 gallons of oil, which weighs 300 pounds. 7.2 barrels of oil weigh one ton.

At the current rate of world's oil production, the "known" oil reserves should last for about 100 years in SAUDI ARABIA, 150 years in IRAQ, 250 years in KUWAIT, 70 years in UNITED ARAB EMIRATES, 60 years in LIBYA, 35 years in GREAT BRITAIN, and between 100 and 200 years in RUSSIA. It is no wonder that a push for alternate sources of energy is not being vigorously pursued. The notion of "known" oil reserves is partly manipulated by the oil producing nations for political reasons. Some scholars also argue that the relevant measure is NOT how long oil reserves will last but when will the oil production start to decline as that resource dwindles. As Dr. M. King Hubbert theorized in the 1950's, oil is a finite resource and there are basic laws which describe the depletion of any finite resource. These can be summarized in the following statements:

- production starts at zero
- production rises to a peak which can never be surpassed
- once the peak is passed, production declines until the resource is depleted

The point of maximum production is known as **Hubbert Peak**.

The theory proved, correctly, that the peak of the production of oil in the USA would be reached in the 1970's. It is, however, much more difficult to predict the peak for the world as more oil reserves are discovered. The fact is that oil is a finite resource and the prices will increase dramatically as the demand increases and the supply can not keep pace with the demand.

A Historical Perspective of Oil in the Middle East

Over one-third of the western world's oil is now supplied by the Persian Gulf nations. Western Europe's economies would be devastated if the flow of oil from the Middle East was disrupted. United States would also be adversely affected since the country now imports over half of its total oil consumption. Up to the early 1970's, the United States was self sufficient in its oil needs based on internal production. By 1973, the demand for oil exceeded the country's ability to supply those needs, and the United States became an importer nation of foreign oil. In that year, the price of a barrel of oil jumped from under $17 to over $42. The major reason for this increase, led primarily by the Arab nations, was the U.S. backing of Israel in its war with the Arab states. Another was the realization by petroleum producing and exporting nations that the United States could no longer extract enough oil from its fields to satisfy its internal needs. It would, therefore, pay the higher prices.

It must be kept in mind that majority of the nations in the Middle East were created by the European colonial powers after the defeat of the Ottoman Empire in World War I. Great Britain and France were the primary players as they drew the boundaries for the new nations and established their spheres of influence. When oil began to flow from the region, these two nations, later joined by the American oil companies, got the favorable deals with the leaders of these nations. It was not until the more nationalistic leaders in the Middle East got better deals from the oil companies that the huge profits began to pour into those nations.

The creation of Israel after World War Two and the support for that country by the western powers did not sit well with the Arab oil producing nations. In all the conflicts between Israel and the Arab States, the USA and other western European powers backed Israel. This uneven treatment (in the eyes of the Arabs), led to retaliatory actions. One was to increase the cost of oil to the western nations and manipulate the production of oil. Another was to create a powerful oil cartel – the Organization of Petroleum Exporting Nations (OPEC).

<u>Organization of Petroleum Exporting Countries (OPEC)</u>

The Organization of Petroleum Exporting Countries is made up of <u>12 nations</u> (as of April 2010) located in various parts of the world. <u>Seven</u> of the member states are Arab nations including ALGERIA; IRAQ; KUWAIT; LIBYA; QATAR; SAUDI ARABIA and UNITED ARAB EMIRATES (Abu Dhabi is the largest sub-division of UAE). IRAN (former Persia) is also a member located in the Middle East but not an Arab nation. NIGERIA – the most populous nation in Africa and ANGOLA represent Africa south of the Sahara, while VENEZUELA and ECUADOR are members from South America.

<u>Indonesia</u>, an island nation in Asia and the largest Muslim nation in the world (240 million people), was a former member before leaving the organization last year.

The origin of OPEC dates back to the late 1940's when Venezuela approached a number of Arab oil producing nations to discuss the standardization of oil prices. After a decade of discussions, the OPEC was officially proclaimed in <u>1960</u> with the signing of five nations in Baghdad, Iraq. After a number of moves, its official base is now located in Vienna, Austria.

The organization grew to 13 nations until Ecuador and Gabon withdrew in the mid-1990's. In August of 1990, outbreak of hostilities between two OPEC members, Kuwait and Iraq, brought the United States to defend Kuwait in a war with Iraq. As a result of the hostilities, nearly 5 million barrels of oil per day was withdrawn from the market. The United States, with its superior military power, destroyed the Iraqi forces enabling Kuwait to remain independent and hold a seat in OPEC. By the late 1990's, OPEC was producing some 25 million barrels per day, with Saudi Arabia producing one third of the total (8 million), following by Iran with over 3 million barrels a day. When the US invaded Iraq in 2003, more oil was withheld from the market as hostilities escalated. The United States is still in Iraq trying to help that fragile regime to survive. The fighting between the different factions in the country, especially between the Sunnis and Shiites, has slowed the production of oil. The country is in a desperate need for revenues from oil to rebuild its devastated infrastructure.

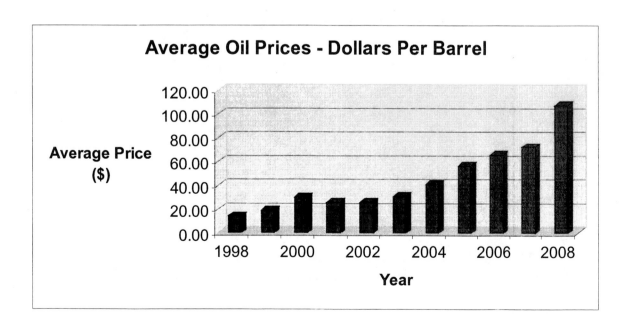

## Top 10 Oil and Gas Net Exporters in 2007:

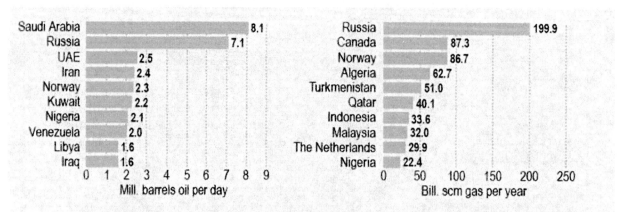

**Figure 1.1** The largest oil exporters (oil includes NGL and condensate) and gas exporters in 2007

*(Source: KBC Market Services)*

## OPEC Member Countries:

| Country | Joined OPEC | Location |
|---|---|---|
| Algeria | 1969 | Africa |
| Angola | 2007 | Africa |
| Ecuador(**) | rejoined 2007 | South America |
| Iran* | 1960 | Middle East |
| Iraq* | 1960 | Middle East |
| Kuwait* | 1960 | Middle East |
| Libyan AJ | 1962 | Africa |
| Nigeria | 1971 | Africa |
| Qatar | 1961 | Middle East |
| Saudi Arabia* | 1960 | Middle East |
| United Arab Emirates | 1967 | Middle East |
| Venezuela* | 1960 | South America |

*founder Members

** Ecuador joined OPEC in 1973, suspended its membership from Dec. 1992-Oct. 2007

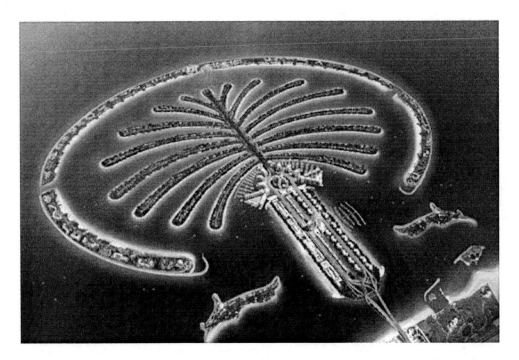

The currently high oil prices have created windfall profits for the countries that are significant oil exporters. This is especially noticeable in Persian Gulf countries such as Kuwait, Bahrain, Qatar, and the United Arab Emirates where the population level is low and oil exports are high. (According to the International Monetary Fund, Qatar was the wealthiest country in the world in 2009.) The result has been massive investments in infrastructure, housing, cultural amenities, and so on.

Perhaps the most interesting case is the **United Arab Emirates** (UAE), which is a federation of seven semi-independent emirates, the largest and best known being **Dubai** and **Abu Dhabi**. Almost all of the country's oil is located in Abu Dhabi. While there is some revenue sharing of the oil wealth within the UAE, Dubai has been forced to focus on other forms of economic development, such as tourism, real estate, and positioning itself as a business center for the Middle East. It has been very successful in doing so due to its strategic location, non-existent taxes and cultural openness (in contrast to, for example, Saudi Arabia's strict conservative Islamic practices). Around the world, Dubai is perhaps best known for its outrageous development projects. The tallest building in the world (called Burj Khalifa) was inaugurated in 2009 and for some time now Ski Dubai has been the premier indoor ski resort of the Middle East! And this in a country where the average temperature exceeds 100°F for a good portion of the year. In the image above you can see a residential development in the shape of a palm tree. Look closer and the individual houses are visible on this artificially constructed island. There are several other projects around Dubai that has drastically extended the buildable shoreline; the most famous is arguably a series of islands in the shape of the world's continents. While Dubai itself has very little oil, this development boom is in no small part a result of oil money and investments from elsewhere in the Middle East (and other places). The expansion of the UAE has necessitated an extremely high level of immigration. Immigrant workers from poorer countries are hired in construction and services, although they are exploited, work for little money under poor conditions, and do not share the emerging wealth of the UAE. Finally, the future of Dubai is not all sunny. Its speculative real estate-driven economy was dramatically affected by the 2008-2009 global recession. Many projects were scaled back or halted all together. Empty real estate is common in Dubai as of 2010. Ecologists are also worried about the environmental consequences of large scale projects such as the "the Palm" in the picture.

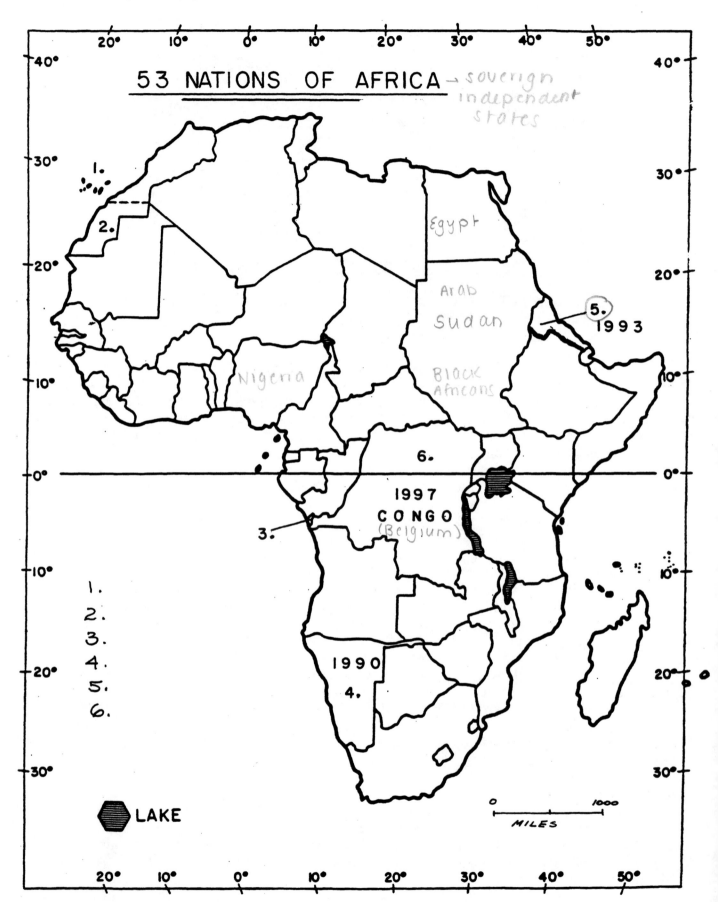

53 NATIONS OF AFRICA → soverign
independent
states

1.

2.

Egypt

Arab

Sudan

5. 1993

Nigeria

Black
Africans

6.

3.

1997
CONGO
(Belgium)

1.
2.
3.
4.
5.
6.

1990

4.

LAKE

0        1000
MILES

— contains 1 billion people → #5

ASSIGNMENT #14                    Name _____

Identify the areas from the Africa map:
1.

2.

3.

4.

5.

6.


List five nations in Africa with the <u>highest</u> population
        NATION    TOTAL POPULATION
1.

2.

3.

4.

5.

List five nations in Africa with the <u>largest</u> area
        NATION    TOTAL AREA
1.

2.

3.

4.

5.

What is one major issue facing Africa today? Explain.


Africa
- is a continent
   - not a country

Sudan
1 million sq mi.
- largest in area

Nigeria
- largest population
            wise
over 100 million
    people

# Mapping the spread of the virus

A look at the spread of HIV in Africa in 1984 and again in 1999, viewed as the percentage of people ages 15 to 49 infected with the virus.

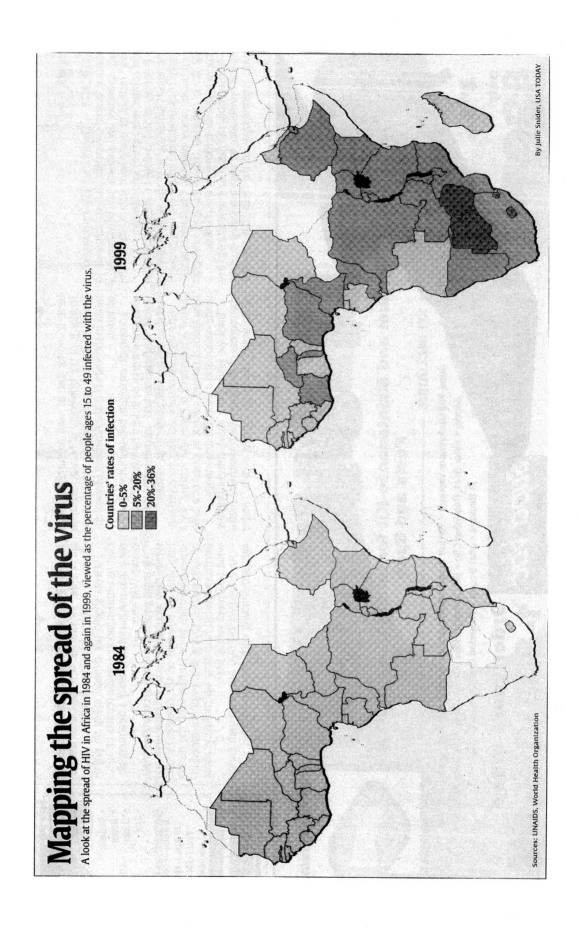

**Countries' rates of infection**

- 0-5%
- 5%-20%
- 20%-36%

1984

1999

By Julie Snider, USA TODAY

Sources: UNAIDS, World Health Organization

180

<u>XVI ~ AFRICA</u>

Africa is a <u>continent</u> made up of 53 countries and having a total population of ONE BILLION people (2010). Most of the African nations gained their political independence from European colonial powers in the decade of the sixties. The long occupation of Africa by the Europeans began to disintegrate with the granting of independence to Guinea by France in 1957 and to Ghana (formerly the Gold Coast) by Great Britain in 1958. In the early 1950's, only four nations on the continent of Africa were independent. They were: <u>Egypt, Ethiopia, South Africa, and Liberia</u>.

Many of the African nations maintain economic ties with their former European ruling nations, and most have retained <u>European languages</u> of their former colonial occupiers as their official national languages. Only in the north, where <u>Arabic</u> was spoken prior to European occupation, did Arabic remain as the official national language of those nations. These northern Arab nations of Africa include <u>Morocco, Tunisia, Algeria, Libya, Egypt and Sudan</u>.

The systematic occupation of Africa by western European countries began in earnest by the middle of the 19th century. Prior to that time, Europeans, for the most part, were content with controlling the coastal regions of the continent. With the growth of nationalism and the coming of the Industrial Revolution in Europe, the scramble for Africa intensified. To resolve any regional disputes, representatives from European nations with interest in Africa, assembled at the <u>Berlin Conference</u> in the winter of 1884 – 1885. At that meeting, the Europeans divided the African continent among themselves, placing boundaries with little regard to populated areas or physical features. The decision regarding which European nation was to get what area was loosely based on: 1. Prior claim to that African territory, and 2. effective occupation and protection of the claimed area. Since <u>Great Britain</u> and <u>France</u> were the most powerful nations at that time, they claimed the bulk of the continent. <u>Portugal, Spain, Germany, Italy,</u> and <u>Belgium</u> got smaller parts. Belgium, though, received an area in central Africa called the **Congo** which was over 100 times bigger than Belgium itself !

Today, few areas in Africa are not independent. With <u>Namibia</u> becoming independent in 1990, and <u>ERITREA</u> (see following page) gaining independence from Ethiopia in 1993, only <u>Western Sahara</u>, which is occupied by Morocco, remains as a non independent territory.

<u>The following African nations were the former colonies of:</u>

GREAT BRITAIN – Kenya,

FRANCE ~ Sénégal,

PORTUGAL ~ Angola,

## Eritrea: Independence From Ethiopia

Eritrea announced its independence from Ethiopia on April 27, 1993, after its referendum on the question. After this announcement, the US recognized Eritrea as an independent state. Eritrea's independence day celebrations were held on May 24. The US has established diplomatic relations with Eritrea, and the United Nations has admitted Eritrea as a member.

The conventional short-form name of this new state is Eritrea, and the conventional long-form name is State of Eritrea. Both names have been approved by the US Board on Geographic Names (BGN).

The national capital of Eritrea is Asmara. The Ethiopia-Eritrea international boundary is the former Ethiopian provincial boundary of Eritrea (see map, below).

— Angela M. Bottom  Geographic and Global Issues
Summer 1993

# Eritrea

Names and boundary representation are not necessarily authoritative

2353 5-93 STATE (INR/GE)

## Africa in the world community

Africa's 53 nations are politically independent and as different from each other as are l the European nations. Each, however, has a colonial legacy and each must strive to unite all its different ethnic groups into one nationality. All 53 countries are members of the United Nations (UN) and, as a block, make up almost 30% of UN's membership.

The African continent covers an area of 11,709,000 square miles and comprises slightly over 20% of the earth's land area. The nations range in size the very large ones like SUDAN (nearly one million square miles, making it the largest on the continent), ALGERIA, CONGO and LIBYA, to very small ones like SWAZILAND (15,000 square miles), DJIBOUTI (9,000 square miles); GAMBIA (4,000 square miles) and even smaller island nations.

The nations also differ in their total population. <u>NIGERIA</u> is the largest nation on the continent having close to 153 million people in 2010. It is followed by ETHIOPIA (84 million), EGYPT (80 million), CONGO (70 million) and SOUTH AFRICA (51 million). In addition, Algeria, Morocco, Sudan, Kenya, and Tanzania all have over 30 million people. The continent has one of the highest birth rates in the world (almost 40 births per 1000 population, compared to 14 in the USA) and its fertility rate (the number of children a female will have in her reproductive years) is nearly 5 (it is 2 for the USA).

Many nations of Africa have suffered from natural and human induced disasters. In the past, thousands of people have died from hunger and disease in nations like Ethiopia, Sudan, Somalia, Liberia and Burundi. Tribal, religious, ideological and regional conflicts have also taken a great toll on human lives. The recent war in the CONGO (formerly ZAIRE) may have resulted in as many as 100,000 casualties, along with many thousands who became homeless. The genocide in Rwanda and Burundi some years back resulted in an estimated one million casualties. The tragedy in Darfur, a province in western Sudan on the border with Chad, has been going on for almost a decade. The conflict is between the Sudanese government which represents the majority Arab population in the country and the black African population in the south. The later complain that the government oppresses and discriminates against them in favor of the Arab population. It is estimated that some two hundred thousand people have died (mostly civilians) in combat or from starvation and disease brought on by the conflict. Millions have been forced into refugees camps or moved across the border into Chad.

<u>Liberia</u>, a nation located in West Africa with close historic ties to the United States, is another example of a nation which was involved in a bloody civil conflict. The war has decimated the country, with a fourth of its population either killed or living in exile. Liberia has had close historical ties to the United States and is the oldest Republic on the continent of Africa, declaring its independence in 1847. The nation's constitution and flag are similar to that of the United States, and Liberia's capital city – Monrovia – is named after the American president. The nation is in the process of rebuilding with the help of the international community, but the damage caused by the conflict will be hard to overcome.

Africa is the place of origin of the human family. The discoveries of skeleton remains in east Africa, especially in Kenya, Tanzania and Ethiopia by anthropologists and other experts led to the dominant view among scientists that Africa, indeed, is the original home of the human species.

## Example of African Nations

### THE REPUBLIC OF SOUTH AFRICA

The Republic of South Africa has undergone major political and social changes in the 1990's. The political power has passed from the white minority population to the black majority, and the policy of <u>APARTHEID</u> (apartness of the races) no longer exists. Under the new regime, the classifying of population into four **racial categories (whites, Asian, colored, and black)** has been abandoned. The new South Africa has an elected black president (blacks could not vote under the old regime), and a new constitution has been adopted.

The English and Dutch settlers colonized this area of Africa in the 17th century, with the Dutch establishing a settlement of Cape Town in 1652. The mild, Mediterranean type climate was one of the main attraction for the European migration to south Africa. There were continuous armed conflicts with the various African tribes, with the Zulus providing the fiercest opposition to the white settlers. There were also conflicts between the British settlers and the Dutch (who called themselves AFRICAANERS) with the British finally winning and with Great Britain establishing a protectorate. In 1910, South Africa became independent with the descendents of British settlers controlling the government.

After World War II, the Nationalist Party, dominated by the descendents of the Dutch settlers, came to power. Although the white settlers discriminated against the African majority from the beginning, in 1948 new laws made racial discrimination legal and institutionalized. Four groups of people were recognized (see above) with the whites having control of the government, economics, best residential areas, best schools, best jobs and general control of the country. Marriage between whites and non-whites was forbidden, schools were segregated and Africans could not vote.

In 1961, South Africa became a Republic and withdrew from the British Commonwealth. As the racial laws became more and more repressive, the international community, led by Great Britain and the USA imposed economic sanctions on the country. Internally, armed resistance by the native Africans intensified and pressure mounted for social and political change in the nation. In 1994, after the nation rewrote its constitution emphasizing racial equality, Nelson Mandela representing the African National Congress party won the presidency by a land slide. This native African leader, who was jailed by the former regime for a quarter of a century, was able to unite the racially diverse population and bring legitimacy, dignity and respect to the new Republic of South Africa. Mandela was awarded the Nobel Peace Price in 1993.

South Africa has an abundance of natural resources including gold, diamonds, uranium, coal, chromium, iron ore and platinum, among others. It also has deposits of natural gas and a rich agricultural base. Foreign investment is booming and there is an increasingly visible middle class.

In spite of all the positive changes in the country, problems do exist. The nation has a high birth rate, economic inequality among different racial groups still exists, the nation has one of the highest rates of AIDS in the world, pollution is a problem and urban centers have a problem keeping up with increasing demands for services by large influx of migrants.

The unequal treatment of racial groups in South Africa, practiced under the old regime, can be seen on the following page.

South Africa under the old regime.

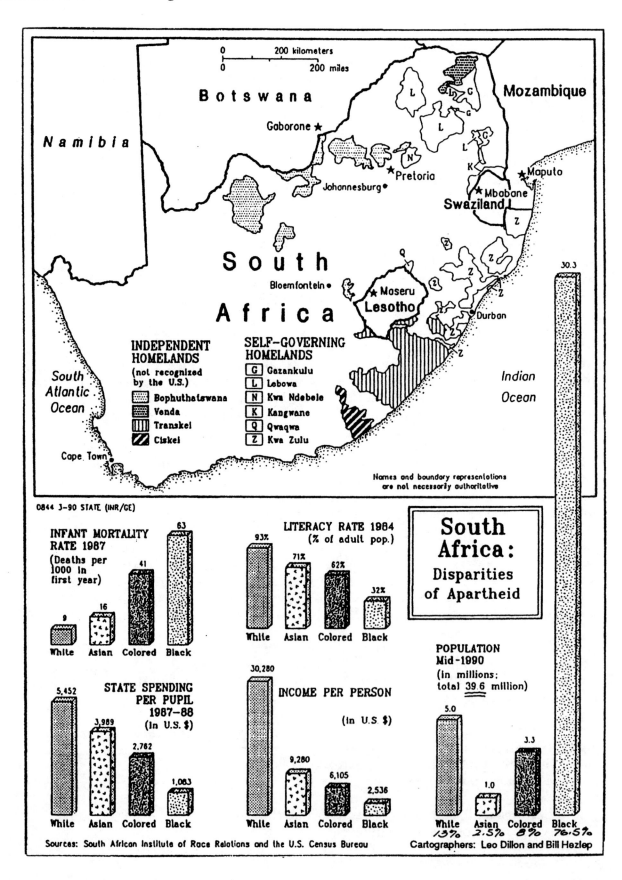

INDEPENDENT
HOMELANDS
(not recognized
by the U.S.)

- Bophuthatswana
- Venda
- Transkei
- Ciskei

SELF-GOVERNING
HOMELANDS

G Gazankulu
L Lebowa
N Kwa Ndebele
K Kangwane
Q Qwaqwa
Z Kwa Zulu

Names and boundary representations
are not necessarily authoritative

0844 3-90 STATE (INR/GE)

**INFANT MORTALITY RATE 1987**
(Deaths per 1000 in first year)

White 9, Asian 16, Colored 41, Black 63

**LITERACY RATE 1984**
(% of adult pop.)

White 93%, Asian 71%, Colored 62%, Black 32%

**South Africa: Disparities of Apartheid**

**STATE SPENDING PER PUPIL 1987-88**
(In U.S. $)

White 5,452, Asian 3,989, Colored 2,762, Black 1,083

**INCOME PER PERSON**
(In U.S. $)

White 30,280, Asian 9,280, Colored 6,105, Black 2,536

**POPULATION Mid-1990**
(In millions: total 39.6 million)

White 5.0 (13%), Asian 1.0 (2.5%), Colored 3.3 (8%), Black 30.3 (76.5%)

Sources: South African Institute of Race Relations and the U.S. Census Bureau

Cartographers: Leo Dillon and Bill Hezlep

186

## THE REPUBLIC OF LIBERIA

The Republic of Liberia has strong historical ties to the United States. The nation was created by the American Colonization Society with funds provided by the US government. In 1822, the first ship of freed slaves arrived from America and deposited some 300 people on the shores of western Africa. More ships, with freed slaves from the United States, followed and in1847, these settlers, who called themselves Americo–Liberians, established a new nation – the Republic of Liberia. Liberia, thus, became the oldest independent republic on the continent of Africa.

The constitution of Liberia was modeled after the American constitution, its flag is similar to that of the United States, the government has three distinct branches, same as the US, the capital city is Monrovia – named after the American president and there are numerous other similarities between Liberia and the United States.

The black settlers from the United States and their descendants, however, viewed themselves superior to the native population, who were members of about a dozen distinct indigenous tribes. The settlers, and their descendants, held political power in the country, controlled the nation's wealth and held the top positions in all segments of the society. These "Americo–Liberians", who were mostly Christian, had the best education and practiced customs which they brought from America. Every President, from Roberts (the first President of the country) to Tolbert (the last) came from their ranks. All had American names and had little in common with the native population of Liberia. They ruled by force, intimidation, bribery and wit.

In 1980 there was a military coup, led by indigenous population, and President Tolbert was assassinated. After nearly 140 years, the continuous rule by the Americo–Liberians was over. But the problems were just beginning. The leader of the military coup became President and ruled the nation as a dictator. After ten years of oppressive rule, the opposition overthrew and murdered the President and the civil war engulfed the whole country. The bloody conflict lasted for over a dozen years, taking the lives of some 200,000 Liberians. Many more were left homeless in this nation of under three million inhabitants. Finally, with the help of the USA and the international community, the civil war ended and elections were held in 2005. Ellen Johnson Sirleaf was democratically elected President, making her the first female head of state on the continent of Africa!

Liberia, located on the west coast of Africa just north of the equator, has a tropical-rainforest type climate. It is rich in natural resources and in a variety of tropical plant life. Its rich deposits of iron ore in the north are exported to Japan and other nations. Its lumber is shipped out throughout the world, and its recently discovered diamond veins are said to be rivaling those of the Republic of South Africa. Liberia was one of the leading producers and exporters of natural rubber, started in the country by the Firestone Rubber Company of Akron, Ohio.

rubber tree

# LIBERIA'S ADMINISTRATIVE DIVISIONS: 13 COUNTIES

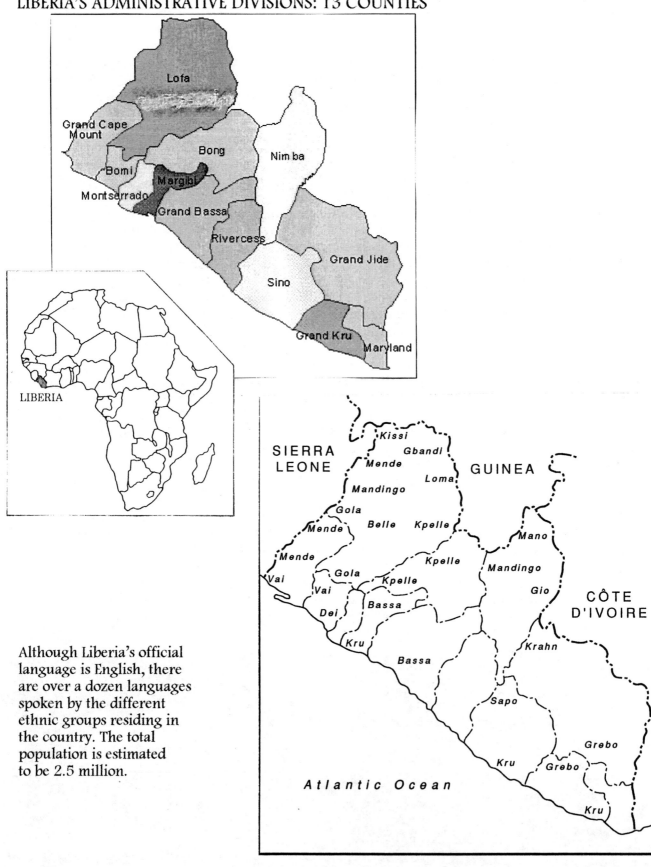

Although Liberia's official language is English, there are over a dozen languages spoken by the different ethnic groups residing in the country. The total population is estimated to be 2.5 million.

Liberia: ethnic groups

## KENYA

Kenya is located in eastern Africa, with the equator cutting the nation in half. The Indian Ocean washes its western shores and Lake Victoria lies to the east of the country. It is surrounded by the nations of Ethiopia, Somalia, Uganda and Tanzania. Kenya's capital city of Nairobi lies in the Southern Highlands in the interior of the country, with its major port city of Mombasa situated on the Indian Ocean. The country was a British colony before getting independence in 1963.

Kenya is the "big-game" country in Africa. Elephants, giraffes, lions, baboons, hippos, zebras and a variety of other animals are found in the country. Its wildlife, along with the flora, attracts tourists from every part of the world. Tourism, in fact, is Kenya's major industry.

Lake Rudolph in the north and the shores of Lake Victoria in the west serve as additional tourist attractions. Part of the Great Rift Valley is located in western Kenya where most of the nation's arable land is found. The rest of the nation's land is plagued by drought, floods and mass scale erosion and leeching. Under 10 per cent of Kenya's land is suitable for agriculture, yet nearly 70 percent of the labor force is engaged in agriculture. One of the problems facing the country is its very high birth rate. The nation also has a high incidence of AIDS among its population, with an estimated 3 million people infected with the disease.

The south-central part of Kenya is the home of the famous Masai people. These tribesmen, who are great herdsmen roam across the boundary between Kenya and Tanzania unimpeded. Their cattle is their wealth and provide the people with their livelihood.

EGYPT

Egypt is located in the north-eastern part of Africa covering an area of nearly 400,000 square miles. The nation is mostly covered by a desert with a few exceptions, including a shoreline along the Mediterranean Sea in the north and land on both sides of the Nile River. Egypt, the "Gift of the Nile", is a cradle of one of the world's greatest civilizations, with a recorded history dating back to 3200 B.C. As in any desert region, the greatest range in temperature occurs between day and night; the difference in temperature can reach between 70 to 80 degrees in a 24 hour span! The most humid area in the country is located along the Mediterranean coast, where the average annual rainfall is about 8 inches. Precipitation decreases rapidly to the south.

The vegetation of Egypt is confined to the Nile delta, the Nile Valley and the oases. Crops are grown along the Nile River and irrigated with the water from the Nile River regulated from the Aswan Dam. The most widespread native tree is the date palm, which grows where some water is available.

Egypt has a wide variety of mineral resources, some of which, like gold and copper, have been mined since ancient times. Today, the most important resource for the country is petroleum, found primarily in the coastal region of the Red Sea. Some natural gas is also extracted in the country, along with uranium, phosphates, manganese and other minerals.

Egypt's economy is dependent upon revenues generated by:
1.  Sale of PETROLEUM
2.  Fees from the SUEZ CANAL and
3.  TOURISM

The petroleum industry plays a key role in the Egyptian economy, accounting for approximately 40% of the nation's export earnings. Although Egypt is not a member of OPEC, it is an important oil producing nation in north Africa.

The Suez Canal is another important source of revenue for Egypt. Finished and opened in 1869, it connects the Mediterranean Sea with the Red Sea. Ships, which otherwise would have to travel around Africa, save thousands of miles using the canal. Some 50 ships a day use the canal over its 110 mile distance from Port Said in the north to Port Suez in the south.

*Ships lie off Port Said prior to entering Suez Canal*

## ANCIENT EGYPT

It is, however, Egypt's ancient civilization that captures people's imagination and accounts for the nation's booming tourist industry. The Giza Plateau, with its three major pyramids and the Great Sphinx (see next page), may be the most frequently visited tourist spot on the face of the earth. Of the Seven Wonders of the Ancient World, the three Great Pyramids are the only ones still standing. The largest, Pyramid of Khufu, was built some four and a half thousand years ago and stands 450 feet high. It, like other pyramids, was built as a tomb for the pharaoh and his queen. Inside the pyramid, there is a chamber where the pharaoh was buried. The chamber was filled with treasure so that the pharaoh could maintain his life style in the after life. The treasure was looted long ago.

The technology to built such a structure so long ago is truly astonishing. Over two million fine chiseled stones were used in the construction of the pyramid, some weighing as much as twenty tons! No stone was under a ton and all were placed on each other in almost perfect symmetry. In addition, the chamber had to be constructed in the middle of the structure. The process of how the pyramids were constructed is still debated today.

More than seventy pyramids survive from the ancient times. Most were built in the Valley of the Kings and Queens on the western side of the Nile River. The area is some three miles south of Cairo, the capital of Egypt, across the river from the present day city of Luxor. The tomb of Tutankhamen, discovered in the Valley of the Kings in 1922, was the only one found (so far) not looted by early robbers. The tomb contained the mummified body of the boy-king and many treasures including the golden mask, a wooden gold-plated throne, art objects, semi-precious stones and many more. Most of the material is now housed in the Cairo museum of antiquity in Egypt.

Standing near the three Great Pyramids of Giza is the SPHINX. The Sphinx, carved out of natural sandstone rock, is a human-headed structure of a lion which was buried under the sand for a long time. The body of the Sphinx measures 200 feet in length and is 65 feet high. The face, with a missing nose, is 13 feet wide and the beard from the face is now displaced in the British museum in London. Why the Sphinx was constructed is a mystery, as is the symbolism of the figure. The fact is that the statue is crumbling today due to wind erosion, humidity and the smog generated from the city of Cairo. The city's suburbs are encroaching on the Giza plateau as the nations' population continues to grow at one of the fastest rates on the continent.

The Sphinx and the pyramids of Egypt

# The Giza Plateau

A year of digging has filled in pieces of the mosaic of the 70 years of the fourth dynasty in which Cheops, Chephren and Mycerinus built the famous Giza Pyramids. This map shows the Giza Plateau as it would have appeared after Cheops built the Great Pyramid during his rule from 2551-2528 B.C. and before his son Chephren built the Sphinx and his own pyramid to the southwest of Cheops'.

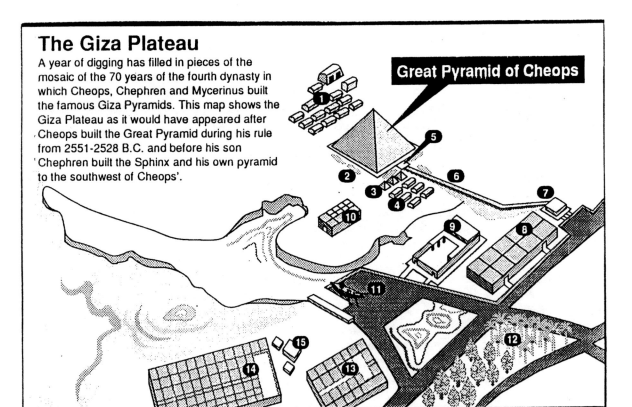

**Great Pyramid of Cheops**

## The legend

1. Tombs of the officials.
2. Boat pits. There are five in all; four uncovered so far. One yielded a magnificent royal boat. The pit still covered contains a sister ship, dismantled.
3. Three queens' pyramids.
4. Tombs of the royal family.
5. Mortuary temple, where final rites were said for Cheops.
6. The 810-meter causeway linking two temples. Cheops' body was carried over the causeway to burial within the pyramid.
7. Valley temple, where the body was purified.
8. Pyramid city, stretching over three square kilometers.
9. King's Palace or rest house.
10. Workmen's shop.
11. Harbor.
12. Royal farms.
13. Artists' village.
14. Workers' city.
15. Cemetery for the middle class (foremen, supervisors, etc.).

The Sphinx Avenue in Karnak, Egypt

Hatshepsut's Temple in Luxor, Egypt

Every nation on the continent of Africa has a unique history. Although most of the countries are on the road to economic development, the continent's contribution to human civilization is rich and lasting.

Another example of an African nation:

Namibia:  This was a former German territory called "German South–West Africa". At the end of W.W. I (1919), Germany lost its colonies in Africa and this area came under the administration of the Republic of South Africa. South Africa fought against Germany in World War I and was awarded this territory by the victorious Allies. The odd shape of the county was the result of Kaiser Wilhelm's demand for a piece of the Zambezi River at the Berlin Conference of 1884-1885, when Africa was divided among the European colonial powers (see map below). In 1990, the nation of Namibia became independent, but the odd shape of the country remains.

The nation is also the home of the famous Namib Desert. This coastal desert is located between the Atlantic Ocean to the west of the country and the Kalahari Desert east of the nation and extends some 1,700 miles north to south. Its aridity is caused by cooling of the dry air descending towards the cold Benguela ocean current along the nation's Atlantic coast. The sand dunes of the Namib Desert are among the highest in the world, reaching heights of 1,200 feet. In the most arid part of the desert, the rainfall is under one inch per year.

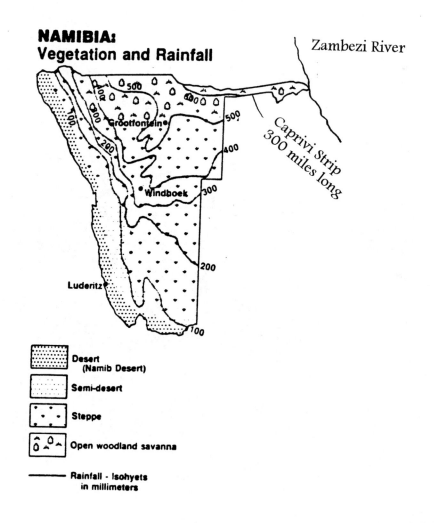

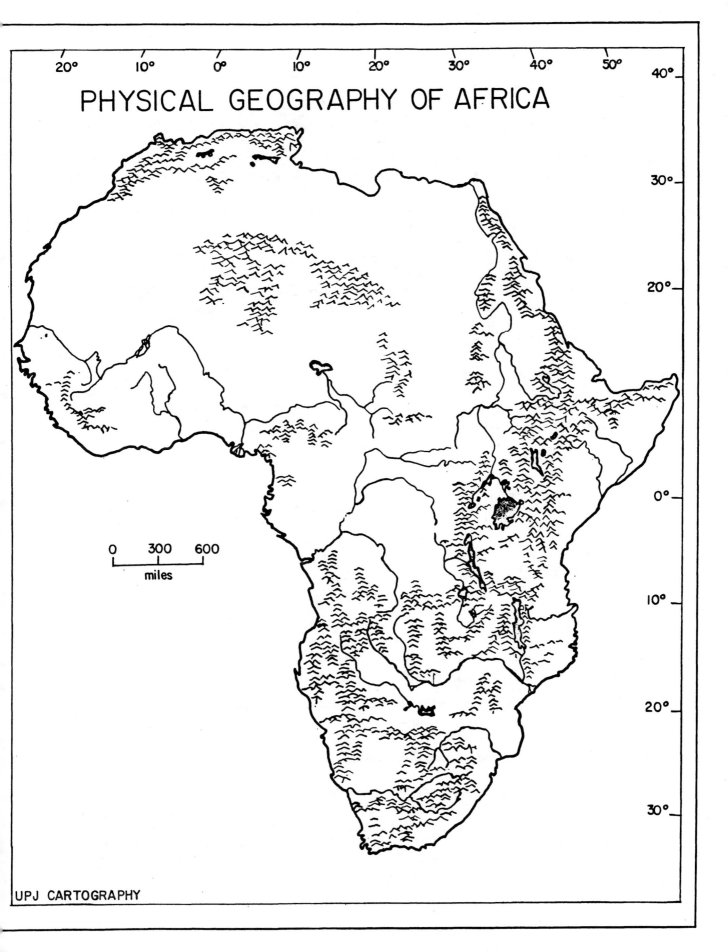

PHYSICAL GEOGRAPHY OF AFRICA

20° 10° 0° 10° 20° 30° 40° 50°

40°

30°

20°

0 300 600
miles

0°

10°

20°

30°

UPJ CARTOGRAPHY

195

## PHYSICAL GEOGRAPHY OF AFRICA

The African continent is a massive tropical plateau covering 20% of the world's land surface. One third of the continent lies under a desert. Its area measures slightly over 11.8 million square miles. Some parts of the plateau are comprised of metamorphic rock containing metallic ores, others are sedimentary rock formations. Many of the continent's rivers flow over steep falls and rapids near the edge of the continent before emptying into the Atlantic Ocean in the west or the Indian Ocean in the east. The longest river on the continent, the Nile, flows northward and empties into the Mediterranean Sea.

Ten percent of Africa is covered by tropical rainforest, located in the coastal west Africa and in the Congo basin of central Africa. One third of the total area lies under a desert, mainly in the north-Saharan Desert and the south-west-the Namib Desert. The mountainous regions of Africa are located primarily in the eastern and southern part of the continent, with the majestic Atlas Mountains hugging the extreme north-west. The rest of the continent is sometimes referred to as "Low Africa" based on its elevation.

Africa is separated from Europe by the Mediterranean Sea. The Atlantic Ocean washes the continent's western shore, while the Indian Ocean forms its eastern boundary. Both the Prime Meridian and the Equator pass through Africa. The two lines cross in the Gulf of Guinea, approximately 400 miles south of Accra, the capital city of Ghana.

### Deforestation in Africa

One of the most serious ecological problems facing Africa is DEFORESTATION. The term can be defined as a process of clearing forests without replacing them. In the tropical forest regions of Africa, deforestation is an every day occurrence and is a cause of concern. Recent estimates by the United Nations Food and Agricultural Organization (FAO) showed that West Africa led the world with over two percent annual loss of its tropical forests. Ivory Coast (over 5 %) had the highest deforestation rate in the region. Liberia, Ghana and Nigeria now have less than 15% of the original forest vegetation.

Central Africa contains over forty percent of its original forest. This is because the region has a low density of rural population, and less forest is cut for subsistence agriculture. In fact, the major reason for deforestation in Africa is the conversion of forest lands to agriculture. Logging and using trees for fuel also contribute to deforestation.

The loss of tropical rainforest, with its irreplaceable hardwoods like ebony, mahogany and iron wood, causes accelerated erosion in the area. In addition, faunal and floral diversity declines with the depletion of tropical forests. Africa's tropical rainforests provide a home to more than half of the world's plants and animals.

Most important, perhaps, are the losses of potential medical herbs, native to tropical rainforest. Some of these include rosy periwinkle, used in treatment of leukemia, curare, used as a muscle relaxant during surgery, and quinine, used in treatment of malaria. Other species of medical plants collected from the tropical forests have been used for treatment of diarrhea, fever, intestinal problems, and snakebites. Herbs from tropical rainforests may provide future cures for cancer, AIDS, and other diseases.

Nurturing a small crop in the semi-desert region of Africa

**Cocoa beans**

# REGIONAL MAPS OF THE WORLD

The following regional maps should be used in conjunction with the maps found in WORLD ATLAS (newest edition). These include:

NORTH AND CENTRAL AMERICA

CENTRAL AMERICA

SELECTED CARRIBEAN ISLANDS

SOUTH AMERICA

EUROPE

ASIA

AFRICA

WORLD

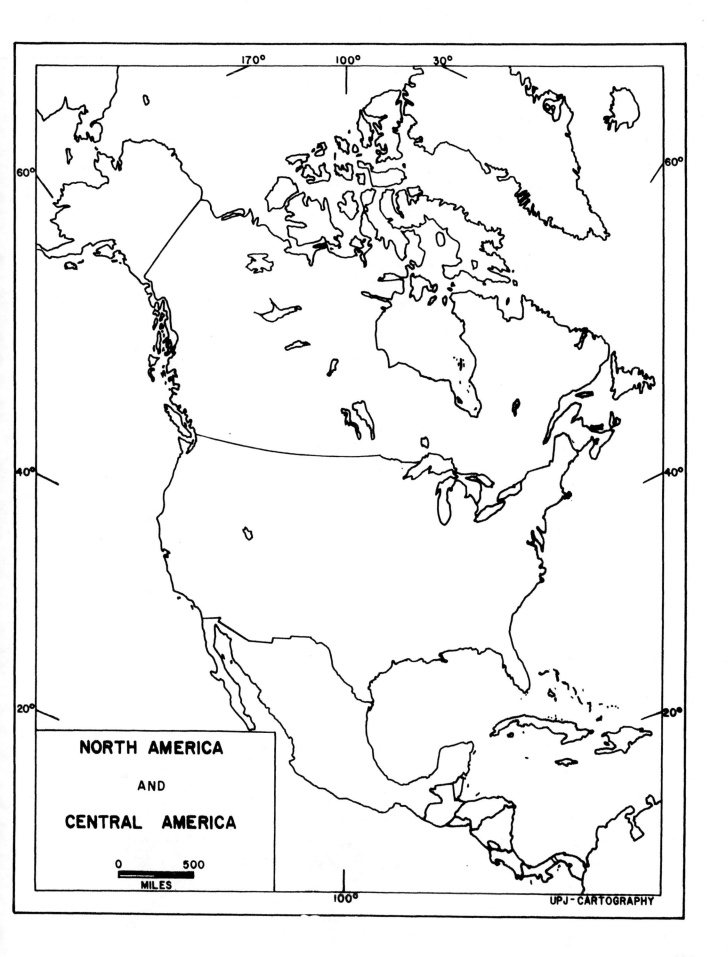

NORTH AMERICA

AND

CENTRAL AMERICA

0        500
MILES

170°  100°  30°

60°

40°

20°

100°

UPJ-CARTOGRAPHY

199

North and Central America

Three **nations** of North America:

1.

2.

3.

What is the political status of GREENLAND ?

The SEVEN nations of Central America are:

Which nation of Central America has English as an official language ?

_____

GRAND CANYON – USA

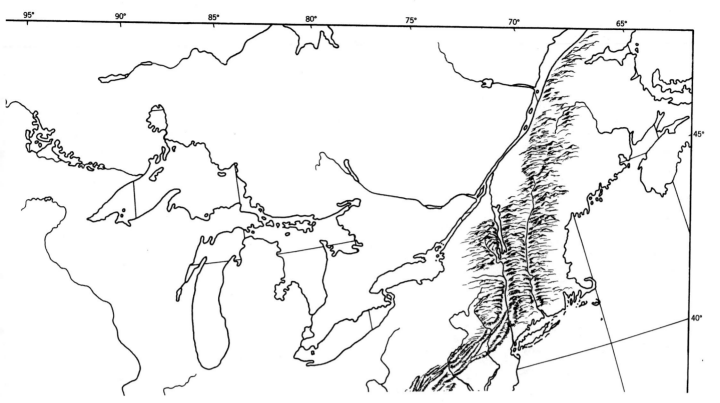

## The Great Lakes of North America

The FIVE Great Lakes of North America, including (west to east) Lake Superior, Lake Michigan, Lake Huron, Lake Erie and Lake Ontario hold 20% of the world's fresh water and, by surface, constitute the largest group of lakes on earth. They range in size from Lake Superior (largest) covering an area of nearly 32,000 sq. mi. to Lake Ontario (smallest) with an area of 7,540 sq. mi. The average depths of the lakes range from 62 feet for Lake Erie to the deepest – 483 feet for Lake Superior.

Lake Michigan is located entirely within the boundaries of the United States while the other four form the border between the USA and Canada. The Lakes touch the following eight states: Minnesota, Wisconsin, Michigan, Illinois, Indiana, Ohio, Pennsylvania and New York. They are bounded in the north be the Canadian Province of Ontario. The Saint Lawrence River is the primary outlet for the lakes. It follows a path through the Canadian Provinces of Quebec and Ontario in the north-easterly direction to the Atlantic Ocean.

The Lakes provide drinking water to millions of people in the bordering areas. Recreational boating and tourism are the major industries, while commercial fishing of salmon, trout, and whitefish brings in some $3 billion per year. Niagara Falls, located on the Niagara River between Lake Erie and Lake Ontario, attracts tourists from around the world. The falls is actually comprised of two major sections: the Horseshoe Falls, located primarily on the Canadian side and the American Falls on the US side.

The Great Lakes have been plagued by toxic contamination, shrinking wildlife habitat and invasive species. The U.S. government has recently developed a $2 billion plan to clean-up the most heavily polluted sites of the lakes, restore wetlands, and improve water quality. Sixteen federal agencies working with state, local and tribal governments and private groups will be involved in this undertaking. One of the many goals is to save species such as the lake sturgeon, an endangered species because of habitat degradation.

Mississippi and Missouri Ricers

Two great rivers, the Mississippi and the Missouri drain the central part of the USA between the Rocky and the Appalachian Mountains.

The MISSISSIPPI River's source is Lake Itasca (elevation 1,475 feet), located in northern Minnesota. It flows southward for a distance of 2,320 mile and empties into the Gulf of Mexico.

The headwaters of the <u>Missouri River</u>, known as the "Big Muddy" because of its high silt content, are located in the Rocky Mountains in southwestern Montana near the continental divide. The Jefferson, Madison, and Gallatin Rivers come together near Three Forks, Montana to form the Missouri. The Missouri River and its tributaries run through Montana, North Dakota, South Dakota, Nebraska, Iowa, Kansas, and Missouri. The Missouri River eventually joins with the Mississippi River just north of St. Louis.

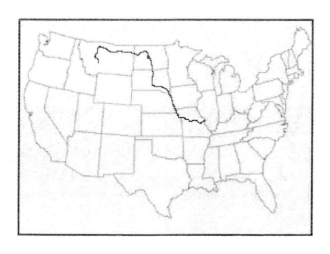

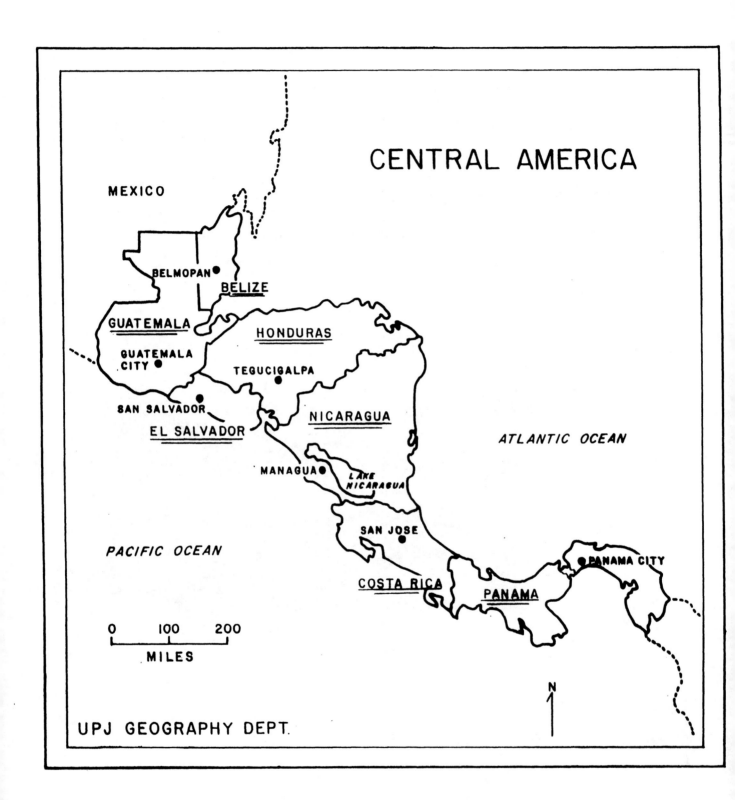

CENTRAL AMERICA

MEXICO

BELMOPAN

BELIZE

GUATEMALA

HONDURAS

GUATEMALA
CITY

TEGUCIGALPA

SAN SALVADOR

EL SALVADOR

NICARAGUA

ATLANTIC OCEAN

MANAGUA

LAKE
NICARAGUA

PACIFIC OCEAN

SAN JOSE

PANAMA CITY

COSTA RICA

PANAMA

0    100    200

MILES

N

UPJ GEOGRAPHY DEPT.

Short Outline of Central America's nations.

BELIZE is located in northern Central America and is bounded by Mexico, Guatemala and the Caribbean Sea. It is the home of the largest barrier reef in the Western Hemisphere, running for some 160 miles along the entire length of the country. The nation's unspoiled tropical rainforest is another attraction for tourists who provide the major source of income for Belize. This former colony of Great Britain, the nation was known as British Honduras until 1973.

GUATEMALA has a long history of unrest and civil war. In 1996, a peace agreement was signed after 36 years of civil war during which 100,000 people were killed and one million became refugees. The Maya civilization flourished here in the first millennium A.D. The Spaniards ruled the area for three centuries before independence came in 1821.

HONDURAS gained its independence from Spain in 1821. The nation was ruled by a series of dictators until 1982 when a freely elected government came to power. The country was devastated by Hurricane Mitch in 1998 which caused nearly 7,000 deaths and over 2 billion dollars worth of damage. The nation is still recovering from that disaster.

EL SALVADOR borders the nations of Honduras and Guatemala. The nation has the strongest economy in Central America and has been politically stable since 1992. In that year, the leftist guerillas and the government signed a peace treaty ending 12 years of civil war which caused 75,000 casualties. The country is also known for its many earthquakes. In 2001, two quakes killed over 1,000 people and destroyed 20 % of the nation's housing. Three quarters of the nation's crops were also destroyed, causing severe famine in the country.

NICARAGUA borders the nations of Honduras and Costa Rica. The nation has three distinct regions; the Pacific Lowlands, North-Central Mountains and the Atlantic Lowlands. The Pacific Lowlands, located in the west, are the broad, fertile plains where a variety of crops are grown. Coffee is grown in the North-Central Mountain region while the Atlantic Lowlands are the home of the nation's tropical rainforest.

COSTA RICA borders Nicaragua on the north and Panama to the south-east. Both the Atlantic and the Pacific Oceans wash its shores. The country is a haven for biodiversity and over one-fourth of the nation's land is comprised of protected forests and reserves. There are a variety and diversity of national parks in the country which are home to big cats and tapirs. The latter are pig-like animals with short tusks which are found in huge numbers. In addition, the parks provide a habitat for an endangered green turtle and a variety of other living creatures including spiders, white-throated monkeys, three-toed sloth and big hunting cats. There are over three hundred species of birds, with some only found here. The parks contain over 2,000 variety of plans and are a draw for tourists from all over the world.
Costa Rica has the highest standard of living in Central America and has had a democratically elected government for some time. There is a wide practice of land ownership and the nation has been relatively stable politically. Although agriculture is the mainstay, the nation is expanding its industrial base. Tourism has always been an important industry due to the safety and accommodations for the visitors.

## THE PANAMA CANAL

Opened in 1914, the 51 mile long canal has served as a link between the Caribbean Sea and the Pacific Ocean. Build by the United States of America, after Panama declared independence from Columbia in 1903, the project took 10 years to complete. The USA paid Panama ten million dollars and a yearly sum of money for the Canal Zone – a 10-mile strip across the isthmus administered by the US.

Many lives were lost during the construction in this tropical rainforest type region. Workers died from malaria and other tropical diseases, accidents and injuries. The finished product, however, was an engineering marvel.

In 1974, President Carter signed a treaty with Panama giving that nation gradual control of the canal. The US Senate ratified the treaty in 1978. In 1999, the USA formally handed over control of the Panama Canal to Panama.

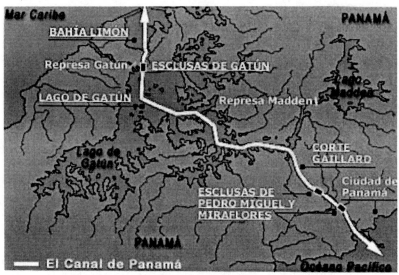

Courtesy: Instituto Paname–o de Turismo (IPAT)

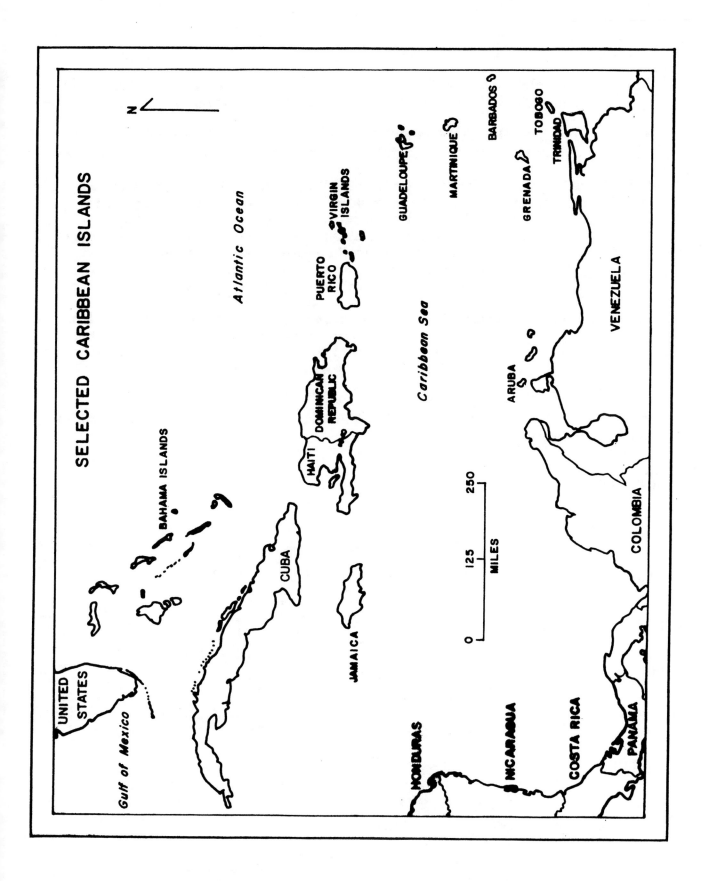

SELECTED CARIBBEAN ISLANDS

207

The four major island in the Caribbean include:

CUBA – located just 90 miles from Key West, Florida. This Spanish speaking island of over 11 million people has been ruled by Fidel Castro's communist regime since 1959.

JAMAICA – this former British colony of 2.7 million people gained its independence in 1962. It serves as one of the major tourist attractions for the North American population

PUERTO RICO – is a possession of the United States having a legislature consisting of a 27-member Senate and a 51-member House of Representatives, all elected to four-year terms. In addition, the island's governor is also elected for a four year term. The residents of Puerto Rico are American citizens but do not vote in the US presidential elections. In the latest polls, about half of the island's population favored its present political status, 46% were in favor of statehood and only four percent wanted political independence.

THE ISLAND OF HISPANIOLA: The island is made up of two independent nations. HAITI, the French speaking country, is located in the western part while the DOMINICAN REPUBLIC, the Spanish speaking nation, occupies the eastern part of the island.

Some of the smaller islands in the Caribbean include ARUBA, GRANADA, BARBADOS, MARTINIQUE, TRINADAD, and VIRGIN ISLANDS. Thousands of even smaller island dot the region of the Caribbean Sea.

GRANADA

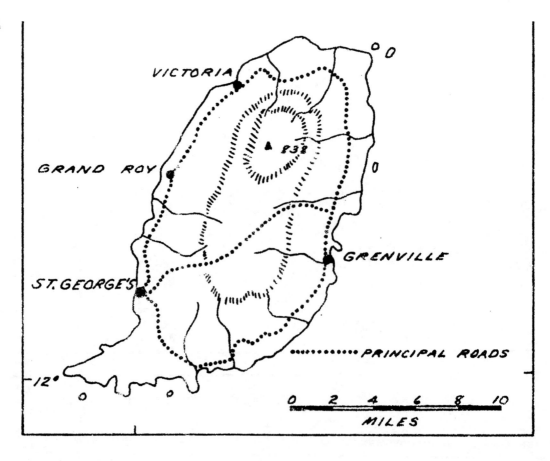

208

SOUTH AMERICA

0   300   600
MILES

UPJ-CARTOGRAPHY

209

SOUTH AMERICA

Most of the nations of South America were former Spanish colonies and use Spanish as their official language. There are four exceptions:

1. BRAZIL was a former Portuguese colony and uses that language as it official language. This largest nation in South America in size and population may be divided into the Brazilian Highlands, or plateau, in the south and the Amazon River Basin in the north. Over a third of the nation is drained by the Amazon River and its more than 200 tributaries. This area, covered by the tropical rain forest, is not well suited for agriculture. In fact, only 5 per cent of Brazil's land is arable.
2. GUYANA is a nation located north of Brazil with a population of well under one million people. The former British colony became independent in 1966 and uses English as its official language.
3. SURINAME was a former Dutch colony which was granted independence in1975. The country of under half a million ethnically diverse people exports lumber, aluminum and oil from recently discovered fields.
4. FRENCH GUIANA located north of Brazil and east of Suriname is an Oversees Department of France. The French used the area as its penal colony from 1852 to 1939. Today, only 5 percent of the population which consists of under 200,000 people favor independence from France.

Rainforest along the Amazon River

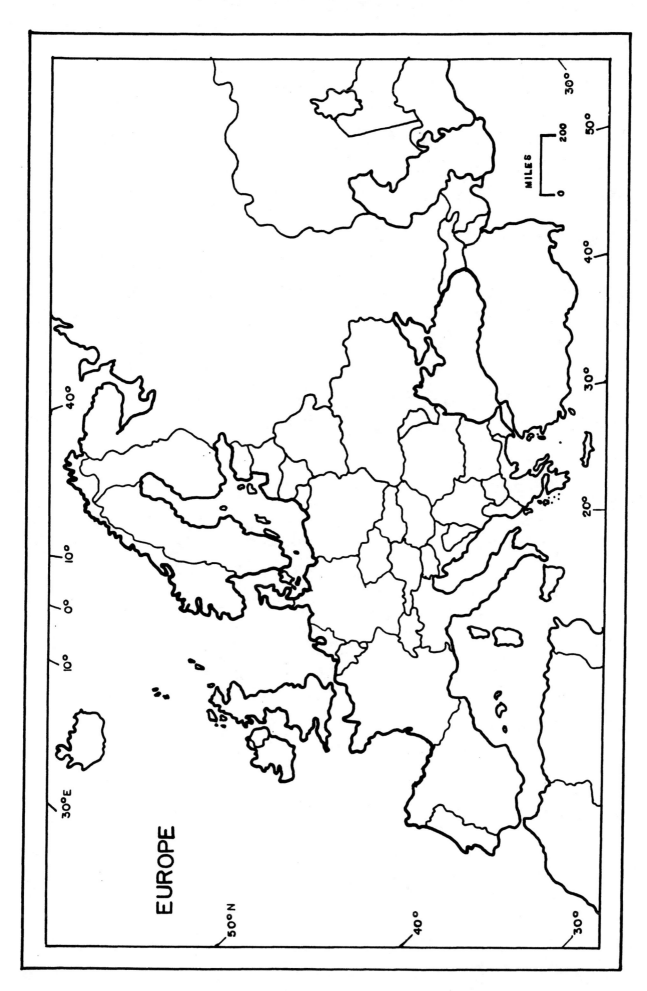

EUROPE

211

# EUROPE

Iceland

Norway Sweden Finland

Estonia
Latvia
Lithuania

Russia

Denmark

Ireland

United Kingdom

Netherlands

Belgium Germany

Luxembourg

Poland

Belarus

Czech

Ukraine

France

Liechtenstein

Austria Slovakia

Moldova

Switzerland

Hungary

Slovenia

Romania

Monaco

Croatia

Bosnia

Serbia

Portugal

Spain

Italy

Andorra

Vatican
City

Albania

Bulgaria

Macedonia

Greece

Malta

Cyprus

EUROPE

The micro states of Europe:

Scandinavian Nations:

Benelux nations:

Former Republics of the Soviet Union:

Nations comprising former Yugoslavia:

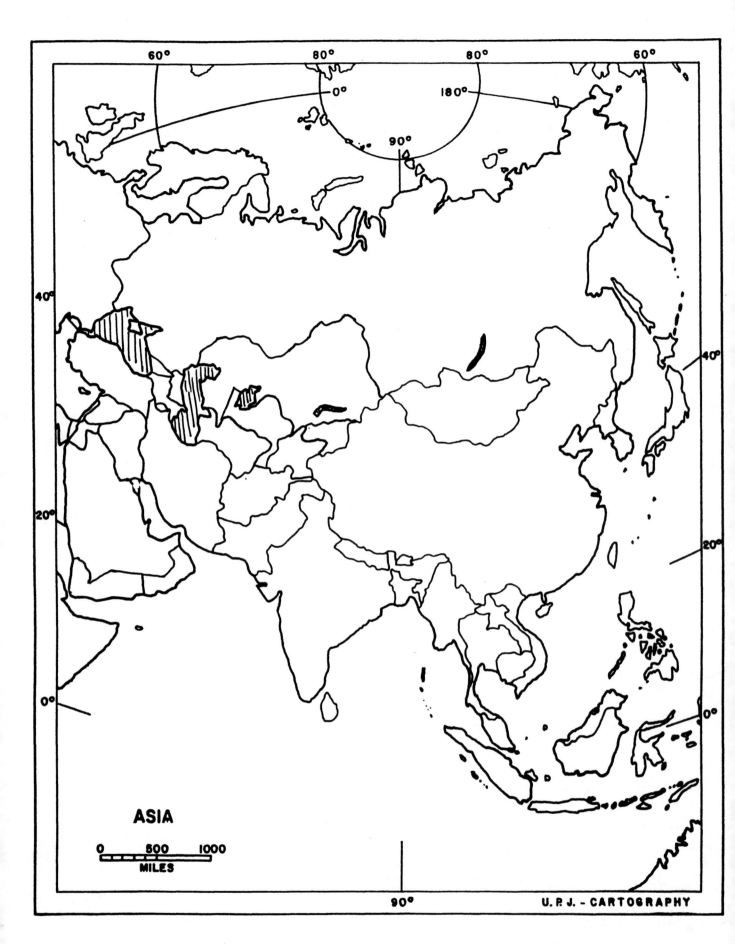

ASIA

0     500     1000
MILES

60°     80°     80°     60°

0°     180°

90°

40°

20°

0°

90°

U. P. J. - CARTOGRAPHY

ASIA

Nations of Asia with over 100,000,000 people:

| Nation | Total Population |
| --- | --- |
| 1. | |
| 2. | |
| 3. | |
| 4. | |
| 5. | |
| 6. | |

Five nations located east of the Caspian Sea which were the former Republics of the Soviet Union:

1.

2.

3.

4.

5.

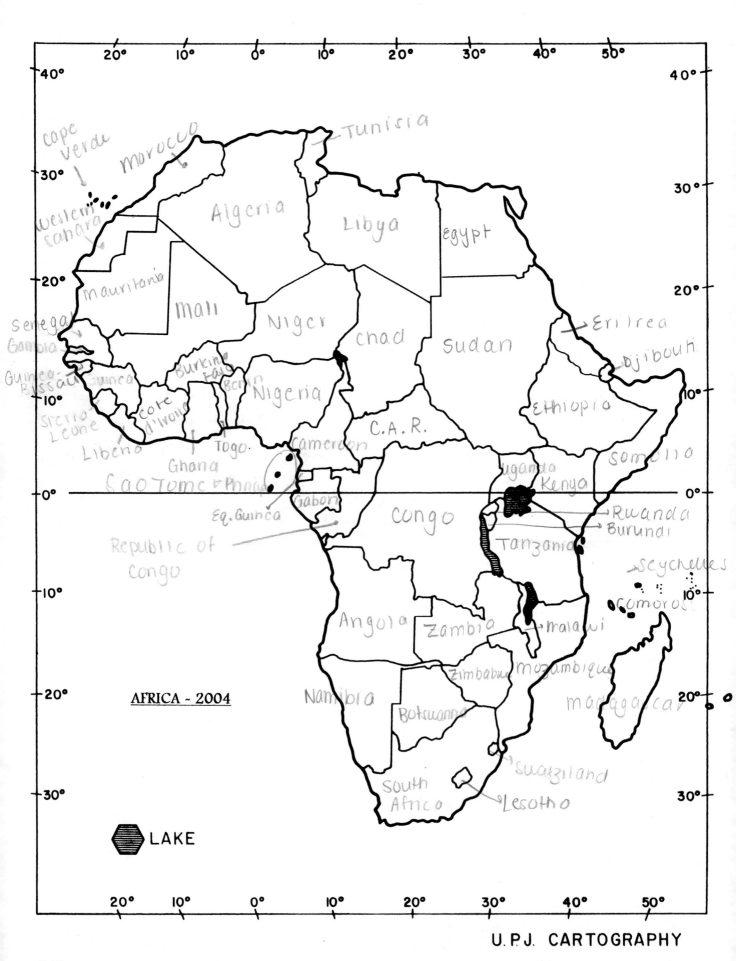

AFRICA ~ 2004

LAKE

U.P.J. CARTOGRAPHY

216

## AFRICA

INDEPENDENT ISLAND NATIONS AROUND AFRICA:

Landlocked Nations of Africa:

Nations of Africa bordering the Indian Ocean (excluding the island nations)
1.

2.

3.

4.

5.

African nations bordering the Mediterranean Sea
1.

2.

3.

4.

5.

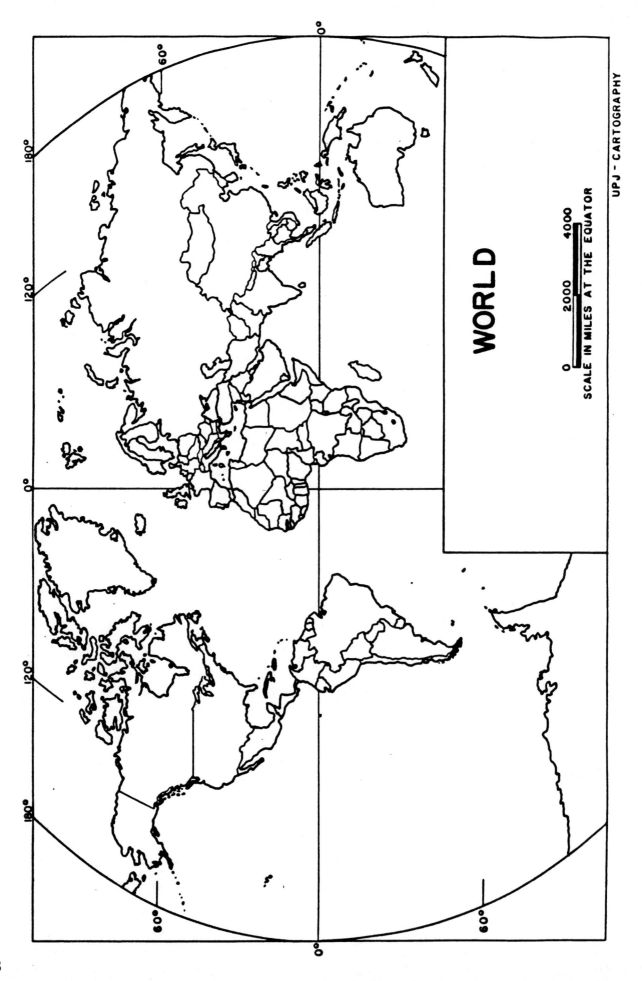

WORLD

SCALE IN MILES AT THE EQUATOR

0    2000    4000

UPJ – CARTOGRAPHY

THE WORLD

What are the FIVE largest nations in the world (in area)

    Name             Area (in square miles)

1.

2.

3.

4.

5.


The most populous nations in

NORTH AMERICA –

SOUTH AMERICA –

AFRICA –

ASIA –

EUROPE –

What does this map shows ?

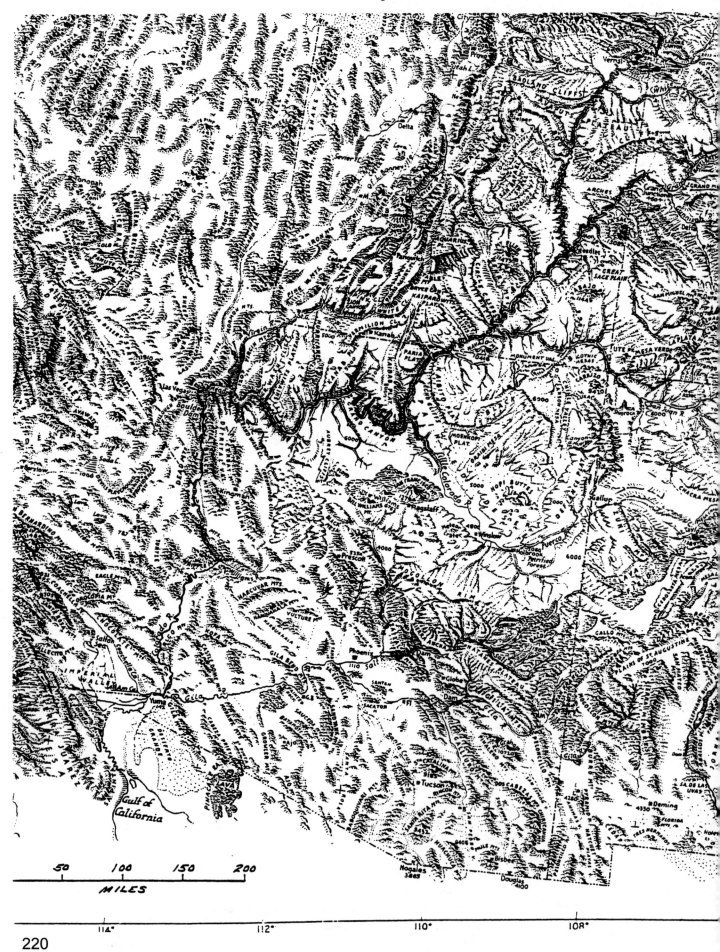

50    100    150    200

MILES

114°        112°        110°        108°

220

**AFRICA:** To enhance geographic research and scholarship on matters relating to Africa by encouraging effective communication of knowledge and information and supporting innovative approaches to geographic education on Africa. Dues $3 (student $2). Barbara E. McDade, Department of Geography, University of Florida, Gainesville FL 32611-7315 Voice 904-392-0494 Fax 904-392-8855 Internet bmcdade@nervm.nerdc.ufl.edu

**AGING AND THE AGED:** To support research, teaching, and service pertaining to the geography of aging and the aged. Dues $2 (student $0). Susan Macey, Department of Geography and Planning, Southwest Texas State University, San Marcos TX 78666-4616 Voice 512-245-3903 Fax 512-245-8353 Internet sm07@swt.edu

**AMERICAN ETHNIC GEOGRAPHY:** To promote the common interests of persons working in American ethnic geography, to provide a forum for the exchange of ideas and information for its members, and to undertake activities within the AAG. Dues $5 (student $3). Douglas Heffington, Department of Geography and Geology, Middle Tennessee State University, Murfreesboro TN 37132 Voice 615-898-2726 Fax 615-898-5592 Internet jheffing@frank.mtsu.edu URL http://everest.hunter.cuny.edu/aegsg

**AMERICAN INDIAN:** To foster communication and the pursuit of shared concerns among the group's membership and others, including research, education, and the application of knowledge in all geographic and related matters involving past, present, and future cultures, habitats, economies, and societies of American Indians and other indigenous peoples of North America. Dues $5 (student $5). Douglas Heffington, Department of Geography and Geology, Middle Tennessee State University, Murfreesboro TN 37132 Voice 615-898-2726 Fax 615-898-5592 Internet jheffing@frank.mtsu.edu

**APPLIED GEOGRAPHY:** To increase the visibility of applied geography in the profession and the general population; promote and facilitate communications among the Group members; promote and recognize individual excellence in applied geographic research. Dues $5 (student $0). Nancy Torrieri, Demographic Statistical Methods Division, Bldg 3 Rm 3725, US Bureau of the Census, Suitland MD 20746 Voice 301-457-3602 Fax 301-457-8611 Internet nancy.k.torrieri@ccmail.census.gov URL http://agsg.freac.fsu.edu

**ASIAN GEOGRAPHY:** To promote geographic research and to facilitate teaching the geography of Asia through professional meetings, publications and establishing contacts with Asian geographers, and developing an agenda for research and teaching grants. Dues $5 (student $5). Members receive the Bulletin of Asian Geography edited by Bimal K. Paul, Department of Geography, Kansas State University, Manhattan, KS 66506. Thomas R. Leinbach, Department of Geography, University of Kentucky, Lexington KY 40506-0027 Voice 606-257-1276 Fax 606-323-1969 Internet leinbach@ukcc.uky.edu URL http://www.uky.edu/ArtsSciences/Geography/AGSG/Welcome.htm

**BIBLE:** To use the Bible as a source of geographic information for the study of the geography of ancient Israel. Dues $1 (student $1). William A. Dando, Department of Geography, Geology and Anthropology, Indiana State University, Terre Haute IN 47809 Voice 812-237-2444 Fax 812-237-8029 Internet gedando@scifac.indstate.edu

**BIOGEOGRAPHY:** To promote interactions between biogeographers, stimulate active research and teaching development in biogeography, and facilitate the exchange of ideas. Dues $7.50 (student $5). George Malanson, Department of Geography, University of Iowa, Iowa City IA 52242-1316 Voice 319-335-0158 Fax 319-335-2725 Internet george-malanson@uiowa.edu URL http://www.geocities.com/RainForest/2498/bsghome.htm

**CANADIAN STUDIES:** To stimulate a more visible series of activities and increased research on Canadian topics. Dues $3 (student $3). Peter H. Meserve, Geography/Geology, Columbia College, Columbia MO 65216 Voice 573-875-7630 Fax 573-875-7209 Internet pmeserve@mail.coin.missouri.edu URL http://web.syr.edu/~tppratt/cssgmain.html

**CARTOGRAPHY:** To encourage cartographic research, promote education in cartography and map use, and facilitate the exchange of ideas and information about cartography, promote interest in and correct utilization of maps and other cartographic products, promote and facilitate the cartographer's role within the geographic profession, promote and coordinate activities and directions with other professional organizations involved with cartography. Dues $6 (student $2). Scott Freundschuh, Department of Geography, University of Minnesota, Duluth MN 55812 Voice 218-726-6226 Fax 218-726-6386 Internet sfreuds@d.um.edu URL http://www.csun.edu/~hfgeg003/csg

**CHINA:** To promote the study of the geography of China, including Taiwan, and to serve as a clearinghouse of information for persons interested in Chinese geography. To increase contacts with Chinese geographers and encourage professional activities, including the development of research projects. Dues $3 (student $1). K.C. Tan, Department of Geography, University of Guelph, Guelph ON, Canada N1G 2W1 Voice 519-824-4120 Fax 519-837-2940 Internet kctan@uoguelph.ca

**CLIMATE:** To support research and teaching in climatology, especially as part of the discipline of geography. Dues $5 (student $1). Robert E. Davis, Department of Environmental Sciences, University of Virginia, Charlottesville VA 22903 Voice 804-924-7761 Fax 804-982-2137 Internet red3u@virginia.edu URL http://www.geog.ucla.edu/csghome.html

**COASTAL AND MARINE:** To encourage the intellectual exchange of knowledge related to coastal and marine environments and resources. Dues $3 (student $1). Paul Gares, Department of Geography and Planning, East Carolina University, Greenville NC 27858-4353 Voice 919-328-6084 Fax 919-328-6054 Internet gegares@ecuvm.cis.ecu.edu URL http://www.ecu.edu/geog/faculty/gares/gares.html

**CONTEMPORARY AGRICULTURE AND RURAL LAND USE:** To promote the common interests of geographers working on agriculture and rural land use problems in the U.S., Canada, and other developed countries. Dues $4 (student $2). Lisa Harrington, Department of Geography, Kansas State University, Manhattan KS 66506-0801 Voice 785-532-6727 Fax 785-532-7310 Internet lharrin@ksu.edu

**CRYOSPHERE:** To foster communication between practitioners dealing with the various elements of the cryosphere, to establish linkages with related organizations, and to enhance research on and teaching of cryospheric topics. Dues $5 (student $0). Brian Hanson. Department of Geography, University of Delaware, Newark DE 19716 Voice 302-831-8268 Fax 302-831-6654 Internet hanson@udel.edu

**CULTURAL ECOLOGY:** To promote and conduct scholarly activities on cultural ecological topics ranging from pre-history to third world development, and from environmental to economic problems. Dues $5 (student $0). Oliver Coomes, Department of Geography, McGill University, 805 Sherbrooke St W, Montreal QC, Canada H3A 2K6 Voice 514-398-4943 Fax 514-398-7437 Internet coomes@felix.geog.mcgill.ca URL http://www.cwu.edu/~geograph/cult.html

**CULTURAL GEOGRAPHY:** To encourage and facilitate intellectual exchange between scholars of all ages working in every branch of the subfield of cultural geography, Dues $5 (student $2). Garth A. Myers, Department of Geography, University of Kansas, Lawrence KS 66045-2121 Voice 785-864-4291 Fax 785-864-5378 Internet gmyers@falcon.cc.ukans.edu URL http://www.geocities.com/Athens/5802/cgsg.html

**ECONOMIC GEOGRAPHY:** To facilitate the exchange of information and ideas among its members and other specialists; to stimulate research, teaching, and applications in industrial and economic geography; to aid in the advancement of its members and the field of industrial and economic geography; and to help represent industrial and economic geography within the discipline of geography and to related disciplines, agencies in government, the private sector, and the general public. Dues $5 (student $0). J.W. Harrington, Department of Geography, University of Washington, Box 353550, Seattle WA 98195-3550 Voice 206-543-5843 Fax 206-543-3313 Internet jwh@u.washington.edu

**ENERGY AND ENVIRONMENT:** To promote interaction and research among geographers interested in energy and environmental issues, to enhance the contributions of geographers to energy and environmental research and practice, and to assist in developing related educational curricula. Dues $4 (student $2). Martin J. (Mike) Pasqualetti, Department of Geography, Arizona State University, Tempe AZ 85287-0104 Voice 602-965-4548 Fax 602-965-8313 Internet pasqualetti@asu.edu URL http://saguaro.la.asu.edu/eesg/

**ENVIRONMENTAL PERCEPTION AND BEHAVIORAL GEOGRAPHY:** To advance the theoretical and applied interests of environmental perception and behavioral geography within the discipline of geography, developing links to related disciplines through communication and organization. Dues $5 (student $1). Christina (Tina) Kennedy, Department of Geography and Public Planning, Northern Arizona University, NAU Box 15016, Flagstaff AZ 86011-5016 Voice 520-523-0983 Fax 520-523-1080 Internet tina.kennedy@nau.edu URL http://geog.ucsb.edu/epbg

**EUROPEAN:** To foster research, teaching, and scholarly interaction on the geography of Europe. broadly defined; to promote work on all parts of Europe and to advance scholarship that moves beyond the traditional East-West bifurcation of the continent; to promote the study of Europe within the discipline of geography; and to encourage contacts between its members and those working on Europe in other disciplines, government, and private agencies. Dues $4 (student $2). Boian Koulov, School of International Service, American University, 4400 Massachusetts Ave NW, Washington DC 20016-8071 Voice 202-885-2463 Fax 202-885-2494 Internet bkoulov@american.edu URL http://ezinfo.ucs.indiana.edu/~aagesg/home.html

**GEOGRAPHIC INFORMATION SYSTEMS:** To promote the development and practice in computer-based hardware, software and graphic capabilities that encode, analyze and display natural, cultural and economic information. Dues $4 (student $0). Stephen Walsh, Department of Geography, University of North Carolina, Chapel Hill NC 27599-3220 Voice 919-962-3867 Fax 919-962-1537 Internet walsh@geog.unc.edu URL http://www.cla.sc.edu/gis/aaggis.html

**GEOGRAPHIC PERSPECTIVES ON WOMEN:** To promote geographic research and education on topics relating to women and gender. Dues $5 (student $0). Karen Falconer Al-Hindi, Department of Geography and Geology, University of Nebraska, Omaha NE 68182-0199 Voice 402-554-3585 Fax 402-554-3518 Internet falconer@unomaha.edu URL http://www.masu.nodak.edu/hssdiv/meartz/gpow/gpow.htm

**GEOGRAPHY EDUCATION:** To promote research, development, and practice in the learning and teaching of geography and to examine and strengthen the role of geography in education by focusing on the development of learners, teachers, curricula, and programs. Dues $2 (student $1). James M. Dunn, PO Box 6115, Boulder CO 80306-6115 Voice 303-440-7505 Fax 303-440-1322 Internet jmdgigi@aol.com URL http://www.colorado.edu/geography/COGA/geoed/

**GEOGRAPHY OF RELIGIONS AND BELIEF SYSTEMS:** To further the geographic study of religious phenomena, including but not limited to religious groups, behavior, material culture, and human-environment relations from a religious perspective. Dues $5 (student $1). Richard H. Jackson, Department of Geography, Brigham Young University, Provo UT 84602 Voice 801-378-6063 Fax 801-378-5978 Internet geosec@fhss.byu.edu URL http://www.ndsu.nodak.edu/instruct/balachan/sp_grps/gorabs/

**GEOMORPHOLOGY:** To foster better communication among those working in the geomorphic sciences, especially in geography. Dues $7 (student $0). Jeffrey Lee, Department of Economics and Geography, Texas Tech University, Lubbock TX 79409-1014 Voice 806-742-2201 Fax 806-742-1137 Internet j.lee@ttu.edu URL http://www.cla.sc.edu/geog/gsgdocs/home.html

**HAZARDS:** To promote research, education, and the application of knowledge about natural, technological, and social hazards; to strengthen communication and collaborative activities among geographers pertaining to hazards; to encourage communication between geographers and the members of other disciplines and professions that share an interest in hazards. Dues $5 (student $2). Burrell E. Montz, Department of Geography, Binghamton University, Binghamton NY 13902-6000 Voice 607-777-2615 Fax 607-777-2288 Internet bmontz@binghamton.edu URL http://www.cla.sc.edu/geog/hrl/hsg/index.html

**HISTORICAL GEOGRAPHY:** To promote the common interests of persons in the field, provide a forum for the discussion of matters that pertain to the membership, and establish procedures for activities within the AAG. Dues $10 (student $1). James R. Shortridge, Department of Geography, University of Kansas, Lawrence KS 66045-2121 Voice 785-864-5539 Internet shortrid@falcon.cc.ukans.edu URL http://www.maxwell.syr.edu/geo/histgeo/histgeo.htm

**HISTORY OF GEOGRAPHY:** To promote research and the exchange of information pertaining to the history of geography and advance scholarship that contributes to a deeper understanding of the evolution of the discipline. Dues $4 (student $0). Paul B. Frederic, Department of Social Sciences & Business, University of Maine, Farmington ME 04938-1720 Voice 207-778-7442 Fax 207-778-7452 Internet frederic@mail.caps.maine.edu URL http://www.geog.psu.edu/HoG

**HUMAN DIMENSIONS OF GLOBAL CHANGE:** To promote the varied interests of geographers who are united by research, teaching, or service that in one way or another involves the human dimensions of global-scale processes that affect or are affected by environmental changes. Dues $5 (student $1). Brent Yarnal, Department of Geography and Earth System Science Center, Pennsylvania State University, University Park PA 16802-5011 Voice 814-863-4894 or 8017 Fax 814-863-8018 Internet alibar@essc.psu.edu URL http://www.geog.utah.edu/~hdgcsg/index.html

**HUMAN RIGHTS:** To encourage scholarly geographic research and teaching about human rights issues, as well as to encourage a sustained interest in human rights concerns at all scales of analysis, in all parts of the world, for all time periods. Dues $4 (student $0). Jeremy J. Brigham, Department of Geography, University of Iowa, Iowa City IA 52242-1316 Voice 319-335-0165 Internet jbrigham@uiowa.edu

**LATIN AMERICAN:** To promote education, research and other activity relating to Latin American geography and to advance communication among geographers and others with an interest in the region. Dues $5 (student $1). Deborah A. Salazar, Department of Geography, Oklahoma State University, Stillwater OK 74078 Voice 405-744-3293 Fax 405-744-5620 Internet salazar@okstate.edu

**MATHEMATICAL MODELS AND QUANTITATIVE METHODS:** To aid and enhance research and teaching on mathematical models, statistical methods and other computational approaches in geography, and to promote their application in the form of scientific methodology in all subfields of geography. Dues $3 (student $1). Harvey Miller, Department of Geography, University of Utah, 260 S Central Campus Dr Rm 270, Salt Lake City UT 84112-9155 Voice 801-585-3972 Fax 801-581-8219 Internet harvey.miller@geog.utah.edu URL http://www.geog.utah.edu/~hmiller

**MEDICAL GEOGRAPHY:** To provide a forum for disseminating research on geographical epidemiology, spatial aspects of health care delivery, health care policy and the political economy of health care, and ethnomedicine and to promote medical geography within the discipline of geography and to related disciplines, agencies in government and the private sector, and the general public. Dues $5 (student $5). Mark W. Rosenberg, Department of Geography, Queen's University, Kingston ON, Canada K7L 3N6 Voice 613-545-6030 Fax 613-545-6122 Internet rosenber@post.queensu.ca URL http://www.pop.psu.edu/aag/mgsg.html

**MICROCOMPUTERS:** To investigate ways in which microcomputers can be used as a tool in geographical research and teaching and to provide a forum for the exchange of information and knowledge regarding the use of microcomputers. *Nonmember newsletter subscription $6. Dues $4 (student $1). Gregory Chu, Department of Geography and Earth Science, University of Wisconsin, La Crosse WI 54601 Voice 608-785-6675 Fax 608-785-8332 Internet chu@mail.uwlax.edu URL http://lambert.ship.edu

**MILITARY GEOGRAPHY:** To promote research and the exchange of information pertaining to military geography and advance scholarship that contributes to a deeper understanding of the discipline. This field is broadly defined to include those interested in physical, human, cultural, political, remote sensing, GIS, and other applications as they relate to military or security issues. Dues $5 (student $3). Mike Besch, 37 Castle Blvd, Akron OH 44313 Voice 330-972-7059 Fax 330-972-4904 Internet besch@cc.uakron.edu

**POLITICAL GEOGRAPHY:** To provide a central focus and organization for political geographers by which they can achieve scholarly growth and to improve the status and cohesion of the subdiscipline. Dues $4 (student $4). Jeff R. Crump, Department of Geography, Western Illinois University, Macomb IL 61455 Voice 309-298-2956 Fax 309-298-2400 Internet jr_crump@wiu.edu URL http://garnet.acns.fsu.edu/~dpurcell

**POPULATION:** To promote research, teaching, and service in the general field of population geography, to stimulate the exchange of information among members of the group, to encourage the development of population geography as a science and a profession, and to develop close relations and interchange with other sciences. Dues $8 (student $2). Brigitte Waldorf, Department of Geography & Regional Development, University of Arizona, Harvill Box 2, Tucson AZ 85721 Voice 520-621-7486 Fax 520-621-2889 Internet bwaldorf@ccit.arizona.edu URL http://www.pop.psu.edu/aag/psg.html

**RECREATION, TOURISM, AND SPORT:** To provide a forum and to encourage research and teaching of applied and academic aspects of recreation, tourism, and sport geography. Dues $3 (student $1). Barbara Carmichael, Department of Geography, Wilfrid Laurier University, Waterloo ON, Canada N2L 3C5 Voice 519-884-1970 Fax 519-725-1342 Internet bcarmichael@mach1.wlu.ca URL http:\\www.for.nau.edu/geography/rts

**REGIONAL DEVELOPMENT AND PLANNING:** To encourage and promote research, teaching, service and communication among members of the group; to publish and distribute newsletters twice a year featuring upcoming activities and other items of interest. Organize special sessions or events at AAG meetings. Dues $2 (student $1). George M. Pomeroy, Department of Geography and Planning, University of Akron, Akron OH 44325-5005 Voice 330-972-7620 Fax 330-972-6080 Internet pomeroy@uakron.edu

**REMOTE SENSING:** To foster an understanding of remote sensing science. Emphasis is placed on developing a meaningful dialogue among geographers interested in understanding and applying remote sensing technology in research, instruction, public service, and private enterprise. Dues $5 (student $1). William A. Tyler, ERIM International, Earth Sciences Group, PO Box 134008, Ann Arbor MI 48113-4008 Voice 734-994-1200, ext 3609 Fax 734-665-6559 Internet tyler@erim-int.com URL http://www.earthsensing.com/rssg/index.html

**RURAL DEVELOPMENT:** To promote sharing of ideas and information among geographers interested in the many facets of rural development. Dues $4 (student $2). Bradley H. Baltensperger, Department of Social Sciences, Michigan Technological University, Houghton MI 49931 Voice 906-487-2113 Fax 906-487-2468 Internet brad@mtu.edu

**RUSSIAN, CENTRAL EURASIAN, AND EAST EUROPEAN:** To promote the professional competence and knowledgeability of its members for Russian, Central Eurasian, and East European region and to enhance communication among members. Dues $8 (student $0). Beth Mitchneck, Department of Geography and Regional Development, University of Arizona, Tucson AZ 85721 Voice 602-621-9681 Fax 602-621-2289 Internet bethm@u.arizona.edu URL http://weber.u.washington.edu/~reecas/RCEEE-SG/

**SEXUALITY AND SPACE:** To promote and facilitate scholarly and other geographic inquiry into human sexualities and related issues. Dues $5 (student $2). Glen Elder, Department of Geography, University of Vermont, Burlington VT 54170 Voice 802-656-3060 Fax 802-656-3042 Internet gelder@zoo.uvm.edu & Heidi J. Nast, International Relations, DePaul University, 2320 N Kenmore Ave, Chicago IL 60614-3298 Voice 773-325-7882 Fax 773-325-7452 Internet hnast@wppost.depaul.edu URL http://www.ndsu.nodak.edu/instruct/balachan/sp_grps/sassg/

**SOCIALIST GEOGRAPHY:** To promote critical analysis of geographic phenomena, cognizant of geographic research on the well-being of social classes; to investigate the issue of radical change toward a more collective society; and to discover the impact of economic growth upon environmental quality and upon social equity. Dues $6 (student $0). Andrew J. Herod, Department of Geography, University of Georgia, Athens GA 30602-2502 Voice 706-542-2856 Fax 706-542-2388 URL http://www.staff.uiuc.edu/~dwilson2/sgsg.html

**TRANSPORTATION GEOGRAPHY:** To develop transportation geography as a subfield of the discipline. Dues $5 (student $4). Mike Kuby, Department of Geography, Arizona State University, Tempe AZ 85287-0104 Voice 602-965-6850 Fax 602-965-8313 Internet mikekuby@imap1.asu.edu URL http://web.syr.edu/~rcaxsiom/TGSG.HTML

**URBAN GEOGRAPHY:** To facilitate communication of information and ideas among urban geographers and other urban specialists through a newsletter, meetings, correspondence and other media. Dues $7 (student $0). Helga Leitner, Department of Geography, University of Minnesota, Minneapolis MN 55455 Voice 612-625-9010 Fax 612-624-1044 Internet eqj6139@vx.acs.umn.edu URL http://www.staff.uiuc.edu/~dgrammen/ugsg.html

**VALUES, ETHICS, AND JUSTICE:** To support inclusive and informed discussion by geographers throughout the discipline on substantive and professional normative concerns, both theoretical and applied, working together with existing AAG Specialty Groups and Committees whose areas of focus touch on these concerns. Dues $3 (student $0). James D. Proctor, Department of Geography, 3611 Ellison Hall, University of California, Santa Barbara CA 93106-4060 Voice 805-893-8741 Fax 805-893-3146 Internet jproctor@geog.ucsb.edu URL http://www.geog.ucsb.edu/vejsg

**WATER RESOURCES:** To provide its membership with services that enhance professional opportunities to communicate research progress and results within the professional community and to announce events and discuss major developments in the field of water resources. Dues $5 (student $2). William C. Rense, Department of Geography & Earth Science, Shippensburg University of Pennsylvania, 1871 Old Main Drive, Shippensburg PA 17257-2299 Voice 717-532-1662 Fax 717-530-4029 Internet wcrens@ark.ship.edu URL http://www.geog.ucla.edu/wrsghome.html

# AFFINITY GROUPS

**COMMUNITY COLLEGE:** Seeks to give community college geographers a stronger voice within the discipline and within the AAG by disseminating information about funding opportunities for projects relevant to community college geography, enhancing research and professional development opportunities for community college faculty, and promoting curriculum development of GIS and other technical areas. Dues $1 (student $1). Joan Clemons, 3240 Tilden Ave, Los Angeles CA 90034 Voice 310-825-7053 Fax 310-206-4743 Internet jclemons@msn.com

**RETIRED GEOGRAPHERS:** Provides opportunities for retirees to keep in contact with colleagues and professional friends through newsletters, distinctive travel opportunities, social activities, and service projects. Dues $10. Robert A. Harper, 410 Deer Lake Dr W, Carbondale IL 62901 Voice 618-457-7081 Internet raharper@midwest.net

Selected Bibliography

Abrahams, Peter W. & Parsons, Julia A.; "Geography in the Tropics: A Literature Review", The Geographical Journal, Vol. 162, #1, March 1996, pp. 63-72.

Aguado, Edward and James E. Burt; Understanding Weather and Climate, Prentice Hall, NJ, 2006.

Alwin, John A.; "North American Geographers and the Pacific Rim: Leaders or Laggards", The Professional Geographer, Vol. 44, #4, November 1992, pp. 369-376.

Andrews, Sona Karentz; "Applications of a Cartographic Model to Tactual Map Design", The American Cartographer, Vol. 15, #2, April 1988, pp. 183-196.

Auty, Richard M.; "Third World Response to Global Process: The Mineral Economies", Professional Geographer, Vol. 43, #1, February 1991, pp. 68-75.

Bailey, Adrian J. & Ellis, Mark; "Going Home: The Migration of Puerto Rican Born Women from the United States to Puerto Rico." The Professional Geographer, Vol. 45, #2, May 1993, pp. 148-158.

Baker, Earl J.; "Public Responses to Hurricane Probability Forecasts", The Professional Geographer, Vol. 47, #2, May 1995, pp.137-147.

Barnes, Kent; "Geographical Information Systems and Water Resources: An Assessment and Survey of Applications." The Pennsylvania Geographer, Vol. 32, #1, Spring/Summer 1994, pp. 47-59.

Begg, Robert B.; "Pennsylvania in the International Economy", The Pennsylvania Geographer, Vol. XXX, #2, Fall/Winter 1992, pp. 3-20.

Bencloski, Joseph W. & Tepper, Leonard P.; "Population Concentration and Redistribution in Pennsylvania 1850-1990", The Pennsylvania Geographer, Vol. XXX, #1, Spring/Summer 1992, pp. 3-12.

Bierly, Gregory D.: "An Investigation of the Influence of Cyclonic Airstreams on Midwestern Snowfall", Professional Geography, Vol. 51, No. 3, August 1999, pp.340-348.

Blacksell, Mark; Political Geography, Routledge, New York, 2004.

Blouet, Brian W., "The Political Geography of Europe: 1900-2000 A. D." Journal of Geography, Vol. 95, #1, January/February 1996, pp. 5-14.

Bonner, Nigel W.; "The Future of Antarctic Resources", The Geographical Journal, Vol. 152, #3, July 1986, pp. 248-255.

Bosh, Patricia K.; "The Oceans: Their Hidden Treasures", The Journal of Geography, Vol. 90, #4, July-August 1991, pp. 182-188.

Bromley, Rosemary D.F. & Jones, Gareth A.; "Identifying the Inner City in Latin America", The Geographical Journal, Vol. 162, #2, July 1996, pp.179-190.

Brunn, Stanley D.; "A World of Peace and Landscapes", Journal of Geography, Vol. 86, #6, Nov./Dec. 1987, pp. 253-260.

Buckwalter, Donald W.; "Pennsylvania and the Changing Economic Geography of the United States", The Pennsylvania Geographer, Vol. 30, #2, Fall/Winter 1992, pp.37-54.

Butler, David R.; "Teaching Natural Hazards: The Use of Snow Avalanches in Demonstrating and Principles", Journal of Geography, Vol. 87, #6, Nov.-Dec. 1988, pp. 212-221.

Butzer, Karl W.; "From Columbus to Acosta: Science, Geography and the New World", The Annals of the AAG, Vol. 82, #3, September 1992, pp. 543-566.

Byklum, Daryl; "Geography and Music: Making the Connection", Journal of Geography, Vol. 93, #6, Nov.-Dec. 1994, pp. 274-278.

Campbell, James B.; Map Use and Analysis, McGraw/Hill, New York, 2001.

Carter, Harold; The Study of Urban Geography, Edward Arnold, London, 2005.

Castles, Stephen and Mark J. Miller; The age of Migration: International Population Movement in the Modern World, Guilford Press, New York, 2003.

Cohen, Joel E.; "Human Population Grows Up", Scientific American, pp. 48-55, September 2005.

Cope, Meghan; "Participation, Power, and Policy: Developing a Gender-Sensitive Political Geography", Journal of Geography, Vol. 96, #2, March/April 1997, pp.91-96.

Cox, Kevin R.; Political Geography, Blackwell Publishing, Malden, Massachusetts, 2002.

Cutter, Susan and William H. Renwick; Exploitation, Conservation, Preservation: A Geographic Perspective on Natural Resource Use, John Wiley and Sons, New York, 2003.

Diamond, Jared; Collapse: How Societies Choose to Fail or Succeed, Viking Press, New York, 2005.

deBlij, Harm; Why Geography Matters, Oxford University Press, New York, 2005.

Dow, Kirstin; "Caught in the Currents: Pollution, Risk, and Environmental Change in Marine Space.", The Professional Geographer, Vol. 51, #3, August 1999, pp. 414-426.

Eflin, James C. and Julie T. Eflin; "Thinking Critically about Global Environmental Issues", Journal of Geography, Vol. 98, #2, March/April 1999, pp. 68-78.

Enger, Eldon D. and Bradley F. Smith; Environmental Science: A Study of Interrelationships, McGraw/Hill, Boston, 2004.

Fowler, W. M.; Empires at War, Walker and Company, New York, 2005.

Geiger, Charles; Pennsylvania's Landscapes and People, Kendall/Hunt Publishing Company, Dubuque, Iowa, 2005.

Getis, Arthur, Getis Judith and Fellmann, Jerome D.; Introduction to Geography, McGraw/Hill, Boston, 2006.

"Global Warming", National Geographic Magazine, Washington, D.C., pp. 2-75, September 2004.

Higgs, Linda S; "Where Will the Garbage go?, The Future of Landfills Sitting in Pennsylvania." The Pennsylvania Geographer, Vol. 30, #2, Fall 1992, pp. 80-86.

Harley, J.B. and Woodward, David; "Why Cartography Needs its History", American Cartographer, Vol. 16, #1, January 1989, pp. 5-15.

Hartman, Jeffery and Ingoil Vogelor; "Where in the World is the U.S.?" Journal of Geography, Vol. 92, January 1993, pp. 2-11.

Hartshorne, Richard; "Where in the World are We?, Geographic Understanding for Political Survival and Progress," Journal of Geography, Vol.89, #5, September 1990, pp. 198-201.

Hausladen, Gary J; " Murder in Moscow," The Geographical Review, Vol. 50, March 1995, pp. 63-77.

Haverluk, Terence; "The Changing Geography of U.S. Hispanics, 1850-1990", Journal of Geography, Vol. 96, #3, May/June 1997, pp. 134-145.

Henderson, Martha L; "Cultural Diversity in Geography Curriculum, The Geography of American Indians." Journal of Geography, Vol. 90-91, October 1991-1992, pp. 113-122.

Griffith, Daniel A., Philip G. Doyle, David L. Wheeler, David Johnson; "A Tale of Two Swaths: Urban Childhood Blood-Lead Levels Across Syracuse, NY", Annals of the Association of American Geographers, Vol. 88, #4, December, 1998, pp. 640-665

Holloway, Steven R. and Wheeler, James O; "Corporate Headquarters Relocation and changes in Metropolitan Corporate Dominance," Economic Geography, Vol. 67, #1, January 1991, pp.54-72.

Hupy, J.P. et al; "Mapping Soils, Vegetation and Landforms: An Integrative Physical Geography Field Experience", Professional; Geographer, Vol. 57, #3, August 2005, pp. 438-45

Hull, Suzanne; "Mapping Migration: Experiencing Geography through Travelers Diaries", Journal of Geography, Vol. 93, #4, July 1994, pp. 172-179.

"Inequality in Latin America: A Stubborn Curse", The Economist, November 6, 2003.

Kaplan, David, James O. Wheeler and Steven Holloway; Urban Geography, John Wiley and Sons, New York, 2004.

Kinsella, Kevin and David R. Phillips; "Global Aging: The Challenge of Success", Population Bulletin 60, #1, Population Reference Bureau, Washington, D.C., 2005.

Klare, Michae; "The New Geography of Conflict", Foreign Affairs, Vol. 80, No. 3, 2001, pp. 49-61.

Knox, J.W. and E.K. Weatherfield; "The Application of GIS to Irrigation Water Resource Management in England and Wales", The Geographical Journal, Vol. 165, #1, March 1999, pp. 90-98.

Kump, Lee, James Kasting, and Robert crane; The Earth System, Prentice Hall, NJ, 2003.

Marsh, William M. and John M. Grossa; Environmental Geography: Science, Land Use, and Earth Systems, John Wiley and Sons, New York, 2004.

Martin, Geoffrey J.; All Possible Worlds: A History of Geographical Ideas, Oxford University Press, New York, 2005.

McVey, David; "Reexamining Russia's Geographical Identity", A Case for Historical Eurasianism", The Pennsylvania Geographer, Vol. 44, #1, pp. 50-63, Spring/Summer 2006.

Mitchell, Don; Cultural Geography: A Critical Introduction, Blackwell Publishing, Malden, MA, 2005.

Mitchell, Jennifer; "Before the Next Doubling", World Watch, January/February 1998, pp. 20-27.

Newbold, K. Bruce; Six Billion Plus: World Population in the Twenty-First Century, Rowman and Littlefield Publishers, Inc., New York, 2007.

Pannell, Clifton W. and Jeffrey S. Torguson; "Interpreting Spatial Patterns from the 1990 China Census" The Geographical Review, Vol. 81, #3, July 1991, pp. 304-317.

Pacione, Michael; Urban Geography: A Global Perspective, Routledge, London, 2005.

Pattison, William D.; "The Four Traditions of Geography", Journal of Geography, Vol. 75, pp. 520-30, 1976.

Pritchard, Sandra F.; "The Agricultural Landscape of Summit County, Colorado", The Pennsylvania Geographer, Vol. XXXIII, #1, Spring/Summer 1995 pp. 3-22.

Ryan John C. and Durning, Alan Thein; "The Story of a Shoe", World Watch, March/April 1998, pp. 29-32.

Saainen, Thomas F. and MacCabe, Charles L; "World Patterns of Geographical Literacy based on Sketch Map Quality", The Professional Geographer, Vol. 47, #2, May 1995, pp. 196-202.

Sachs, Jeffrey; "Can Extreme Poverty Be Eliminated?", Scientific American, September, 2005, pp. 56-65.

Sagers, Matthew J and Maraffa, Thomas; "The Spatial Structure of Air Passenger Service for Kiev and Tashkent", Soviet Geographer, Vol. 32, May 1991, pp. 314-346.

Savage, Melissa, "Ecological Disturbance and Nature Tourism", Geographical Review, Vol. 88, July 1993, pp. 290-299.

Sechrist, Robert; "Results of a Survey on Map and Gas use by local Government in Pennsylvania", The Pennsylvania Geographer, Vol. 22, #1, Spring 1994, pp.69-84.

Scharnberger, Charles K.; "Could Earthquake Disaster Strike Pennsylvania", The Pennsylvania Geographer, Vol. XXVIII, #2, Fall/Winter 1990, pp.27-38.

Schein, Richard H; "Urban origin and form in Central New York", Geographical Review, Vol. 81, #1, January 1991, pp. 52-69.

Schmelzkopf, Karen. "Urban Community Gardens as Contested Space", Geographical Review, Vol. 85, #3, July 1995, pp. 364-381.

Shawn, Wendy; "The Spatial Concentration of Affluence in the United States", Geographical Review, Vol. 87, Issue 4, October 1997, pp. 544-548.

Sommers, Brian J.; "The Freshman Experience and Geography; Linking Student Retention and the Introductory Geography Class", Journal of Geography, Vol. 96, #5, September/October 1997, pp. 243-249.

Spencer, Edgar W.; Earth Science: Understanding Environmental Issues, McGraw/Hill, Boston, 2003.

Sporton, Deborah. "Mixing Methods in Fertility Control", Professional Geographer, Vol. 51, #1, February 1999, pp 68-76.

Starrs, Paul F ; "Looking for Columbus", Geographical Review, Vol. 82, #4, October 1992, pp. 367-374.

Taft, Lou A;  "Reflections of the Past: Using Architecture to Understand the Culture and Economic Development of a Small Town", The Pennsylvania Geographer, Vol. 21, #2, Fall 1993, pp. 92-104.

Trifonoff, Karen M. "Going Beyond Location: Thematic Maps in the Early Elementary Grades", Journal of Geography, Vol. 94, #2, March/April 1995, pp. 368-374.

Tuan, Yi Fu. "A View of Geography", Geographical Review, January 1991, pp. 99-107.

Voeks, Robert. "African Medicine and Magic in the Americas", Geographical Review, Vol. 83, #1, January 1993, pp. 66-77.

Vogeler, Ingolf. "Cold War Geopolitics: Embassy Locations", Journal of Geography, Vol. 94, #1, January/February 1995, pp. 323-329.

Walford, Rex, "Careers for Geographers: What Prospects for the 1990's, The Pennsylvania Journal, Vol.#2, July 1991, pp 199-205

Wilke, Thomas A; "Geographic Patterns of Membership in U.S. Environmental Organizations", Professional Geographer, Vol. 47, #1, February 1995, pp.41-48.

Wilson, Veronica R.; "Expected Impact of Tourism on the Business Community of Windber, PA" The Pennsylvania Geographer, Vol. XXXIII, #1, Spring/Summer 1995, pp.71-87.